THE LIGHTNING BOOK

THE LIGHTNING BOOK

by PETER E. VIEMEISTER

with diagrams by READ VIEMEISTER

DOUBLEDAY & COMPANY, INC., GARDEN CITY, NEW YORK, 1961

ACKNOWLEDGMENTS

Photographs were reprinted through the courtesy of the following:
  Plate II: American Museum of Natural History
  Plate III: Public Service Company of Colorado
  Plate IV: Burndy Library
  Plates V and VI: American Philosophical Society Library
  Plates VII, VIII, IX, X, XIV, XX, XXVII, XXVIII, XXXII, XXXVI, and
    XXXVII: General Electric Company
  Plate XI: John Stroud
  Plates XII, XIII, XXVI, XXIX, XXX, XXXI, XXXIII, and XXXVIII:
    Westinghouse Electric Corporation
  Plates XV, XVI, and XVII: Beech Aircraft Corporation
  Plate XVIII: Wide World Photos
  Plate XIX: Thompson Lightning Protection Company
  Plates XXI, XLVI, and XLVII: U.S. Department of Agriculture
  Plate XXII: Paul's Photos
  Plates XXIII, XXIV, and XXV: National Park Service
  Plate XXXIV: Lightning Protection Institute
  Plate XXXIX: U.S. Naval Ordnance Laboratory
  Plates XL and XLI: United Press International Photos
  Plate XLII: *Journal of Geology,* copyright 1946 by the University of Chicago
  Plate XLIV: Academy of Natural Sciences of Philadelphia
  Plate XLV: *Stanford Research Institute Journal*
  Plates XLVIII and L: U.S. Air Force
  Plates XLIX, LI, and LII: Grumman Aircraft Engineering Corporation
  Plate LIII: *Weatherwise*

To my wife, Suzie
for her encouragement, suggestions, and diligent typing

CONTENTS

LIST OF PLATES AND SOURCES OF PHOTOGRAPHS

Ever since I can remember, I have been intrigued by lightning. As the years have passed, I have realized that I was not alone in my interest. Most people seem to be fascinated, impressed, or frightened by lightning. Everyone seems to have some question about what it is, why it behaves as it does, and what can be done to protect against it. To answer these questions, I have written this book. It is intended for the reader who wants to know more about the subject than his ten-year-old son without having to delve into advanced textbooks. It has been great fun putting the facts together, and I hope that these pages will give you a better understanding of lightning and how it affects you.

This book has been made possible by the hundreds and thousands of scientists, engineers, and interested laymen who have troubled themselves to search for a better understanding of the world around us. The majority of the facts and ideas that are presented here belong to these investigators. To cover every facet of lightning in extensive detail would fill many volumes, therefore much of the information here is necessarily restricted to the more significant phenomena. I apologize to the experts for leaving some things unsaid. To the reader who wants to know more about any particular aspect of lightning, I suggest he obtain the pertinent papers or books listed in the Bibliography. Out of this rich fund of knowledge came most of this book, and the reader who studies these fascinating sources will be well rewarded. Three books were particularly valuable. Dr. B. F. J. Schonland's *Flight of the Thunderbolts* (Oxford, 1950), *Henry F. Kretzer's Lightning Record* (Kretzer, 1895), and *Playing with Lightning*, by K. F. McEachron and K. G. Patrick (Random House, 1940) have provided inspiration and ideas.

The suppliers of photographs, listed on pages 9–10, were most generous and many government agencies co-operated in providing statistical information. Headquarters, offices, and personnel of the U.S. Weather Bureau were always co-operative and generous in giving their help. This book touches many fields of science and has required suggestions and comments from qualified experts in separate fields. I am indebted to hundreds of people for their help. But I am especially grateful to Julian H. Hagenguth, Manager of High Voltage Research at the Pittsfield plant of the General Electric Company, and P. N. Bosworth, Manager of Electrostatic & High Voltage Engineering at the General Engineering Laboratory of General Electric Company, and to S. B. Griscom, Advisory Engineer of Westinghouse Electric Corporation. Meteorologist Donald M. Fuquay and his associates of the U.S. Forest Service supplied much of the information about lightning and our national forests. Kenneth Spengler of the American Meteorological Society uncovered many of the supporting documents and Rexford Wilson of the National Fire Protection Association provided important statistics. Others who aided by offering suggestions, facts or ideas include:

Professor John W. Barrett, State University of Forestry, Syracuse, New York

R. D. Bienemann, Security Manufacturing & Contracting Co.

Albert De Ronde, Flight Safety Foundation

H. S. Ingham, Director of Research, Metallizing Engineering Co.

Charles Keller, Aviation Historian, Sea Cliff, New York

Robert W. Lindquist, Thompson Lightning Protection Co.

Dr. D. M. Ludlum, Editor, *Weatherwise*

Dr. Brian H. Mason, Curator of Geology, American Museum of Natural History

R. D. Miller, Chief Engineer, Pacific Telephone & Telegraph Co.

Captain William Moss, Pan American World Airways

R. B. Pfeifer, Bridge Engineer, Franklin County, Ohio

F. W. Preston, Aviation Products Service, General Electric Co.

Dr. Horace G. Richards, Associate Curator, Academy of Natural Sciences of Philadelphia

L. M. Robertson, Manager of Engineering, Public Service Company of Colorado

H. B. Robinson, Chief Park Naturalist, Sequoia and Kings Canyon National Parks

Dr. J. L. Rosenholtz, Head, Department of Geology, Rensselaer Polytechnic Institute

Arthur Sugden, Engineering Manager, Long Island Lighting Co.

Dr. Bernard Vonnegut, Arthur D. Little Co.

Dr. William K. Widger, Jr., Geophysics Research Directorate, Air Force Cambridge Research Center

Credit also belongs to my associates at Grumman Aircraft Engineering Corporation who contributed ideas and comments in informal discussions. Richard Imgram, Chief of Antenna Design, was particularly helpful in the subject of lightning protection for aircraft. Research Physicist Anthony Favale reviewed most of the manuscript and made constructive comments and suggestions. Donald Imgram, Advanced Design Projects engineer, deserves special commendation for reviewing the entire manuscript. To the man behind the scenes, Dick Winslow of Doubleday, I owe my thanks for his guidance in converting my drafts into a readable book. It was a pleasure working with my brother Read, who, in spite of heavy obligations to his industrial design business, took time out to make the fine diagrams and illustrations.

At this very minute about 1800 thunderstorms are raging over the face of the earth, hurling savage lightning bolts to the ground. We've had thunderstorms almost since the world began. And yet, common as it is, lightning is perhaps the most misunderstood phenomenon of nature.

Powerful enough to dig deep holes or split huge trees and throw heavy chunks of wood hundreds of feet, lightning seldom fails to be impressive in its display of nature's tremendous energy. It causes millions of dollars of damage and kills hundreds of people every year in the United States alone, while at the same time performing a fascinating role in maintaining the balance of nature.

Thunderstorms occur in some sections of Florida more than ninety days each year, while in Kampala, Uganda (Africa), they are so common that thunder is heard 242 days each year. On the other hand, thunderstorms are so rare in some parts of California that when one occurred during World War II, some citizens scurried to their cellars thinking they were being bombed!

Lightning was universally feared in primitive civilizations and generally thought to be a manifestation of the power and wrath of the gods. Thunder and lightning have often been symbolic of gloom, mystery, and terror. The fictional Frankenstein monster was born in a thunderstorm and the witches in Shakespeare's *Macbeth* always performed their most sinister deeds amid thunder and lightning. Television script writers like to use flashing lightning and booming thunder to set a somber mood.

Almost everyone has read of strange happenings because of freak behavior of lightning. You may have heard the story of the train wreck that was averted because of lightning, or the story of a New York farmer who survived a lightning bolt although a companion was killed just a few feet away. A respected resident of Lake Placid tells of the experience of a friend in Ontario. Standing on a boulder, the man was struck by "lightning from a clear blue sky." The boulder was split to pieces and the man's hair was removed but he was merely dazed.

Many of the stories involve "ball" lightning. A favorite recounts the tale of a Frenchman in Marseille. While reading, he was suddenly dazzled by a "ball of lightning" that bored through the floor, sizzled up the chimney, and exploded on the roof with a resounding bang. From Long Island comes the story of another "ball of fire" that drifted through a hall, went out a window and silently disappeared.

Many of these freak stories have happy endings. But unfortunately most of man's contacts with lightning do not end so pleasantly. Golfers have been struck, homes set afire, school children killed, boats badly damaged, electrical power service disrupted, and timberland destroyed by lightning. During the past ten years an average of 180 Americans were killed by lightning each year.

There are hundreds of thousands of people who have a false sense of security. Homeowners think that they are protected by their TV antenna or because a tall tree is near their home. Some men continue to play their round of golf or "take shelter" under a tree when lightning flashes nearby. A common misconception is that shutting windows and doors will "keep the lightning out."

Some people enjoy sitting on the front porch, gleefully watching the fireworks while their neighbors may be hiding in closets or under blankets, shivering in terror. Lightning should not be taken lightly or ignored. But neither should it be overrated: falling down stairs kills sixteen times more people than lightning does. Today we find people harboring unjust fears. You may even know someone like the New York woman who, upon hearing a thunderstorm approach, dons rubbers, raincoat, and bathing cap and then huddles in the center of the living-room floor, even though the steel frame of her apartment building shields her from any harm.

Old wives tales say that thunder is caused by clouds bumping together and that thunder can kill unborn chicks or even make milk turn sour. Rapidly fading is the erroneous belief that lightning never strikes the same place twice.

We hear there are such things as heat lightning, sheet lightning, ball, bead, hot, and cold lightning, and even "petrified lightning." Some say it is no more hazardous to take a bath than to talk on the telephone during a thunderstorm. Lightning is sometimes falsely blamed for calamities caused by something else.

What are the facts?

Although some of the stories and beliefs are substantiated by fact, others are ridiculous and without foundation. Many of the classic lightning tales have probably been distorted through the years.

In 42 B.C. Publilius Syrus said, "It is vain to look for a defense against lightning." Benjamin Franklin and other scientists have proven Syrus wrong. But in spite of increased scientific knowledge, lightning damage continues to sap our national resources and to bring on personal tragedy. The understanding of lightning and application of simple precautions can significantly reduce these losses, and perhaps save your life.

This book explains lightning: why it happens, what it does, and what you can do about it.

PART ONE

THE SEARCH FOR KNOWLEDGE

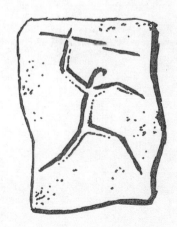

Long before man came onto the scene, lightning was bombarding the earth. It is even possible that lightning played a vital role in the evolution of life.

The earth's early atmosphere is believed to have consisted of a mixture of ammonia, methane, hydrogen, and water vapor. Dr. Harold C. Urey, Nobel Prize-winning University of Chicago chemist, has suggested that the action of ultraviolet radiation or lightning discharges split and converted these gases into molecular components that then combined into more complex molecules. As time passed these more complex molecules reacted with each other in the waters of the oceans, combining and recombining again and again into even more complex molecules. Later, proteins, which are vital constituents of all living cells, were evolved, leading to subsequent reactions and life itself.

One of Urey's students, Stanley L. Miller, recently demonstrated that this may well have been the case. Using an electric spark to imitate lightning, Miller set up an experiment in which he simulated the primordial atmosphere with a mixture of ammonia, methane, and hydrogen. He circulated this "atmosphere" over the "lightning" by artificial evaporation and precipitation: boiling and condensing water. He carefully excluded living organisms from the test apparatus. At the end of a week he analyzed the mixture and found that it contained amino acids, the building blocks of proteins.

Mystery and Myths

The story of lightning is the story of man's endless quest for understanding the world about him. Originally regarded with terror, lightning was a mystery to the first men who sought to understand it. The sequence of man's attempt to explain the mystery of thunder and lightning started with magic and then passed into primitive religion and superstition. Today the story is one of science. But the search for understanding has been long and circuitous. Even today there is considerable conflict of theory and a surprising lack of information about lightning.

Early man rose above animals when he learned how to control the fires started by lightning bolts. Observing how animals avoided fire, he recognized that fire could be a valuable ally. Flaming wood from a fire started by lightning was carried to a pile of dry sticks in front of his shelter and nursed until a steady blaze burned. Lightning thus helped man protect himself from predatory beasts, and therefore contributed to the development of man's superiority over creatures larger and stronger than himself. Legends of the Cherokee Indians say that the world was a cold place before lightning started the first fire. As late as the 1600's, many aborigine tribes of Tasmania had not yet learned how to make fire. If their campfires went out, they had to either borrow some fire from a friendly neighboring tribe or wait until lightning started a brush or forest fire.

What primitive man thought about lightning is purely a matter of speculation, since records of man's thoughts only go back a mere 6000 years or so. That man has always feared and respected lightning is evidenced by the extent to which thunder and lightning enter into the primitive religions and legends handed down from the ancients. The folklore of primitive peoples is rich in "thunder magic."

Several thousand years before Christ, in the ancient civilizations of Egypt, Greece, and Rome, thunder and lightning were believed to be manifestations of the power and wrath of the gods. As man embraced religion, he associated a flash of lightning or the boom of thunder with the appearance of a god. The Bible relates that before Moses climbed Mount Sinai to receive the Ten Commandments ". . . there were thunders and lightnings and a thick cloud upon the mount and the voice of the trumpet exceeding loud; so that all the people that was in the camp trembled." The Bible also states, in Second Samuel, "The Lord thundered from heaven, and the most high uttered His voice." David's psalm of thanksgiving mentioned "And He sent out arrows and scattered them; lightning and discomfited them."

The ancient Greeks believed that they lived in the middle of a circular but flat earth. The elements air, fire, and water were subject to religious adoration and their gods were the personification of natural powers. Lightning was the weapon of Zeus, father of all gods. Zeus' favorite bird, the eagle, bore his thunderbolts, which were forged by Vulcan, the lame ironsmith. Even today, the eagle on the back of our dollar bill clasps lightning arrows in its claws. Mythology credits the invention of thunderbolts to Minerva, the goddess of wisdom. Zeus used lightning to indicate his displeasure with wrongdoers or punish wayward mortals. He is also reported to have turned the tide of battle for his favorites by hurling thunderbolts at the enemy.

Fig. 1   Early Greeks believed that lightning was the weapon of Zeus.

The Romans, who inherited many of their religious beliefs from the Greeks, respected Jupiter (Zeus Pater) or Jove, the Roman equivalent of Zeus. Jupiter, who is said to have subdued the monsters with thunderbolts, presented Venus to Vulcan for a bride in gratitude for forging the thunderbolts. Since lightning was a manifestation of the father god, the Greeks and Romans revered any spot struck by lightning. Temples to Jupiter and Zeus were often located on these sacred sites.

These civilizations regarded thunder and lightning as belonging exclusively to the gods. Legends tell of the punishment meted out to Salomoneus, the King of the Elis, for attempting to mimic Zeus.

Salomoneus tried to imitate the father of the gods and impress his
people by throwing flaming firebrands from his chariot as he clamored
over a bronze bridge. For this irreverent behavior Zeus caused Salomoneus to be struck by a real thunderbolt, teaching him the difference
between Divine and Mortal weapons.

Fig. 2   Salomoneus irreverently tried to imitate Zeus by throwing flaming
brands.

The ancient Persians also believed that divine wrath was manifested
by lightning. In about 450 B.C. the Greek historian Herodotus wrote,
"You may have observed how the thunderbolt chastises the insolence
of the more enormous animals whilst it passes over without injury
the weak and the insignificant; before these weapons of the gods you
must have seen how the proudest palaces and the loftiest trees fall and
perish. . . . God permits none but Himself to entertain grand ideas.
. . . God loves to truncate all those things that rise too high." The
Moslems also attribute thunder and lightning to their god. The Koran
says, "He it is who showeth you the lightning" and "He launcheth the

thunderbolts and smiteth with them whom He will while they dispute (in doubt) concerning Allah, and He is mighty in wrath."

But not all early religions vested the primary god with the power to control thunder and lightning. Scandinavian mythology alludes to Thor (the thunderer), a foe of all demons, as the custodian of thunder rather than the father god, Odin. In the multigod Hindu religion, Indra was the god of heaven, thunder, lightning, storm, and rain, but the Maruts were actually in charge of storm clouds and used the thunderbolts as weapons.

Omens and Politics

The appearance of lightning or the sound of thunder was often taken as an omen by people of ancient civilizations. To the Greeks thunder on the right was a good omen, and they planned their personal behavior accordingly. The Romans, however, regarded thunder on the left as a favorable sign. Since the Greeks faced north and the Romans faced south while watching for these signs, they both agreed that thunder or lightning in the east was more favorable than in the west. Weather generally moves from west to east and thunder in the east usually indicated that the storm had passed.

The Romans relied on these omens for personal guidance and for government affairs as well. They established a College of Augurs to appraise portents in the sky. Organized prior to 300 B.C. with three members, the College grew to sixteen by the time of Julius Caesar and was active in guiding the affairs of state up to at least A.D. 300. The members of the college were highly respected and their judgment or interpretations could not be questioned by lay observers. With an exclusive franchise on interpretations of omens and with its members appointed by incumbent rulers, the College eventually degenerated into a political device.

An augur watched for lightning, birds, and shooting stars. A lightning flash passing from left to right indicated that Jupiter approved the activities of the Forum. Flashes passing from right to left were an unfavorable omen. But the appearance of any lightning at all while an augur was on duty was sufficient cause to have all assemblies adjourned for the day. If an election or plebiscite was required by law but the rulers suspected that the population might vote against them,

it was not unusual for the College of Augurs to notify the magistrate
that the plebiscite should be postponed "because of unfavorable
omen." If the public mood did not change, the postponement was
often indefinite. Cicero criticized this process in 45 B.C. when he remarked, "We regard lightning on the left hand as a most favorable
omen, for everything except an election." When the people refused to
tolerate this chicanery any longer, the College fell into disrepute and
went out of existence in the fourth century A.D.

Early in the same century lived Barbara Dioscorus, a convert to
Christianity. Barbara's wealthy heathen father became incensed when
she became a Christian. He had the governor condemn her to death,
and then Dioscorus personally beheaded her. But he himself was immediately struck by lightning and killed. Barbara entered martyrdom
and became the patron saint of protection against thunder, lightning,
and fire. In the days of the gunpowder cannon, Santa Barbara was
adopted by military ordnance men as their patron saint, first by the
French cannoneers in 1417 and later by ordnance men in other countries. The anniversary of her martyrdom, December 4, was celebrated
as a feast day by Greeks, Romans, and early Russians. As recently as
1940 a painting of Santa Barbara hung in the office of the Chief of the
U.S. Navy Bureau of Ordnance in Washington, D.C.

Magic and Mimicry

Although most legends associate lightning and thunder with
human-like gods, some primitive civilizations believed that magical
animals or birds were responsible. The American Indians had many
myths that related thunder and lightning to the thunderbird. Some
tribes thought that lightning was the flash of the thunderbird's eye as
he winked. Others harbored the idea that lightning was the bird's
weapon and that the peeled bark of a tree struck by lightning was
evidence of the thunderbird's sharp claws. Some Bantu-speaking tribes
of South Africa still believe that a thunderbird, Umpundulo, creates
thunder and lightning. Lightning is created by its bright plumage and
thunder sounds from its beating wings when it dives to earth. Again,
the bark torn from trees hit by lightning is supposed to be a mark of
its claws.

The uncivilized Bantu of the twentieth century, who have pro-

gressed little from ancient times, provide insight into possible atti-
tudes and practices of early man. They place great faith in the magic
ability of witch doctors.

While his fellow tribesmen hide in their huts, the witch doctor of
these Bantu braves thunderstorms and bids lightning strike far away.
He seeks out areas and objects that have been struck by lightning,
believing that they have special powers. He uses these objects to prepare protective mixtures; trees and animals hit by lightning make excellent ingredients of magic potions.

The thunderbird takes different forms from tribe to tribe—it may be
a flamingo, stork, or sea hawk—and is believed to leave its eggs or urine
where lightning has struck. The witch doctors find such places, dig
up gelatinous or chalklike substances, and mix them with feathers and
bones to make special mixtures. Rubbed into incisions, put on pegs, or
buried in the village, the brew is expected to provide protection from
lightning. If a hut is struck by lightning in spite of an anointment of
the magic mixture, the witch doctor shrugs his shoulders and claims
that the prescription should have been renewed.

The American Navahos ascribed great power to lightning. Many of
their healing rituals revolved about the benevolent war god, Slayer of
Enemy Gods. When trying to heal a patient, the Navaho priest or
singer made a sand painting of the benevolent god standing on lightning and holding lightning in his hand.

Like the ancient Greeks and Romans, some of today's Africans believe that a person hit by lightning has incurred spiritual wrath. If the
victim lives, he is shunned as being unclean. If killed, he is buried immediately and without ceremony.

Reliance upon practitioners of magic has not been restricted to jun-
gle natives of Africa who looked to their witch doctors for health and
to the rainmakers for rain. It appears that as late as the 1800's in parts
of Russia people relied upon rainmakers to bring the showers essential
for crops. Sir James George Frazer, in his classic treatise on magic and
religion, *The Golden Bough*, relates, ". . . in a village near Dorpat,
Russia, when rain was much wanted, three men used to climb up the
fir-trees of an old sacred grove. One of them drummed with a hammer
on a kettle or small cask to imitate thunder; the second knocked two
fire-brands together and made sparks fly, to imitate lightning; and the
third, who was called 'the rain-maker,' had a bunch of twigs with

which he sprinkled water from a vessel on all sides." Rainmakers usually utilized mimicry to get results.

Wood and Lucky Charms

Wood has played a part in many religious and superstitious considerations of lightning. When the Thompson Indians in British Columbia wanted to set fire to the homes of their enemies, they would take fragments from a tree struck by lightning and attach them to their incendiary arrows, believing that more destruction could be wrought by such a flame than from an ordinary one. Some tribes in Northern Rhodesia used such wood for their fires because they felt that lightning was a spiritual phenomenon and that the burning of this wood yielded physical and spiritual benefits. But the Thonga tribes in South Africa and the Wendish peasants of Saxony so revered the wood that they would refuse to use it for fuel, no matter how much they needed a fire. The Wendish feared that such fuel might make their house burn down.

Fire festivals in Europe, dating back to the Middle Ages, were thought to promote protection from lightning. In many parts of Germany on Easter Eve a hilltop bonfire was made and consecrated near a church. Townspeople called their hill Easter Mountain and brought sticks of oak, walnut, or beech to kindle the fire. After being charred in the fire, the sticks were taken home and burned in a new fire with the prayer that the homestead be protected from fire, hail, and lightning. Some people kept the sticks throughout the year and put them back into the hearth during heavy thunderstorms. Other pieces were inserted in the roof to prevent the house from being struck. As recently as the nineteenth century Easter Eve fires could be seen on these Easter Mountains of many towns of North and Central Germany.

In Prussia and Lithuania ceremonial fires ignited on Midsummer Eve or Midsummer Day in June were supposed to give protection from thunder, hail, cattle disease, witchcraft, and sundry other hazards of life.

As late as 1850, the custom of the Yule log was an active rite in some parts of Central Germany. The Yule log was customarily a heavy block of oak. The log was laid on the bottom of the fireplace for a fire that was started on Christmas Eve and burned until Twelfth Night. People in Westphalia would withdraw the Yule log after it was slightly charred, set it aside, and replace it on the hearth only when thunderstorms threatened, on the notion that lightning would not strike while a Yule log smoldered. Similarly, in England the remains of the Yule log were supposed to avert lightning. In Flanders and France, the charred pieces of the log were kept under a bed to keep lightning away. However, even in the seventeenth century this practice was denounced by some French writers as superstition.

The European reverence for an oak Yule log is believed to have evolved from the legend that the oak was the favorite tree of Jove. To many early European observers it seemed that the oak was struck more frequently than any other tree in European forests and was therefore symbolic of divine powers. The special charm of mistletoe in our own Christmas customs may have stemmed from an old belief that mistletoe was no natural plant, but rather an aftermath of lightning.

The Roman historian Pliny (A.D. 23–79) stated that the Druids worshiped mistletoe as a token from heaven. The rarity with which mistletoe grows on oak may have contributed to its special sanctity. Frazer concluded that the Druids thought that the mistletoe growing on an oak was "a visible emanation of the celestial fire; so that in cutting the mistletoe with mystic rites they were securing for themselves all the magical properties of a thunderbolt. 'Thunder-besom' is a popular name in Germany for any bushy nest-like excrescence growing on a branch, because such a parasitic growth is actually believed by the ignorant to be a product of lightning."

Faith in the power of charms and talismans to provide immunity to lightning was displayed as early as Roman times. The laurel bush, according to Pliny, offered protection from thunderbolts. Emperor Tiberius is said to have worn a laurel wreath during thunderstorms to guard himself from lightning. Even in the nineteenth century, belief in the effectiveness of talismans persisted. John Leigh wrote in 1835 that "A document known as 'Christ's Letter' is carried about the person as a charm against the fatal effect of lightning, and other sundry calamities. Sprigs of thorn bushes, carried about the person, or placed in the different rooms of the house are also supposed to insure

safety, from an absurd and false idea that thorns are not damaged by
lightning."

Beginnings of Science

While most men invented myths to explain the unexplainable, some
men were trying to bring Nature's phenomena within the grasp of
understanding in a more scientific manner. Early glimmerings of understanding came with the philosophers Herodotus, Aristophanes, and
Aristotle. Aristophanes records how Socrates looked beyond mysti-
cism. To calm a frightened farmer who was cringing under a storm,
Socrates said, "That is not Zeus up there but a vortex of air."

Aristotle attempted to put the explanation of weather on an orderly
physical basis. He suggested that any change seen in the sky was
caused by changes that occurred in the regions of fire and air that lay
between the earth and the moon. Fire, as a principle rather than an
actual flame, was thought to be caused by hot dry "exhalations" rising
up from the ground due to heating or movement and it produced
such phenomena as auroras, shooting stars, and comets in the sphere
of fire. In the sphere of air, these same hot dry exhalations created
thunder, lightning, and wind. On the other hand, rain, snow, hail, and
clouds were supposedly the product of cool, damp exhalations in the
sphere of air that fell on water.

Rudimentary principles of lightning behavior were observed by
Herodotus who had noticed that tall objects were the most susceptible
targets. The Mongols recognized that bathing was hazardous during
lightning activity: the laws of Genghis Khan specifically forbade Mon-
gol subjects from washing their garments or bathing in running water
during thunderstorms.

Leonardo da Vinci (1452–1519) associated updrafts with storm
clouds. He observed that "When the movement of two contrary winds
brings two clouds to strike together, these clouds then become incorporated in each other, and not being able either to expand or lower
themselves because of the wind passing beneath them, these clouds
extend in that direction in which their passage is least impeded, that
is upwards." These early weather suppositions did not include consideration of electricity. Little was known about electricity and, as a
result, no attempt was made to relate electricity with lightning.

The earliest nonmeteorological thoughts about electricity are attributed to the Greek philosopher Thales, who, in about 600 B.C., found that after a piece of amber was rubbed briskly with a dry substance it would attract small pieces of straw or feathers. Pliny the Younger, the Roman philosopher, duplicated this simple experiment in the second century B.C., but was unable to explain it. Today we refer to this as a manifestation of static electricity. But knowledge about electricity progressed no further during the Dark Ages that followed.

Interest was renewed in the late 1500's by William Gilbert, brilliant court physician to Queen Elizabeth. He repeated the demonstrations of Thales and Pliny and named the science of studying such phenomena *vis electrica*, after the word *electra*, which is Greek for *amber*. Our word *electricity* was derived from these terms.

In France, Charles François de Cisternay Du Fay followed these experiments and investigated the effects of rubbing on different kinds of materials. He noticed that two charged pieces of amber repelled each other, but that a charged piece of amber attracted a charged piece of glass. Evidently, he concluded, electrified materials behave something like magnets: bodies with the same electrification (or magnetization) repel each other while bodies with unlike electrification (or magnetization) attract each other. This led Du Fay to the conclusion that there must be two different kinds of electricity. He named one *resinous*, because it involved resinous materials like amber, and the other *vitreous*, because it involved material like glass. Du Fay believed that any material had some sort of invisible conducting "fluid" in it and that rubbing released the fluid. Benjamin Franklin, as we will see later, changed Du Fay's concepts, but Du Fay did make a lasting contribution to electrical science. He had observed that some materials, such as metals, permit electricity to pass through them easily and he called such substances *conductors*. Materials that resist the passage of electricity through them were called *insulators*.

Electrical Entertainment

By the middle of the seventeenth century scientists throughout Europe were beginning to perform electrical experiments. Machines for generating static electricity, first created by Otto Von Guericke in

1663, relieved experimenters from arduous rubbing to produce electrification. Von Guericke's first machine utilized a ball of sulfur, "the size of an infant's head," that could be turned with a crank. By rub-

Fig. 3   Otto Von Guericke invented a "friction machine" that generated static electricity.

bing the sphere with his hand as he turned the handle, Von Guericke showed that the sulfur became electrified. Bits of paper would stick to it and the charge could be transferred to other balls of sulfur or used for experiments. Many other "friction machines" followed, including one built by Sir Isaac Newton, and a version designed by F. Hauksbee in 1709 that used a rotating glass globe with a rubbing chain for collecting the charge.

Another valuable tool for the "electrician," as these electrical experimenters were popularly known, was a device that could store considerable charges of electricity for long periods of time. It was called the *Leyden jar* and its invention is credited to Pieter van Musschenbroek, at the University of Leyden in 1745. After he had charged his invention with electricity from a friction machine, Van Musschenbroek found that the jar could truly store electricity: he touched the top and received a severe shock. He wrote later "my whole body was shaken as by a thunderbolt. . . . I thought it was all up with me."

Since the Leyden jar or "electric phial" could be "filled with electricity" and carried around and discharged at will, it became an item of considerable interest to scientists and laymen alike. Traveling dem-

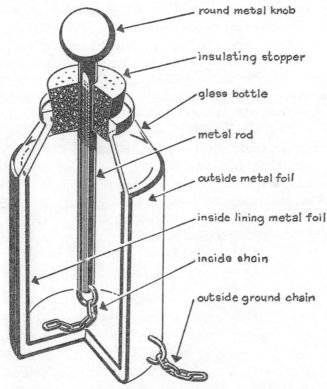

round metal knob

insulating stopper

glass bottle

metal rod

outside metal foil

inside lining metal foil

inside chain

outside ground chain

Fig. 4   Cutaway view shows make-up of a Leyden jar.

onstrators in Europe staged shows of "electrical magic" for the amusement of royal courts. Everyone was eager to see the Leyden jar in action, and some demonstrators were able to earn fortunes. Brave souls actually wanted to feel its effects. As I. Bernard Cohen relates in *Lives of Science*, "Seven hundred monks from the Convent de Paris, joined hand to hand, had a Leyden jar discharged through them all. They flew up into the air with finer timing than could be achieved by the most glorified corps of ballet dancers."

There were no practical applications for electricity and as a science it was in its infancy. Permeating all of scientific thought was Sir Isaac Newton's philosophy that basic mathematical laws were the foundation for understanding nature. But mathematical analysis could not be applied to electrical phenomena because of a lack of facts based upon orderly experimental investigation and measurement. Without this necessary groundwork, science's characteristic ability to predict natural phenomena in electricity was impossible.

In 1746 a Dr. Spence, who had just arrived from Scotland, introduced electrical experiments to Benjamin Franklin. Although he had done some reading in science for a few years prior to the meeting, Franklin was delighted and impressed with what he saw. He bought the electrical apparatus. At about the same time, a Quaker merchant friend in London, Peter Collinson, sent Franklin a glass tube that, through rubbing, could attain and hold an electrical charge. These simple events were to trigger a dramatic change in the course of electrical discovery and understanding. Benjamin Franklin, a man without extensive mathematical training, soon brought from the morass of random electrical amusements a new understanding that was to lay the foundation for modern electrical theory.

2 BENJAMIN FRANKLIN

Most people remember Benjamin Franklin for his impressive career in government. His prodigious writings, letters, and publications have given us a clear picture of his economic views, his political ideas, and his diplomatic career. But his stature as America's first great scientist is often overlooked. He had one of the most creative minds of the century.

Franklin showed the world how to protect property from lightning by inventing the lightning rod. This invention is virtually unchanged more than two hundred years later.

Born in 1706, Benjamin Franklin was one of ten children. He attended school in Boston and served as a printer's apprentice for an older half-brother. He visited London and later moved to Philadelphia, where he established his own print shop. He bought the *Pennsylvania Gazette*, which soon became the largest paper in the colonies. In 1732, Franklin introduced a new publication, which he called *Poor Richard's Almanack*. Full of wit and wisdom and spiced with interesting hints, the *Almanack* built a personal fortune for Franklin. These widely read publications helped make Franklin one of the most influential and important men in Philadelphia.

Franklin began his career of electrical experimentation immediately after receiving the equipment from Spence and Collinson. He had some additional Leyden jars made at a Philadelphia glass-blowing house. He soon was amusing himself and friends with his friction machine and electric "phials." Franklin became so engrossed in electrical study that almost all of his leisure was devoted to experimenting.

Peter Collinson kept Franklin posted on the progress of electrical experimentation in Europe and Franklin corresponded frequently with the London merchant. In May or June of 1747 Franklin sent a letter to Collinson describing his observations on the ways that pointed bodies draw or throw off "electrical fire." Franklin saw that a needle, when brought near a charged insulated body, will draw off the charge if the needle is grounded, such as to a wire running to the ground or the hand. If the needle is insulated (by a piece of wax, for example) it will not draw off the charge. He also found that a body with a sharp point or jagged edge would lose its charge as fast as he tried to charge it. Breathing on a charged body or surrounding it with smoke, he discovered, would discharge a charged body.

A month later Franklin made his greatest single contribution to understanding electricity: the remarkably simple concept that electrical phenomena can be explained by the action or presence of only one "kind" of electricity. On July 11 Franklin wrote Collinson that electricity is a single "fluid" and that differently charged bodies had either more or less of the same kind of electricity rather than two different kinds of electricity. This was a radical concept at the time, since most students of electricity adhered to Du Fay's Theory that electrified resinous and vitreous substances were charged with different kinds of electrical fluid. An English electrician named William Watson had already suggested that any material, whether charged or not, contains electricity. Franklin pointed out that rubbing or charging merely transfers amounts of electricity from one body to another, leaving one with a surplus and the other with a shortage. Unable to see the electricity itself, Franklin assumed that what had been called vitreous electricity was actually a surplus of the electrical fluid. Such bodies, he said, had a *positive* or *plus* charge. Similarly, Franklin reasoned, bodies charged with resinous electricity had a shortage of the electrical fluid, so Franklin called this *negative*, or *minus*. When the fluid flows, he concluded, the current flows from plus (surplus) to minus (deficiency).

Today we know that the basic "particle" of electricity is the electron. We further know that an electrified resinous substance actually has a surplus of electrons, and not a deficiency of "electrical" fluid as Franklin believed. But since Franklin had called this state of charge "minus" or "negative," the particles causing it had to be called "negative" too. Therefore the electron had to be called a negative particle of electricity.

If a body with a surplus of electrons is brought in contact with a body deficient in electrons, the electrons flow, much as water seeking its own level, from the area of oversupply to the area of undersupply.

Since the electron is negative, a "surplus of electricity" is actually a surplus of negative charges, or a relatively negative condition. *Electrons, therefore, flow from minus to plus.* It is unfortunate that Franklin named the charges as he did, because people still say that "current" flows from plus to minus, even though the actual flow of electrons is

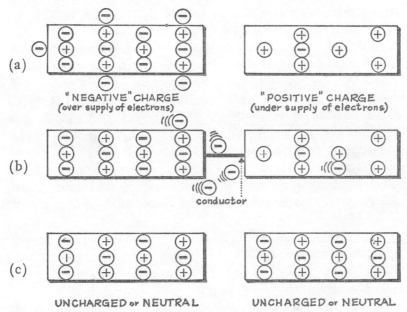

(a)

"NEGATIVE" CHARGE
(over supply of electrons)

"POSITIVE" CHARGE
(under supply of electrons)

(b)

conductor

(c)

UNCHARGED or NEUTRAL   UNCHARGED or NEUTRAL

Fig. 5   Electric charge is a relative measure. (a) Negatively charged body has more electrons than protons. (b) When two charged bodies are connected by a conductor, electrons flow from oversupply (−) to undersupply (+), much as water tries to seek its own level. (c) After conductor is removed, both bodies have the same charge.

from minus to plus, the opposite direction to "current"! Franklin had an even chance to guess right, and he guessed wrong. High-school physics students have been plagued with confusion ever since Franklin made his unfortunate choice of terminology.

Is Lightning Electricity?

The idea that lightning might be electricity predates Franklin's work. This thought was advanced as early as 1708 by the English scientist William Wall. Watching the spark and crackle of a discharge from a charged piece of amber, Wall observed that it seemed "in some degree to represent thunder and lightning." Sir Isaac Newton commented that a spark "putteth me in mind of lightning on a small—how very small—scale."

Franklin suspected that thunderclouds were charged and assumed that lightning was an electrical phenomenon. In April 1749 he wrote to Dr. John Mitchell, a Fellow of the English Royal Society, and speculated on the cause of electrification in clouds. He noted that lightning favored high hills and trees, spires, lofty towers, chimneys, and masts. He reasoned that if two charged bodies in an experiment spark and discharge with a loud snap, "how loud must be the crack" of "10,000 acres of electrified cloud?" He realized that thunder was a result of the lightning discharge.

In order to devote more time to his experiments, Franklin retired from his printing business, and in November of 1749, he wrote, in the minutes he kept of his experiments and proposed investigations, that "Electrical fluid agrees with lightning in these particulars:

1. Giving light.
2. Colour of the light.
3. Crooked direction.
4. Swift motion.
5. Being conducted by metals.
6. Crack or noise in exploding.
7. Subsisting in water or ice.
8. Rending bodies it passes through.
9. Destroying animals.
10. Melting metals.
11. Firing inflammable substances.
12. Sulphureous smell.

The electrical fluid is attracted by points. We do not know whether this property is in lightning. But since they agree in all particulars wherein we can already compare them, is it not probable they agree likewise in this? Let the experiment be made."

A few weeks later Franklin made the first suggestion for a device to protect property from lightning. In a letter to Collinson he wrote, "There is something, however, in the experiments of points, sending off or drawing on the electrical fire, which has not been fully explained, and which I intend to supply in my next. For the doctrine of points is very curious, and the effects of them truly wonderful; and from what I have observed on experiments, I am of the opinion that houses, ships, and even towers and churches may be effectually secured from the strokes of lightning by their means; for if, instead of the round balls of wood or metal which are commonly placed on the tops of weathercocks, vanes, or spindles of churches, spires, or masts, there should be a rod of iron eight or ten feet in length, sharpened gradually to a point like a needle, and gilt to prevent rusting, or divided into a number of points, which would be better, the electrical fire would, I think, be drawn out of a cloud silently, before it could come near enough to strike; and a light would be seen at the point, like the sailor's corpuzante [St. Elmo's fire]. This may seem whimsical, but let it pass for the present until I send the experiments at large." Franklin apparently believed that thunderclouds could be drained of their electricity.

At this time, Franklin had not recognized the need for a ground wire, but the idea of a simple device for protecting property of lightning damage was worth pursuing.

He repeated the suggestion of the lightning rod in July 1750 in a letter to Collinson and the Royal Society, Britain's earliest scientific society. This time he included the concept of a ground wire "down the outside of a building into the ground or down one of the shrouds of a ship and down her side until it reaches the water."

Simultaneously, Franklin made his first proposal for a specific experiment to determine if lightning clouds are electrified. "I would propose an experiment to be tried where it may be done conveniently. On the top of some high tower or steeple place a kind of sentry box . . . big enough to contain a man and an electrical stand [insulating stool or table]. From the middle of the stand let an iron rod rise and pass bending out of the door, and then upright twenty or thirty feet, pointed very sharp at the end. If the electrical stand be kept clean and dry, a man standing on it when such clouds are passing low might be electrified and afford sparks, the rod drawing fire to him from a cloud. If any danger to the man should be apprehended (though I think there would be none), let him stand on the floor of his box and now and then bring near to the rod a loop of wire that has one end fastened to the leads he is holding by a wax handle; so the sparks,

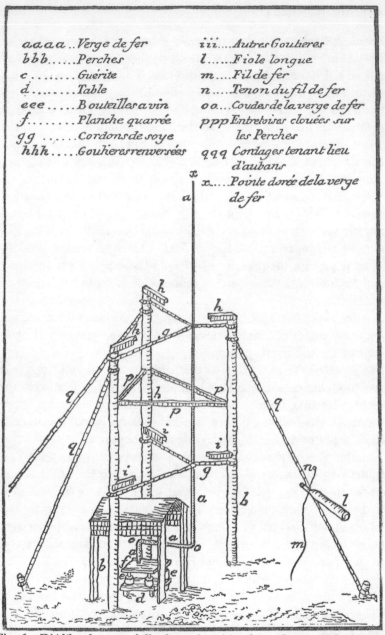

aaaa..Verge de fer   iii....Autres Goutieres
bbb......Perches   l......Fiole longue
c........Guérite   m....Fil de fer
d........Table   n....Tenon du fil de fer
eee.....Bouteilles a vin   oo....Coudes de la verge de fer
f........Planche quarrée   ppp Entretoises clouées sur
gg ......Cordons de soye   les Perches
hhh....Goutieres renversées   qqq Cordages tenant lieu
                          d'aubans
                       x....Pointe dorée de la verge
                          de fer

Fig. 6 D'Alibard successfully drew electricity from the air with this version of Franklin's proposed sentry-box experiment. Note that insulators for the test stand are empty wine bottles. COURTESY OF AMERICAN PHILOSOPHICAL SOCIETY

if the rod is electrified, will strike from the rod to the wire and not affect him." Franklin must not have recognized the potential magnitude of lightning and did not realize that a mere wax handle would be insufficient insulation to deter a powerful bolt of lightning if it struck the rod. Professor Georg Wilhelm Richmann, while performing a similar experiment with an insulated rod, was killed by a bolt of lightning in St. Petersburg (now Leningrad) in 1753. But prior to Richmann's demise, several successful experiments were made as a result of Franklin's suggestion.

Franklin's proposal was read before the Royal Society but was not published in full. Franklin's electrical rival, William Watson, abstracted Franklin's comments that reflected favorably upon his own theories, but ignored the proposed experiment. English scientists did not endorse the idea but French electricians quickly applied the proposal when they received translations. Three experimentalists, Thomas-François D'Alibard, a Monsieur de Lor, and a Monsieur Buffon decided to attempt the experiment. Outside of Paris in Marly, D'Alibard set up a forty-foot iron rod that was topped with a brass point and supported by silk ribbons from wooden posts. For an insulating stand he used a plank with three wine bottles for legs. A glass Leyden jar was kept nearby. An old dragoon named Coiffier was left to tend the rig.

On the afternoon of May 10, 1752, thunder shook the town of Marly. The village prior raced to the scene to see if the old soldier had been killed. Groups of curious villagers followed the priest and arrived to see Coiffier with the phial near the rod. They heard a crackling sound and saw, in broad daylight, sparks jumping between the rod and the glass phial held by Coiffier. This was the first proof that thunderclouds were electrified. De Lor repeated the experiment eight days later in Paris.

Franklin Flies a Kite

Because of the slow communication of the times, Franklin himself was unaware of these activities when in June, only a few weeks after D'Alibard had made his report to the Académie Royale des Sciences, Franklin set out to prove the same fact. He had intended to erect a sentry-box experiment on top of a spire on the new Christ

Church in Philadelphia but grew impatient when construction was delayed. He embarked on a new method to conduct the experiment.

Franklin decided that an ordinary kite would give him access to a thundercloud far better than any spire. He made a kite with two crossed sticks of cedar, using a large silk handkerchief that would not tear in the rain. A sharp, pointed wire extended about a foot above the kite. At the bottom of the kite twine, Franklin attached a key. A few inches of silk ribbon between the key and his hand acted as an insulator. When the first thunderstorm approached, Franklin went into the fields near a convenient shed. Sailing his kite up near the clouds, he was cautious to stay in the shed so that the ribbon could be kept dry.

Fig. 7   Franklin drew sparks from the end of the string of a kite flown near a thundercloud.

For a few minutes nothing happened. Then Franklin noticed that the strands of the twine at the knot by the key began to bristle and stand away from each other, as would the strands of a string attached to an electrified conductor. He raised his knuckle toward the key and, with profound delight, felt a small spark jump between the key and his knuckle.

After rain had wet the kite string, he was able to draw bigger sparks and collect "electrical fluid" in a Leyden jar. His satisfaction was complete when tests with the electricity thus collected demonstrated that electricity from thunderclouds was the same as the electricity from friction machines in his laboratory. Benjamin Franklin, who was first to propose experiments to prove lightning and electricity were one, now had the proof he had wanted. It is typical of his practical ingenuity that he used a simple kite for the purpose.

Franklin saved the announcement of the Electrical Kite for publication in the *Gazette*, with the first account of how to use a kite to draw "electrical fire from clouds," appearing on October 19, 1752. On another page of the same issue of the *Gazette* was an advertisement for next year's issue of *Poor Richard's Almanack*, which was then in the press.

It was in that 1753 *Almanack* that Franklin modestly made the first revelation to the general public of the lightning rod. Squeezed between announcements for meetings of the Mayor's courts and the Quaker general meetings was an eighteen line paragraph, entitled, "How to Secure Houses, &c. from Lightning." Franklin wrote, "It has pleased God in His goodness to mankind, at length to discover to them the means of securing their habitations and other buildings from mischief by thunder and lightning. The method is this: provide a small iron rod (it may be made of rod-iron used by the nailers) but of such length, that one end being three or four feet in the moist ground, the other may be six or eight feet above the highest part of the building. To the upper end of the rod fasten about a foot of brass wire, the size of a common knitting needle, sharpened to a fine point; the rod may be secured to the house by a few small staples. If the house or barn be long, there may be a rod or point at each end, and a middling wire along the ridge from one to the other. A house thus furnished will not be damaged by lightning, it being attracted by the points, and passing through the metal into the ground without hurting any thing. Vessels also, having a sharp pointed rod fix'd on the top of their masts, with a wire from the foot of the rod reaching down, round one of the shrouds, to the water, will not be hurt by lightning." Franklin's lightning rod served a dual purpose: the point was to attract lightning away from other targets and the conducting rod was to provide the "electrical fire" with an easy, safe path to the ground. Franklin received almost unanimous accord on the conducting aspects of his device but, as we will see later, the wisdom of "attracting" lightning has been the subject of considerable controversy almost ever since.

The Franklin Rod in Action

At least some of the ten thousand subscribers to *Poor Richard* were quick to grasp the importance of the lightning rod. "Franklin rods" were soon erected on structures in many areas reached by the *Almanack's* circulation. History is not clear, however, whether rods were first used in France after D'Alibard's experiment or in America on the lower spires of Christ Church in Philadelphia. But one of the first successful demonstrations of the effectiveness of lightning rods concerned the Water Street home of a Mr. West in Philadelphia. The building had been outfitted with a Franklin rod. The conductor was a quarter-inch square iron rod whose base was joined to a ring on the top of an iron stake that had been driven into the ground. The conductor extended upward for four and a half stories to the chimney, where it connected with a half-inch diameter rod which extended more than nine feet into the air. The rod was topped with a pointed brass wire ten inches long. In 1760 lightning scored a direct hit on the rod. The stroke burned off three inches of the brass wire but left the house unharmed. The principle of the lightning rod had been proven under fire.

To the man in the street, Franklin was more than a talented scientist. He was a virtual hero. As Kant said, Franklin was a new Prometheus who had stolen the fire from heaven. Because of his contribution of the lightning rod, which he refused to patent, and his meticulous experiments and theories of electricity, Franklin received virtually every honor that could be bestowed by his contemporaries. Harvard gave him an honorary degree just one year after his kite experiment, the Royal Society awarded him the Sir Godfrey Copley gold medal, and King Louis XIV sent him a letter of compliments.

Most eighteenth-century scientists regarded Franklin as a very talented contributor to physics. His book on electricity became the bible of electrical science, was published in four languages, and was read and admired throughout the learned world. I. Bernard Cohen calls him the "Newton of his age, the one outstanding American scientist, the only one with a world wide reputation."

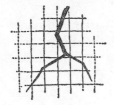

3 LIGHTNING RESEARCH

Franklin's lightning rods began to appear on the rooftops of American buildings. Exactly why they worked was a mystery to most of Franklin's contemporary scientists. But the rods did work, and this was all that mattered to the layman. As is usually true in most fields of technology, practical applications often precede the understanding of the natural phenomena that make the applications possible.

Scientists of the time generally agreed that lightning was a big electric spark and that one essential function of the rod was to provide an easy and safe path for the "electrical fluid." They differed, however, on the explanation of the origin of the electricity in the clouds and they didn't understand the mechanism and character of the lightning discharge itself. It was obvious that lightning, which was seen to come from thunderclouds, was—like rain, snow, and hail—a product of weather. They recognized that the key to the mystery of cloud electrification was inexorably linked to understanding weather.

The exact nature of electricity was unknown. In spite of Franklin's contribution of experimental observations, no one had yet developed a satisfactory theory of what electricity was. No one was able to "catch" a lightning bolt and measure its character. Proper instruments for recording and measuring lightning's power had not been developed.

The understanding of lightning was to benefit from research in both electrical and weather science. Some scientists studied electricity in their laboratories. Other students of electricity looked to the sky for the answers.

Electricity in the Air

Shortly after D'Alibard's success at Marly, Monsieur Lemonnier, the French astronomer, reported to the Paris Academy of Sciences that there is electricity in the air even in fair weather! He had found that sparks could be drawn from an insulated vertical rod even if no thunderclouds were near. Bigger sparks could be drawn from the rod when lightning flashed nearby.

The fact that electricity is in the air even when no lightning occurs was confirmed by Franklin during his investigations of the polarity of the charge of clouds. He erected a conducting rod on his house in September 1752. His purpose was "to draw the lightning down into my house in order to make some experiments on it." By comparing the charge brought down the rod with the charge of a known polarity of a charged Leyden jar, Franklin hoped to determine whether clouds were charged plus or minus. The rod extended nine feet above his house, from which a wire was brought through a glass tube in the roof down through the well in the staircase. The lower end of the wire was grounded to a well pump. "On the staircase opposite to my chamber door the wire was divided; the ends separated about six inches, a little bell on each end; and between the bells a little brass ball, suspended by a silk thread, to play between and strike the bells when electrified clouds passed overhead." Franklin found that "the bells rang sometimes when there was no lightning or thunder, but only a dark cloud over the rod." The tinkling of the bells served notice of approaching clouds or storms.

Using this rod, Franklin concluded by 1753 that the bottom of thunderclouds is usually negatively charged, although there are times when a cloud base is positively charged.

A contemporary of D'Alibard named De Romas also confirmed Lemonnier's discovery by demonstrating that sparks could be drawn from an insulated vertical conducting rod. Realizing that he might produce larger sparks if he were to use a taller rod or a kite, De Romas built a large, 18-square-foot kite to fly far up into the sky. De Romas was not successful until he included a fine copper wire in the kite cord, which was insulated from the ground. Then on June 7, 1753, he found that the end of the cord of his airborne conductor glowed with a sparkling discharge several inches in diameter that was visible in broad daylight. He used a curved wire to conduct the charge from the kite wire to the earth and insulated himself with a long glass handle. De Romas continued his atmospheric explorations and flew his kite to altitudes of nearly 600 feet. He learned that he could get larger sparks when he flew his kite near clouds. His most dramatic flight, made in 1757, produced a spark to earth nearly nine feet long! The obvious hazard of such kite-flying is the reason why today's kites carry this legend: "Do not fly with wire or metallic wrapped string."

Scientists found kite flights useful for producing big sparks that they could then study. These sparks were "artificial lightning" on a small scale. But scientists were more interested in the real thing: the violent bolts of lightning that jumped from thunderclouds to destroy life and property. We shall see here how man learned to measure lightning's character and behavior.

An Italian named Giovanni Beccaria, who had been doing research in the phenomena of fair-weather electricity, conceived a device that could make a record of nearby lightning flashes. He built an instrument in 1770 that he named a "Ceraunograph" that was used in conjunction with an insulated vertical rod. A grounding wire from the rod was led to the Ceraunograph, where a thin strip of wax-coated paper was inserted within a gap in the wire. A clockwork mechanism drove the strip of paper slowly through the points. A nearby lightning stroke would induce an electric arc to jump across the points. The arc burned a hole in the paper so the Ceraunograph could make a record of the frequency of lightning strokes. Beccaria found that an intense discharge burned a bigger hole than a feeble discharge. This was merely a qualitative instrument, which only told that the magnitude of one stroke was greater or less than another. It didn't tell whether a charge was plus or minus.

Seven years later, Georg Christopher Lichtenberg, the witty German satirical writer, then a professor of physics at Göttingen University, discovered a phenomenon that was later to pave the way for an inexpensive lightning research instrument. Lichtenberg experimented with the effect of electric discharges on powdered plates and found that electrical discharges created peculiar patterns. He connected a wire from a charged Leyden jar to a terminal directly above an insulated plate upon which he had sprinkled powder. Underneath this plate he placed a conducting plate that was connected to the other terminal of the Leyden jar. When he completed the connections, a spark jumped, scattering the powder. The peculiar patterns were different when he reversed the connections. A negative discharge from the electrode scattered the powder in a circular pattern, whereas a positive discharge scattered the powder in a fuzzy, flower-shaped pattern. He also found that the size of the "splash" was proportional to the magnitude of the discharge. The patterns produced this way have since come to be known as Lichtenberg figures. In 1924 J. Peters, of the Westinghouse Company, utilized this principle in an instrument he called the Klydonograph. The modern Klydonograph, using photographic film instead of fine powder, is a convenient tool of lightning researchers. The Klydonograph, and a similar instrument called the surge-voltage recorder, serve as silent watchmen on remote locations of modern transmission lines and give engineers an approximate in-

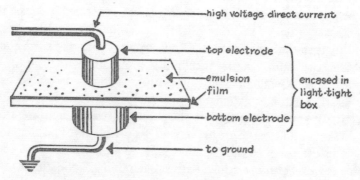

Fig. 8   Klydonograph is inexpensive instrument for measuring lightning current that leads current through a sensitized photo film. Developed image is a "klydonogram" whose size indicates magnitude of current and whose shape reveals polarity. See Plate XII for samples.

dication of the magnitude and polarity of lightning discharges that strike the lines. The shape of the image, or klydonogram, indicates the polarity and the size reveals the magnitude of the voltage. (See Plate XII.)

While the first tools of lightning research were being conceived, scientists were unraveling the mystery of electricity.

The Electron Theory

John Dalton proposed the first atomic theory in 1803, from which we learn that all matter is composed of tiny entities called atoms. All atoms of any element are identical: all nitrogen atoms are alike,

all copper atoms are alike and the atom of any one element is different
from the atom of any other element. Dalton suggested that the atom
is the smallest particle of matter and therefore is indivisible. However,
J. J. Thompson concluded in 1897 that atoms *are* divisible and that
each atom is in reality a miniature universe with moving parts somewhat like our solar system. The center of the atom is a nucleus, as the
sun is the center of our solar system. Whirling around the nucleus
are the planets of the atom, the basic particles of negative electricity
now called *electrons*. Thompson did not attempt to explain the composition of the nucleus, but he did say that the gain or loss of an
electron by an atom changes the properties and behavior of the atom.

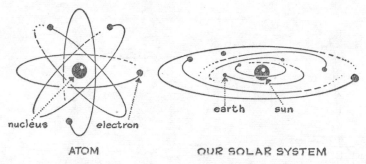

ATOM   OUR SOLAR SYSTEM

Fig. 9   Modern concept of the atom is similar to solar system.

It wasn't long before someone reasoned that if there are negative
charges whirling around in the atom there must be an opposite or
positive charge in the nucleus. Ernest Rutherford suggested in 1910
that the central core or nucleus of each atom was made up of *protons*
and *neutrons*, with the proton being exactly opposite in charge to an
electron. Neutrons have no charge. The Rutherford conception of the
atom, then, consists of a tight nucleus of protons and neutrons with
planet-like electrons revolving around it, and the entire atom is normally in electrical balance. Protons and neutrons each have been
found to be 1836 times as heavy as an electron. The protons and
neutrons stay in the nucleus, but the electrons are free to move if
pushed.

Rutherford's ideas were expanded further by the famous Copen-
hagen physicist, Niels Bohr, who stated that electrons travel in regular,
elliptical-shape orbits at a specific distance from the nucleus. Ameri-

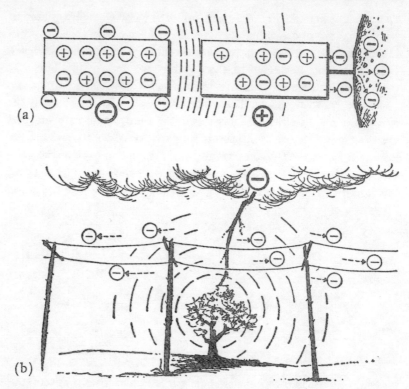

Fig. 10 Charging by induction. (a) In the laboratory. A negatively charged body (excess of electrons) will induce an opposite, or positive charge (shortage of electrons) on a nearby grounded body because of mutual repulsion. (b) In the field. A negatively charged lightning stroke near a long conductor, such as a power line or metal fence, will repel electrons in the conductor, causing a sharp wave of current to move away along the conductor. After the stroke is over, the wave may return to restore conditions back to normal.

can scientist Irving Langmuir showed that there are, in effect, regular, spherically shaped "shells" of orbit paths around the nucleus with each shell having a certain capacity for electron tenants. The atom is most content when its shells are complete. If a shell's quota of electrons is almost complete the atom welcomes additional electrons to fill the ranks. If a shell is almost empty the atom is willing to pass along to other atoms the few electrons it has in the partially filled shell. Elements with just one or two electrons in the outermost shell, such as copper, are generally good conductors of electricity because they are willing to pass electrons along. Atoms lacking only one or two electrons in their outermost shell, such as sulfur, tend to be good insulators and poor conductors.

Electrons, then, can be moved from atom to atom if they are pushed while protons cannot. The electron is so small that the world's most powerful microscope could not reveal it. Within the past few years some scientists have suggested that the electron itself may be a subminiature solar system. But whatever its exact composition, the electron behaves in a way that is now fairly well understood. It likes protons and dislikes other electrons. It dislikes other electrons so much that it tries to push them away in the same manner as two like poles of a magnet repel each other. A body with an excess of electrons will repel electrons on a nearby body even if the two bodies aren't touching each other. The process of inducing an electrical charge this way is called charging by induction. This characteristic of electron behavior will explain much of the lightning phenomena that will be discussed later. See Figure 10.

Engineers Capture Lightning

The increased understanding of electricity paralleled the applications of electrical energy. The electrical age, while fulfilling human needs for convenient power, also stimulated lightning research.

In October 1879, Thomas Alva Edison developed the first practical incandescent lamp. Unlike earlier lamps conceived by other experimenters, the Edison lamp gave forth light for many hours without burning up. With business acumen that typified his career, Edison almost immediately helped organize a company to distribute these lights and supply electrical power to New York City.

The historic Pearl Street power station in downtown New York City ushered in the electrical age on September 4, 1882. Convenient, clean power was made available at the flick of a switch. Generating stations sprang up near cities and networks of poles and transmission lines stretched to outlying areas hungry for the advantages of the electric light. It wasn't long, however, before electrical engineers discovered that their transmission network was a favorite victim of lightning.

As the age of electricity got into full stride in the early twentieth century, the greatest single cause of service disruption or "outage" was lightning. Even though the towers or poles were outfitted with lightning rods, the actual power transmission lines were vulnerable to lightning. Lightning often struck the power lines. This would send tidal waves of electrons surging along the wires to burn out generators and transformers or wreak havoc in the customers' buildings. Power failures were frequent. Faced with disgruntled customers and economic chaos, the power companies needed means of protecting their customers and the power equipment from ravages of lightning. The manufacturers of electric generation and transmission equipment accepted the challenge of learning how to combat lightning. Their first concern, of course, was to provide protection. Some new understanding was needed but the most important task was to get results.

The General Electric and Westinghouse companies played major roles in the search for defense against lightning.

General Electric's staff included Charles Proteus Steinmetz, a German-born immigrant. Steinmetz had taken a $12-a-week job with the electrical manufacturing firm of Eickemeyer and Osterheld in Yonkers, New York, after he arrived in the United States from Zurich in 1889. General Electric acquired his services when they purchased that firm in 1892.

Steinmetz, a dwarf with a distorted, crippled body, overcame his physical handicaps with his brilliant mind that soon received international acclaim. His study of alternating current phenomena resulted in many of the fundamental formulas used by electrical engineers today. Particularly outstanding was his reputation in the field of electrical transients—intense and brief surges of electricity. Steinmetz helped induce scientific talent to work at General Electric. His experiments in high voltages attracted the attention of E. E. F. Creighton, a former Stanford University professor at Union College. Creighton joined Steinmetz at the G.E. laboratory and continued the work in developing improved lightning arresters.

Lightning arresters protect transmission lines from lightning by allowing surges of electricity to bypass the line being protected and escape to the ground, much as excess pressure is released by a steam pressure relief valve. Design of arresters was a trial and error process in the early twentieth century. The only effective method of testing an arrester was actual service. Engineers knew that lightning was of a high voltage, but they could only speculate how high. They faced the difficult task of trying to fight an enemy whose strength they couldn't determine.

Engineers had found that arresters that worked in the lab failed in service when faced with actual lightning. Steinmetz reasoned that it was not merely a problem of high voltage but of the speed of discharge as well. He recognized that it takes time for an arrester to let lightning escape to the ground. A new testing device, called an impulse generator, was built by 1916 to determine the discharge speed of arrester designs. But unless engineers could learn about the time characteristics of lightning, effective arrester designs would be difficult to achieve.

Steinmetz was a prolific writer. He frequently retired to his camp at Viele's Creek on the banks of the Mohawk River, six miles from Schenectady. Here, in a small wooden shack, Steinmetz could forget the formalities of daily work. It was in Camp Mohawk, as he called it, that he wrote several textbooks on alternating-current electricity. A near catastrophe at Camp Mohawk significantly stimulated further advances in understanding lightning.

On a humid Thursday afternoon in Schenectady in August 1920, Steinmetz and an assistant had hoped to visit the camp, but a heavy downpour and thunderstorm made them decide to wait until the next day. It was a fortunate choice for when they arrived the next morning they found the camp a shambles. Lightning had struck a tree next to the building, broken a window, and splintered the table where Steinmetz usually worked. Wooden planks were split, wires were dangling, and a wall mirror lay shattered on the floor. Steinmetz was not only impressed but fascinated. He sent his assistant, Emil Remscheid, back to Schenectady to get his camera. This was one case of lightning damage where the clues would not be disturbed by curiosity seekers.

Steinmetz meticulously photographed, measured, and examined all the evidence nature had provided. Using his knowledge of physics, he calculated the power that must have been in the lightning. Remscheid carefully collected all the pieces and reconstructed the mirror so that the burning pattern of the lightning currents could be deduced from the fused silvering on the back of the mirror. Subsequent study and analysis gave Steinmetz a basis for estimating the power of a lightning stroke. This episode stimulated Steinmetz into a determined course of action.

He became inspired to construct a high-voltage generator that could simulate lightning in the laboratory. In 1921 Steinmetz convinced his company to proceed with the construction of a 120,000-volt generator that could discharge the equivalent of five million horsepower of electrical energy in a hundred thousandth of a second. The generator utilized about 200 huge lead-coated glass plates as condensers that could be charged by high-voltage transformers and special rectifier tubes. After the condensers had accumulated sufficient electrical charges, they would all discharge at once with a dramatic flash. Steinmetz first publicly revealed his "artificial lightning" to a group of guests that included Thomas Edison in the winter of 1922. Safely protected by a heavy screen, the group watched a large block of wood that had been positioned within the discharge gap. After Steinmetz gave the signal, there was a brilliant flash and a resounding bang. When their vision returned, the startled group saw the wood lying in splinters on the floor. But Steinmetz was not really satisfied. Dramatic as this machine was, he estimated that natural lightning was about five hundred times more powerful.

More potent generators were developed later, including one that entertained visitors in "Steinmetz Hall" at the New York World's Fair in 1939. Laboratory lightning with bolts more than fifty feet long gave man his first opportunity to conduct controlled experiments on the effects of sudden discharges of high-voltage electricity. Research with artificial lightning generators led to improvements in arrester design and lightning-protection measures. Steinmetz and his lightning machines helped create a reservoir of information about how materials and things react to high-voltage transients. But engineers had still made little progress in measuring the power of natural lightning when Steinmetz died in 1923. It was apparent that a laboratory lightning bolt that jumps a few feet is puny when compared to real lightning that leaps several thousand feet or even miles in its journey from a cloud to the earth.

Catching a Bolt

The measuring of a lightning bolt is a formidable task. Not only must you be in the right place at the right time, but you need sensitive and quick instruments. A lightning stroke is literally over in a flash. Conventional instruments such as galvanometers involve mechanical motion and are not suitable for measuring transient phenomena. The flash may be over before the instrument even starts to move. Even if the instrument could react quickly enough, some means of recording the reading is needed since a human observer cannot reliably make a mental note of how an indicating instrument behaved during a fraction of a second. These problems were alleviated by the cathode-ray oscillograph, a twentieth-century creation that paved the way for successful lightning measurements.

During the First World War, A. Du Four in France had developed a new kind of cathode-ray oscillograph that became the basis for the modern oscillograph. Unlike electromagnetic oscillographs which use a moving coil to sense electrical phenomena, the cathode-ray device employs a stream of electrons that can be deflected by an electric field. Current to be measured is fed into plates near which the stream of electrons in the cathode beam must pass. Varying the charge on the plates deflects the beam. The negatively charged beam, made of electrons, is attracted by a positive charge and repelled by a negative charge. After passing the charged plates, the beam then impinges upon a coated screen which glows when hit by electrons. J. J. Thompson had first built a cathode-ray tube as a piece of laboratory apparatus to measure the charge-to-mass ratio of the electron in 1897. Du Four, utilizing an improved cathode-ray tube developed by Karl F. Braun, made a special cathode-ray oscillograph that could be used for recording high speed electrical phenomena. Du Four's device was similar to the modern television picture tube but it differed from the TV tube in that the electron beam impinged not on a phosphorescent coating, but upon a sheet of film inside the face of the tube. Harald Norinder, professor of Uppsala University in Sweden, who had been studying lightning for years, recognized that here at last was an instrument swift enough to keep up with lightning.

Norinder visited Du Four in Paris in 1922 and returned home to modify the oscillograph for lightning research. He conceived a special relay, triggered by the electron beam itself, that would actuate the oscillograph. Norinder's relay prevents the beam from exposing the film unless a surge, such as caused by lightning, occurs. Then the beam hits the recording film and the record is made. He set up the first oscillograph for lightning research in a laboratory outside of Uppsala and later outfitted a movable laboratory for making field measurements. Norinder obtained the first oscillograph record of lightning surges on a transmission line in 1925. Science had estimated the brevity of a lightning stroke; now there was direct evidence. Norinder's film record showed that this surge was composed of two major surges and several small ripples, with a total duration being hardly more than one ten thousandth of a second (100 microseconds).

General Electric and Westinghouse engineers acquired cathode-ray oscillographs. The instruments were too large and expensive for easy field operation so American engineers soon developed portable models. Although smaller, the new instruments had limitations: as with Du Four's oscillograph, the film was inside the tube. Whenever the film had to be changed the vacuum was broken so the tube had to be pumped out again. This was inconvenient, particularly when out in the field. Later the engineers evolved a flourescent-screen cathode-ray tube bright enough to permit taking a picture of the wave shape shown on the tube with a camera outside of the vacuum.

After 1928, lightning research accelerated to a faster pace. Both Westinghouse and General Electric established lightning-research stations near high-voltage power-transmission lines that year. The Pennsylvania Power and Light Company built a 220,000-volt transmission line between Siegfried and Wallenpaupack in Pennsylvania's Pocono Mountains. This was one of the highest voltage lines installed in that area and the G.E. engineers designed special new lightning arresters for it. The company officials were concerned whether the lightning-protection methods used were adequate. Summer storms in the Poconos were apt to be both frequent and violent. When the line was first put into operation, engineers had installed surge-voltage recorders at critical points over a 65-mile section to obtain data on the frequency and intensity of lightning strikes to the lines. Late in the summer of 1928 lightning struck, an arrester failed, and the lightning current burned out a transformer. Why did the arrester fail? The Lichtenberg pictures from the surge-voltage recorders revealed part of the story of what had happened, but the engineers needed better data on the transient characteristics of the lightning stroke. The cathode-ray oscillograph was brought into action to get the facts.

The expense and complexity of installing these instruments precluded sprinkling them about an entire transmission network. But the surge voltage recorders had yielded clues as to where lightning was most likely to strike, so the following summer G.E. engineers built a temporary corrugated-metal field laboratory in a likely spot. They attached a wire to one of the supporting towers of the line in the hope that the tower would be hit and some of the current could be shunted into the oscillograph in the hut. Then they settled down to wait. And wait they did. Sunny days found them swimming in a nearby lake. On cloudy days they sat around the radio, listening for static to warn them of an approaching storm. When the engineers heard the static they would get ready for work. But time and time again they waited in vain. Thunder would crash as lightning hit nearby towers, but it seemed as though lightning was determined to ignore the tower that they were ready to measure. Days turned into weeks, and as the summer waned the men grew impatient. Their three-month vigil finally paid off on a hot summer afternoon. Lightning struck their tower!

As the flood of electrons went through the tower to earth, the oscillograph dutifully recorded the voltage wave shape of the lightning stroke. For the first time in the United States, measurements were made within a few feet of where a direct stroke of lightning hit and showed that lightning surges last only a few millionths of a second. Meanwhile, Westinghouse engineers were similarly investigating the 154,000-volt Cheoah-Alcoa line of the Aluminum Company of America in Tennessee.

In 1930 Westinghouse engineers set up a field laboratory near the 110,000-volt line of the Arkansas Power and Light Company to monitor the effect of lightning on the power transmission lines. The engineers learned how brief and how large a lightning surge can be. Lightning once struck the line four miles away but the surge easily flowed along the wires to the oscillograph recorder. A peak of five million volts was reached in less than two-millionths of a second. Lightning moves a mighty tidal wave of electrons!

Engineers garnered considerable data on lightning surges in transmission lines during this period. The research bore fruit in the form of improved lightning arresters and other protective measures for electrical installations. Power interruptions decreased.

Field research tapered off in 1930 and 1931 as the nation bogged down under the Depression. The building of field laboratories was an expensive way to get data. Engineers had to set up their equipment where they expected lightning, only to wait in vain for nature to co-operate. Even Klydonograph devices were costly. Engineers needed a cheaper way to measure the magnitude of lightning strokes.

Students of electricity had long known that the flow of electricity creates a magnetic field. Hans Oersted, a Danish scientist, had dis-covered in 1820 that a magnetic compass was deflected when placed near a wire in which electrical current was flowing. Scientists also knew that certain materials can be easily magnetized. As early as 1901, the German scientist F. Pockels had used small rods of basalt placed near lightning conductors to provide a measurement of how much current passed in the conductor. A lightning stroke passing down the conduc-tor magnetized the basalt rod, and subsequent analysis of the degree of magnetism could be used to compute how much current had passed. This idea was put to work in 1932 in what is now called the magnetic link.

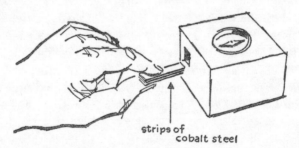

strips of
cobalt steel

Fig. 11 "Magnetic link" that had been near an object struck by lightning is tested to see if it has become magnetized. Amount of magnetism pres-ent indicates magnitude of the lightning current.

The magnetic link is a small bundle of cobalt-steel strips enclosed in a molded tubular container about the size of a cigar butt. The link is attached perpendicularly to a conductor in which lightning currents are anticipated, such as a power line or a tower-grounding wire. After a storm technicians examine the link to see if it has become magne-tized, using a simple compass to sense the magnetism. If the link is magnetized, the technician takes it to a laboratory where the intensity of the magnetism can be measured and the magnitude of the lightning current can be computed. W. W. Lewis and C. M. Faust of General Electric reported in 1934 that magnetic links had revealed that lightning currents down a transmission tower reached values as high as 63,200 amperes. This is enough to light 75,840 ordinary 100-watt bulbs simultaneously.

Cameras in Action

The evidence on the magnitude of a lightning stroke was piling up. But all these measurements and research efforts had not explained the mechanism of the lightning discharge. How does lightning actually come down from a cloud? Does it move all at once, or is it a series of electric discharges? Ordinary cameras are not quick enough to be of much value for analyzing the history of a lightning flash.

The earliest lightning photographers used ordinary cameras. They set the shutter for "time exposure" and left it open until a flash was seen. The shutter was closed. The film had then captured a lightning stroke from start to finish. The picture, however, could not reveal the progress of a lightning stroke, since it showed only the total path. German scientist H. W. Dove once viewed lightning through a slotted rotating disc and deduced in 1835 that a lightning flash can be composed of several strokes along the same path. A countryman of his, B. Walter, proved this photographically in 1901. Walter took a picture of lightning while he rotated or "panned" his camera to spread the picture across the film. His picture showed seven separate strokes.

Sir Charles Vernon Boys, the English scientist who is noted for his work in gravitation, galvanometers, and studies of bubbles, conceived a special camera for lightning studies in 1902. Now called the "Boys" camera, it is a two-lens camera that employs one lens that rotates around a stationary lens. The stationary lens takes a normal picture, while the rotating lens simultaneously spreads a second picture over a large area of the same film in a brief time period. The two pictures can be compared and analyzed.

It is ironic that Boys was never successful in taking a lightning picture with his camera. He tried in vain for more than thirty years. His camera failed to produce useful results until 1933, when B. F. J. Schon-

land, of the Bernard Price Institute of Geophysical Research in South
Africa, had the camera modified. Using his Boys camera, Schonland
captured many lightning strokes on film and was able to formulate
the present theory on how a lightning stroke progresses. This will be
discussed in Chapter 7.

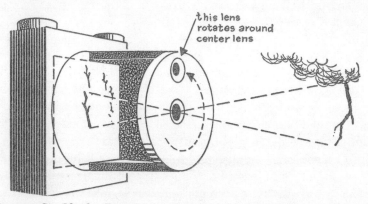

Fig. 12   Sir Charles Boys invented a special lightning camera that takes
two pictures simultaneously on a single sheet of film. Center lens takes
normal "time" exposure, while rotating lens "smears" the same picture
around the film to reveal how the stroke progressed with passing time. See
Plate X for sample.

How could these theories be correlated with ground measurements?
Up to this point engineers and scientists had not produced simultaneous photographic and electrical records of a lightning stroke.

The builders of the Empire State Building in New York City un-
knowingly presented lightning researchers with a novel investigative
tool in the 1930's. This giant, steel-skeleton structure proved to be a
favorite target of lightning in the New York area. The building is
hit more frequently by lightning than most man-made objects. G.E.
engineers decided that here was an ideal spot to conduct lightning
experiments. Under the direction of the late Karl McEachron, the
engineers installed oscillograph equipment in the tower of the building in 1935 to measure lightning strikes to the radio mast. The top of
the mast towered 1250 feet above the street and 38 feet above the
building itself. (The present television transmitter mast was erected
in 1950, increasing the height of the structure to its present 1472 feet.)

The next season they installed super-speed Boys cameras in a building eight blocks to the north. Here, on the 56th floor of the tower of 500 Fifth Avenue, the cameras commanded a clear view of the Empire State Building. They achieved the first satisfactory oscillograph data in 1937, and for the first time science had simultaneous photographic and electrical data of a lightning bolt. The Boys pictures told how the stroke behaved in terms of time and distance and the oscillographs revealed its electrical magnitude in terms of time. During the first three years of the Empire State Building experiments, the building was struck no less than 68 times, amply proving that lightning can strike the same object more than once, and in one year simultaneous photographic and oscillograph information was obtained for 19 strokes.

G.E. discontinued the Empire State research during the war, resumed the program in 1948, and finally terminated activities there in 1950 when the tower space was needed for television transmitting equipment.

Some contemporary scientists have questioned the validity of the Empire State data as not being representative of lightning strokes that normally go an additional 1250 feet or so to the ground, and have maintained that the strokes measured on the building might not have otherwise occurred had the building not been there. Nevertheless, the data from this program forms the backbone of the statistical information on the transient characteristics of lightning.

Weather

While engineers were measuring lightning's effects on the ground, scientists were learning more about lightning as a weather process.

Weather researchers, like the electrical engineers, made real progress only when practical problems provided an impetus. We will see that the airplane provided both the means and the incentive for accelerated weather research that helped to broaden our current understanding of lightning and thunderstorms.

Facts about clouds were hard to get back in the 1700's. For one thing, man was earthbound. He could not get up into the clouds to make measurements. He could not capture samples of clouds. He had only crude instruments for making measurements. Without measurements, theories could not be confirmed and the sphere of man's knowledge could not expand. The study of thunderclouds and weather advanced only as fast as the ability to measure and observe improved.

Weather science had not progressed substantially from Aristotle's time. The Dark Ages added little to scientific advancement in any learned field. Weather science reawakened in the 1600's with the invention of two essential weather instruments, the thermometer and the barometer.

Galileo Galilei first devised a crude air thermoscope in 1607. The Florentines improved upon this by developing a sealed thermometer: the Grand Duke Ferdinand II of Tuscany is believed to have possessed one of these forerunners of the modern thermometer as early as 1654. A German-born physicist, Gabriel Daniel Fahrenheit, made the first mercury-in-glass thermometer in 1714.

Besides temperature, a basic key to the weather process is pressure. Winds arise when air from a region of one pressure flows into a region of lower pressure. Meteorologists needed the barometer before they could properly analyze weather.

In the Middle Ages it was not known that the earth's atmosphere exerts a pressure. At the beginning of the seventeenth century Grand Duke Ferdinand became irritated when engineers failed to get a suction pump to lift water 50 feet from a well. Ferdinand appealed to Galileo to find out what was wrong. Galileo studied the problem for years, but died before he had the answer. When he died in 1642, his investigations were carried on by his student, Evangelista Torricelli. Just a year later, Torricelli concluded that air has weight. He invented the earliest form of the glass-tube mercury barometer and found that air exerts a pressure equal to a 30-inch-high column of mercury. Since mercury weighs 13.6 times as much as water, this pressure is equal to 34 feet of water. Torricelli explained that it was this pressure that determined how high a suction pump could lift water, and that the engineers who tried to pump water 50 feet were up against a basic fact of nature.

Torricelli went on to predict that it was the weight of air above the ground pushing down that created the pressure, about 15 pounds per square inch at sea level, and that pressure should decrease in magnitude at higher altitudes. Blaise Pascal, French philosopher and mathematician, confirmed this in 1647 by inducing his brother-in-law, Florin Perier, to carry a barometer to the top of an Auvergne mountain in

France. Perier reported that in transit from the cloister gardens at the base of the mountain to the 4800-foot peak of Puy de Dôme the mercury fell 3.15 inches. "This filled [me] with wonder and admiration," Perier wrote.

Students of weather climbed mountains to observe the atmosphere from a new viewpoint. But even here, observations were handicapped by air turbulence caused by the earth's irregular surface contours. As any amateur weatherman knows, meteorological phenomena cannot be properly analyzed on the basis of ground measurement alone. The atmosphere must be examined in depth, since much of what happens near the surface results from activity at higher altitudes. The science of meteorology made a major advance when measuring instruments became light enough to be carried aloft by kites. Three years before Franklin's famous experiment, a Professor Alexander Wilson of the University of Glasgow used a chain of six kites to carry thermometers. A thermometer hung on a string below the tail of each kite. A waxed line, ignited before takeoff, burned to the string and released the thermometer when the kite reached altitude. A paper tassel served as a parachute to break the fall. While an assistant held the kite line, Dr. Wilson dashed to retrieve the thermometer before it had a chance to warm up.

Kites could not lift heavy mercury barometers; therefore, they weren't too useful for exploring pressure at altitudes. But in 1845 Vidi patented a new, all-mechanical barometer that contained no mercury and was light in weight. Pressure changes cause deflection of the thin walls of an evacuated chamber. This deflection, working against a spring, moves an indicating needle or recording pen. Now called the aneroid barometer, it could be carried by a kite, even when a clock-driven recording mechanism was attached.

Men in Balloons

Man himself first ventured aloft in 1783 when Jean François F. de Rozier braved the hazards of a flight in the Montgolfier brothers' "fire balloon," which was fed by hot air rising from a fire. J. A. C. Charles, a French physicist, quickly sensed the potential of this as a new meteorological tool and, in December of that same year, he went aboard a hydrogen-filled balloon to become the first scientist to break free from the surface of the earth, rising to 9000 feet. He carried a thermometer and a barometer and found that not only did pressure decrease, but the atmosphere became progressively cooler as the balloon rose. The limit of atmospheric understanding was raised to new heights in 1804 by the noted chemist, Gay-Lussac, who made measurements of pressure, temperature, and electric field from a balloon at the then unheard-of altitude of more than four miles. Capturing samples of air in previously evacuated glass bulbs, Gay-Lussac was able to show that although the pressure and temperature decreased with altitude (he found it a cool 15° at 23,000 feet), the composition of air was essentially unchanged.

The idea of sending weather instruments up in unmanned balloons was suggested as early as 1809, but it wasn't until 1892 that such flights were successfully attempted. An instrument balloon reached 53,000 feet that year. Scientists quickly found that free-flight balloons were not without serious disadvantages. Winds frequently blew the balloons far from the launching point, making recovery of the instruments impossible. Many flights were wasted.

A partial solution to this problem was introduced a year later when Lawrence Hargrave invented the box kite. Hargrave's design could lift far more weight than the ordinary flat kite. Climbing as high as 10,000 feet, these powerful kites easily lifted devices that could record temperature and pressure. Experimenters found it simple to recover their instruments. They just reeled in the metal kite wire. The box kite could be retrieved without trekking over the countryside, but the weight of thousands of feet of wire limited the altitude to which it could be flown.

The U.S. Weather Bureau relied on kites for many years as a means of sending meteorological instruments into the atmosphere. Seventeen Weather Bureau stations were equipped with kites by 1898. These kites could lift about 30 or 40 pounds, over half of which was the weight of the piano wire that held them. The wire was played out from a winch and a reel housed in a small hut. The reel for the wire was grounded to reduce lightning hazards.

But in spite of these precautions, at least one man was killed. In August 1919, Charles Hackelsmiller, a laborer who was helping during a kite flight, was standing near the main kite wire. About a mile of wire was out at the time, when a brilliant flash appeared. Lightning struck: like a skyrocket, the wire became a shower of sparks, the grass was set on fire, and Hackelsmiller fell dead.

The invention of radio brought the ability to transmit instrument measurements from atmospheric balloons, making recovery less essential. Important meteorological data can now be obtained, even if the balloon and its instruments are lost. Developments starting in 1927 led to the perfection of the *radiosonde* and *rawinsonde*, a combination of weather instruments and radio transmitters that can be carried by a balloon. The radiosonde measures such items as temperature, humidity, and pressure while simultaneously transmitting the information by radio signal to a companion radio receiver on the ground. The signals are then converted into numerical data. Since the data is received instantaneously, modern weather balloons are valuable forecasting aids. Radiosondes have been regularly probing thunderstorms and the atmosphere during the last twenty-five years, providing a large share of the data science now has about the first 100,000 feet of the atmosphere.

The growth in aviation proved to be the greatest stimulus to atmospheric research. Not only did the airplane provide the means for carrying heavy loads into the air: it also created a need for more weather information. Weather severely restricted flying activities. Commercial air travel, awakening in the 1920's and expanding in the 1930's, was handicapped by weather. Bad weather forced planes to stay on the ground. Flight experience during the First World War demonstrated the futility of attempting to fly through thunderstorms. New radio navigation aids had improved the ability of planes to find their way at night or in clouds, but encounters with thunderstorms always proved hazardous and sometimes fatal. Newspapers often blamed lightning for unexplainable crashes. The further expansion of air travel in the 1940's, and the necessity for extensive military flying in any weather during the Second World War, accentuated the need for more information about thunderstorms.

During the war, diverse research and development projects were carried out to reduce risks of flying in bad weather. These programs concentrated on weather problems encountered by planes during landing and takeoff. Fog and poor visibility severely limited airport operations. The British FIDO, or fog-dissipation systems, attempted to solve one airport problem. New electronic aids, such as radar, reduced the hazards of blind landings. The phenomenon of ice formation on aircraft was studied and deicing equipment was developed.

But one weather phenomenon still relatively uninvestigated, which caused serious accidents to both military and commercial aircraft, was the thunderstorm. Thunderstorm turbulence caused the demise of many an airplane. And with the necessity for military and commercial airplane operation in any weather, aviation needed better information about the character, structure, behavior, and intensity of the thunderstorm.

The National Advisory Committee for Aeronautics (now the National Aeronautics and Space Administration) began probing thunderstorms in an instrumented XC-35 airplane in 1941 and 1942. These flights gave a brief look at this weather monster and helped in defining the problem of how to study thunderstorms with airplanes.

The Thunderstorm Project

In response to pleas from the military services and scheduled airlines, a committee of experts from the Army Air Force, Navy, Weather Bureau, airlines, Civil Aeronautics Board, M.I.T., University of Chicago, and Carnegie Institute of Washington met in 1944 to plan a program of investigation. Dr. Horace R. Byers of the University of Chicago and L. P. Harrison of the Weather Bureau proposed gathering information about the thunderstorm by having several airplanes, flying at different altitudes, make simultaneous penetrations into thunderheads. They knew that this could be hazardous, but rugged planes had survived thunderstorms in the past. The decision to launch a major research program, the Thunderstorm Project, was made in 1945, and the Weather Bureau assumed responsibility for organizing the program.

Congress appropriated funds that summer and Dr. Byers was appointed director. Just two weeks after he had assumed his duties, the war ended. With hostilities terminated, the armed services released equipment, planes, and personnel for peacetime uses, permitting a more thorough investigation than had been anticipated.

The program was spread over a period of two summers. The first season's activities investigated storms near Orlando, Florida, a region of frequent thunderstorm activity. Then the project moved to Clinton

Air Force Base in Wilmington, Ohio, for the 1947 season to obtain data on storms that frequented the inland regions of the United States. This was research on a grand scale. Twenty-two railroad freight cars were required to carry the equipment when the operation moved from Orlando to Wilmington. This did not include the planes, trucks, or jeeps. Quite a contrast to Franklin's one-man operation with a simple kite!

Dr. Byers worked out the detailed test plans jointly with Commander Maynard of the Navy and Colonel B. Holzman of the Army Air Force. The primary items of interest measured (both vertically and horizontally) in the air were motions and temperatures, electrical field, and gustiness or turbulence. Ground measurements were made of rainfall, temperatures, surface winds, and pressure changes. Radar and radio tracking of aircraft correlated all the observations and related the storms and aircraft in time and space.

Radiosonde balloons carried instruments aloft, primarily to measure vertical motions. The airplane, of course, was the major tool of investigation. Pilots are well acquainted with the fact that the turbulence encountered in a thunderstorm can severely strain, or even break, the structure of an airplane. Most aviators avoid even going near a thunderstorm. Project personnel selected the Northrop P-61C Black Widow for the program because of its rugged structure and its ability to carry heavy instrumentation. It weighed almost fifteen tons. This big twin-engine machine—originally an Air Force night fighter—had sufficient performance to enable it to fly itself out of bad trouble and sufficient endurance to make repeated cloud penetrations. The Air Force made ten planes available.

In spite of the hazards of thunderstorm flying, experienced flight crews volunteered to work on the project. Many were young men just back from military action. Two men—a pilot and a radar officer—manned each Black Widow during the Florida flights. A third member—a weather observer—joined the crew during the Ohio investigations.

The Thunderstorm Project got under way when the first instrumented Black Widow roared down an Orlando runway on June 27, 1946. From that initial flight until the last plane completed its mission in Ohio on September 15, 1947, a total of 1363 thunderstorm penetrations were made by the planes.

As often as possible, five airplanes participated in each mission, with each assigned a particular altitude. Generally the planes flew at constant altitude, separated from each other by 5000-foot increments, with the lowest assigned an altitude of 5000 feet in Florida and 600 feet in Ohio. Each plane made several traverses at its altitude, with flights sometimes being limited only by the amount of film in the data-recording cameras.

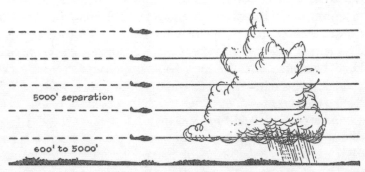

5000' separation

600' to 5000'

Fig. 13   Five pilots of the Thunderstorm Project simultaneously probed thunderstorms at different altitudes with instrumented Northrop P-61 aircraft.

Planes probed more than 76 separate thunderstorms, two of which were at night. The pilots met downdrafts as fast as 79 feet per second that dropped their planes more than 2000 feet, and updrafts as great as 84 feet per second that carried their planes upward more than 5000 feet. Blinding lightning struck the planes 21 times, and hail hammered the aircraft on 51 of the 812 passes in Ohio. Aside from an ocasional jostling about in the cockpit or mild cases of nerves, the crews were unharmed. The airplanes suffered minor hail damage and lightning burns. Pilots all agreed that the thunderstorm, which will be described in the next chapter, is a formidable giant that should be respected and avoided.

The Thunderstorm Project was the most comprehensive program of thunderstorm investigation ever undertaken, costing $863,000 and involving several hundred people. The 1363 airplane penetrations, supplemented by 1375 balloon soundings, yielded data that outlined the major structural features of the thunderstorm and gave new understanding about the generator of lightning.

Our basic knowledge about lightning and the thunderstorm has been built up from both small and big investigations, involving such diverse efforts as those of a Philadelphia printer, a dwarf scientist, and a million-dollar research project. Hundreds and perhaps thousands of other people working alone or as part of organized teams have contributed ideas, information, observations, and inventions over the years that have built the foundation of what we know today about lightning. We know infinitely more about "nature's artillery" than did the first scientists. But the quest for future understanding is still continuing, for there is still much to learn. Today lightning research goes on, with scientists trying to find out more about how thunderstorms become electrified, how to modify clouds, and how to utilize lightning for practical purposes. We will learn more about the present frontiers of lightning research later.

But where do we stand now? In the following chapters you will learn what the thunderstorm is and how it operates as well as what is known about lightning and how to combat it.

PART TWO

ORIGIN AND CHARACTER OF LIGHTNING

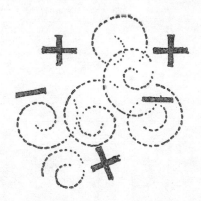

4 BIRTH OF A STORM

Lightning has been reported under the smoke of volcanoes. Lightning has been said to have struck "from a clear blue sky." Where *does* it come from?

Most scientific evidence shows that the generator of lightning is that giant of all clouds, the *cumulonimbus*, or more commonly, the *thunderhead*. An ordinary cumulus cloud gone wild, the thunderhead is a huge storm factory, a monstrous atmospheric machine with the energy of an atomic bomb. Its violent, boiling turmoil of air currents can throw the heaviest airplane about like a cork in a heavy sea. In 1925 the pride of the U.S. Navy dirigible fleet, the *Shenandoah*, was wrenched into three pieces by the turbulent up- and downdrafts of a thunderstorm over the Ohio River valley. Fourteen crew members died.

Although thunderstorms are most impressive for their thunder and lightning, they also bring rain and sometimes hail. Their rain makes them desired visitors to parched summer regions. But citizens of the plains states do not welcome these huge storms because they can lead to tornadoes. Thunderstorm hail, sometimes larger than baseballs, has pounded the noses and windshields of airplanes and smashed valuable crops.

These tempestuous thunderclouds are eternally roaming the globe, with new storms forming as others die. It has been estimated that 1800 are in progress at any one time.

A typical thunderstorm consists of one or more thunderstorm "cells" and covers a land area of from 20 to more than 200 square miles. Plate XVII was taken from an airplane flying at 18,000 feet and shows a parade of thunderstorms nearly 140 miles long. The thunderclouds are big. Measuring many miles across, they usually grow 25,000 feet tall,

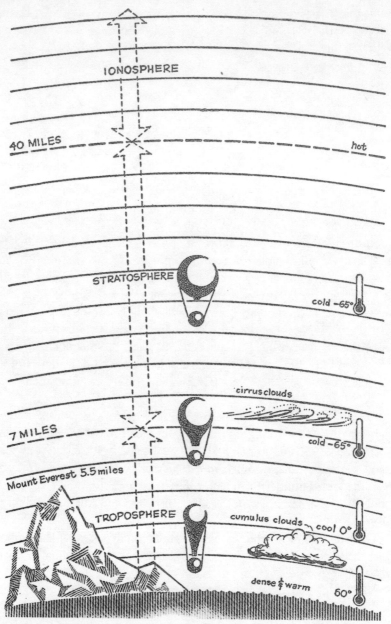

IONOSPHERE

40 MILES   hot

STRATOSPHERE   cold -65°

cirrus clouds

7 MILES   cold -65°

Mount Everest 5.5 miles

TROPOSPHERE   cumulus clouds   cool 0°

dense & warm   60°

Fig. 14   We live at the bottom of an ocean of air.

but pilots have reported seeing thunderheads towering above 60,000 feet—nearly 12 miles high! Moving along at about 15–35 miles per hour, a thunderstorm cell has an approximate life of about 60–75 minutes. When it dies, it frequently gives birth to another that takes its place.

Lightning is born in the conflict of the thunderhead. To better understand where it comes from, let's take a look at how thunderstorms start and how they grow.

Temperature plays a major role in the formation of any cloud. Updrafts or convection currents resulting from temperature variations are a major cause of a cumulus cloud. Picnickers know that a white sheet or blanket laid out in the sun stays cooler than the dirt or dark-green grass nearby. Some parts of the earth, because of differences in material, texture, shape, and color, absorb more sunlight and heat than others. A field of golden wheat stays cooler and heats up slower than a freshly plowed field of dark, rich soil. And a lake or pond absorbs less heat than the field of wheat.

These effects of heating help explain the most familiar type of thunderstorm, the summer afternoon or "heat" thunderstorm. Before dawn, most land regions are approximately the same temperature. But by late morning, after basking in the sun, some areas, materials, and regions are at different temperatures than others. Because of the effect of sunlight and heating, the preponderance of thunderstorms born over land occur between 2 and 8 P.M.

As the earth, trees, and ponds get warmer, they warm the adjacent air. The warmest spots heat the air most. The warming of the air causes it to expand, making it lighter than the cooler nearby air. The heavier, cool air buoys the lighter warm air upward like a stratosphere balloon. As warm smoke from a chimney drifts upward, so does the warm air that forms a cloud. This rising air is called a convection current. It rises rapidly for perhaps several miles but as it rises it starts to cool, transferring some of its heat to the colder air found above the earth. The higher it goes, the colder it gets.

When the air takes off on its vertical journey, it contains some moisture. All air contains some water. It can be in solid form—as snow, hail or ice crystals; it can be liquid like rain or tiny droplets like fog; or it can be in gaseous state such as invisible water vapor. On a clear day, water is in the air in the form of invisible vapor. We see that there is moisture in air when warm air comes in contact with the glass of a cold drink. The water condenses or collects on the glass where the air meets the cold glass. Wipe the walls of the glass dry and it comes right back and happens again. A given volume of warm air can hold more water than the same volume of cold air.

As the bundle of warm air rises skyward it not only expands because of the decreased pressure at higher altitude, but it also gets cooler and cooler and eventually gets to the temperature where it contains all the moisture it can hold: it is saturated. As the air cools still further, some of the water vapor is squeezed out as condensation, forming microscopic droplets of water so small that it would take millions of them to fill a thimble. Most clouds you see are made of these drops. Others, such as high-altitude cirrus clouds, are made of tiny ice crystals.

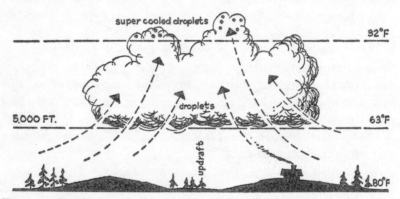

Fig. 15 Simple cumulus cloud is formed when updrafts carry moist air aloft where vapor condenses in the cooler air.

Condensation usually starts around dustlike particles in the air. You "make a cloud" when you exhale on a cold winter day. The air from your lungs contains moisture and as you blow it out into the cold air, the exhaled air is cooled to below its saturation temperature. Some of the water condenses into tiny droplets and you have a visible fog or miniature "cloud." When vapor condenses, heat is liberated.

Most clouds dissipate as fast as they form because the condensed moisture is absorbed by relatively dry air around the cloud and the heat is dissipated. The rate of formation of a cloud is frequently matched by the rate of dissipation so the cloud maintains a steady size. Clouds may deteriorate completely if brisk upper winds scatter the cloud among the cool dry upper air.

The Thunderstorm

A thundercloud outclasses all other clouds. It grows faster than it can dissipate. Only after spending itself with rain and lightning does the thunderstorm dissipate. The major feature of a thunderhead is its strong updraft. In a big, well-developed thunderstorm, several strong updrafts may be present. Each one sets up convection activity as a unit or substorm, called a thunderstorm "cell." A full-blown thunderstorm is like an army of self-contained divisions.

The life cycle of a typical thunderstorm cell can be described in three natural stages:

1. The cumulus stage, typified by strong updrafts throughout the cell.

2. The mature stage, characterized by both up- and downdrafts, at least in lower half of the cell.

3. The dissipating stage, identified by weak downdrafts throughout the cell.

Cumulus Stage

The cumulus stage is sometimes preceded by several small clouds, once believed by Scandinavians to be the messengers of Thor, the thunder god.

An ordinary cumulus cloud may, because of peculiar geographic and atmospheric circumstances, grow faster and faster. For example, a rising warm convection current may get an extra boost from sliding up the side of a mountain, where the added heating helps speed the updraft. Other factors, which will be discussed in the next chapter, nurture thunderstorm growth. The characteristic updraft of a young thunderhead is a rising column of air like a giant chimney, nearly a mile in diameter, thrusting its way skyward at speeds of about 25 miles per hour. The taller it grows, the faster the updraft and the more water vapor carried aloft. The moisture condenses faster than the surrounding air can absorb it, and as it condenses it releases heat that adds to

the updraft, so the cloud keeps growing in all directions. During these
birth throes, there is a gentle inward turning of the winds on the surface, heading toward the cloud. Smoke from ground fires or burning
trash can be seen converging upon the thunderstorm, being drawn by
the surface winds that feed the growing mushroom of rising air.

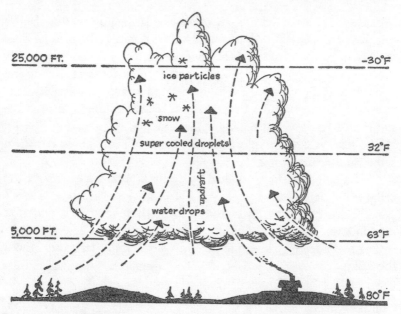

Fig. 16   Cumulus stage of a thunderhead is characterized by updrafts
throughout the cloud cell.

An aid to thunderhead formation is slow winds aloft. If the horizontal winds were faster near the top of the cloud than at the bottom,
the winds might sheer off the chimney and reduce the essential, tall
draft.

Condensation increases while the thundercloud grows larger and
the top reaches higher. Carried upward to at least 25,000 feet, and
sometimes as high as a frigid 60,000 feet, some of the vapor freezes
directly into tiny ice crystals. Snow may be present too. In the lower,
warmer regions of the cloud the condensation takes the form of miniature water droplets. Some of these droplets are tossed by the updraft
up to the colder regions where they collide with the ice crystals and
freeze, layer upon layer, around the crystal, building up sizable hail-

stones. Often there are alternate layers of snow and ice in a hailstone. In the lower regions some of the droplets join together, forming larger raindrops. As the raindrops and hailstones get larger, they soon become too heavy for the updraft to support, so they begin to fall.

When the hailstones fall, they pass through warmer regions and usually melt and turn into raindrops before they reach the ground. As the melted hail and heavy raindrops start to come down, the thunderstorm cell enters the mature stage. Gusty winds near the ground signal that the storm is about to start.

Mature Stage

The falling rain is accompanied by lightning. Almost immediately changes take place in the air circulation of the cell. Where formerly only an updraft was at work, there now appears a downdraft as well. The first rain hits the ground in a limited area of a few square miles. As the cell develops, this area expands, spreading rain over an increasingly larger area. The falling rain produces the downdraft of cool air, which deflects out over the ground to an area even greater than that covered by the rain.

As would be expected, under a moving thunderstorm cell, the area of rainfall moves along the ground at approximately the same speed as the cell itself. The presence of water droplets in the cloud makes it possible for radar to track and observe the progress of a thunderstorm. High-frequency radio waves sent out by the radar transmitter bounce off the droplets of water in the cloud, and return to the radar receiver where they are presented on the radar screen or scope.

The downdraft is first found only in the middle and lower regions of the cloud, but it gradually expands both horizontally and vertically throughout the duration of the mature stage. The warm updraft still persists, with its greatest speed of about 65 miles per hour near the top of the cloud. The downdraft is cooler and weaker than the updraft, and has its highest speed of about 35 miles per hour in the lowest part of the cloud and may be a mile in diameter. These conflicting drafts make it pretty rough going for any airplane that may attempt to fly through a thunderstorm. The plane encounters updrafts that push it upward and downdrafts that throw it downward like a giant roller coaster.

As the cell continues to grow and the downdraft develops, the surface winds switch direction, becoming strong and gusty as they flow outward in all directions. If the storm is traveling fast, these outflowing winds may spread more in one direction than in others.

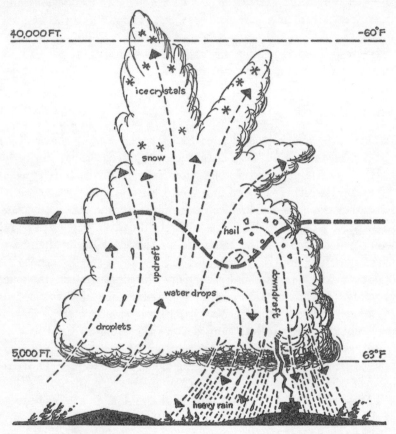

Fig. 17   Mature stage of thunderhead brings rain and/or hail, lightning, thunder, and downdrafts.

Two obvious effects occur almost simultaneously on the ground. The first gust of wind brings a sudden drop in temperature. The rain and downdraft may cool the hot summer air from an uncomfortable 85 to 90 degrees all the way down to a refreshing 65. This cooling is most noticeable at the core of the downdraft or center of rainfall, but the spreading downdraft may bring temperature relief to areas as far as twenty miles away. Humidity also dips. The moisture in the warm air lying on the earth's surface was carried aloft by the updraft, squeezed out, and brought down by gravity as rain.

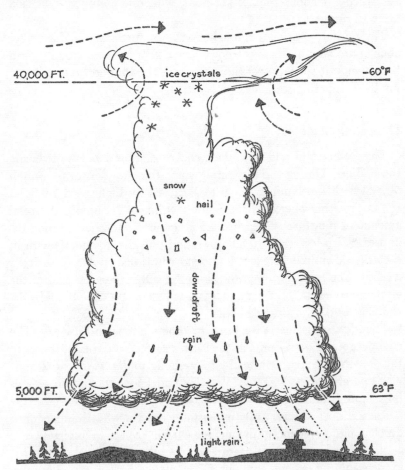

Fig. 18 Dissipating stage of the thunderhead is reached as downdrafts occur throughout the cell. Brisk upper winds may shift the cloud top, producing the familiar anvilhead.

During the mature stage, the cell reaches it greatest height. Periodic protuberances or "turrets" appear at the top of the thunderstorm. Most large clouds usually blossom forth with several such turrets in the course of development. Measurements have shown that each successive turret reaches higher than the previous one and that the throbbing coincides with the amount of rain and lightning that is produced by the storm. Normally the turrets grow at about 12 miles per hour and recede at about 8 miles per hour, with one complete pulsation every 18 minutes.

The rainfall continues throughout the mature stage and lasts for about 15 to 30 minutes as the downdraft area grows and grows. When the downdraft spreads over the entire cell, the thundercloud is entering the dissipating stage.

Dissipating Stage

The falling rain and downdraft cool the ground below, reducing the updraft. During the dissipating stage the thunderstorm is often capped with the familiar "anvil top" caused by high-speed winds in the upper atmosphere. As the updraft chimney is cut off, the total amount of moisture carried upward is reduced and condensation decreases. With less water to fall down and pull the downdraft with it, even the downdraft is reduced. Ground winds disappear as the drafts weaken. The temperature of the air in the cell approaches that of the clear air around it. Thirty minutes is usually enough time to allow the thundercloud to dissipate and die.

Thunderstorms may give birth to others a few miles away. The cold outflow of downdrafts at the earth's surface often contributes to the growth of a new cell nearby by wedging under warm air to start new updrafts of new clouds. Weathermen know that some regions have more thunderstorms than others.

Science does not yet fully understand exactly why thunderstorms develop more frequently in one geographic region in preference to another, but topographical features apparently play an important part in determining where cumulonimbus clouds will form. Thunderstorms are more frequent near and over land masses and continents than over oceans. They are rare in arctic regions and common in tropical areas. In the next chapter we will examine the origin and pattern of these global vagabonds.

The late professor C. E. Brooks of Harvard studied reports from weather stations all over the world and estimated that nearly 1800 thunderstorms are in progress at any given moment. Other meteorologists have calculated that about 44,000 thunderstorms are born every day. These storms do not always occur in the exact same places, but a general global pattern of thunderstorm frequency does exist. Weathermen can now estimate how many thunderstorms will appear in any general area of the earth over the course of a year. They now can also predict thunderstorms on a short time basis with some reliability. But they cannot predict far in advance precisely when and where a storm will start. To understand why the storms occur where they do, we must see how they start.

During the Thunderstorm Project, Dr. Byers studied 584 new clouds observed by radar during 21 summer days in Ohio. He found that fewer new clouds formed over uniform flat plains than over rugged terrain or plains areas that were sharply dissected by streams and rivers. But in neither Florida nor Ohio could Byers find any special cloud starting point.

Other studies show that rivers flanked with bluffs may contribute to thunderstorm development. Islands and peninsulas, mountains or rugged relief, and sharp temperature contrasts between adjoining lakes or swamps and dry land tend to nurture updrafts. Most observers have found that ocean thunderstorms are uncommon, except near islands and coasts. But some coasts, such as Southern California, do not have strong temperature contrasts between land and sea and do not generate many thunderstorms.

A peculiar combination of circumstances gives birth to a thunderstorm. There must be a lifting action to get an updraft started and the air must be conditionally unstable. Conditionally unstable air is stable when at rest near the ground, but becomes unstable when lifted to higher, cooler altitudes where its moisture vapor condenses. The air must also contain enough moisture, because it is the condensation of moisture that releases the heat that feeds the characteristic updraft of a cumulonimbus. The lifting action can come from either solar heating, colliding air masses, converging winds, or upward sliding along a mountain slope. Atmospheric conditions and topography must also condone continued growth. For example, the upper air must be relatively still or the updraft chimney may be cut off.

Once they start, virtually all thunderstorms are similar in structure and general behavior to the one described in the last chapter. However, thunderstorms do have different names, classified according to how they are produced. There are two major categories: frontal and air mass. *Frontal storms* may result when large masses of air collide. *Air-mass storms* occur within a slow-moving or stationary air mass, away from fronts.

Air-Mass Storms

There are two variations of air-mass thunderstorms: the *heat* or *convective* type (described in the previous chapter) and the *oro-*

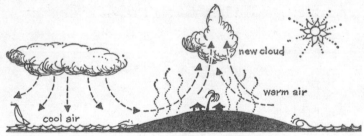

Fig. 19   Heat or convective storms get their initial updraft from different solar heating of the earth's surface.

graphic, or mountain type. The heat thunderstorm grows in relatively still air and may start over land or water almost anywhere in the world. Solar heating of different materials, such as earth, vegetation, or water, may produce an updraft. A shady place under a cloud may feed the updraft above a sunny place. Or rising air over a warm island or peninsula next to cooler water can start the updraft. Although the heat thunderstorm may grow day or night, it is most frequent during summer afternoons and is common over Florida and islands in the tropics. Certain topographical features, such as large inland bodies of water, breed heat thunderstorms. Small "artificial" heat thunderstorms may form from the updraft of a forest fire or the ejectamenta from a volcano, if atmospheric conditions are right. Predicting *where* a heat storm may start is sometimes easy, but forecasting *when* is more difficult. Often a day or two of hot weather are needed to generate the conditions. Heat thunderstorms are usually scattered, and an observer on the ground gets the impression that thunder and lightning are leapfrogging from one place to another.

The *orographic*, or mountain thunderstorm, is similar to the heat or convective thunderstorm. Here again it is the sun's heat that provides the initial energy to drive surface air upward. However, the up-

Fig. 20 Orographic or mountain-thunderstorm updraft starts along warm slopes of a mountain.

draft starts primarily because the slopes of a mountain will absorb more of the sun's energy than the atmosphere. The warm slopes give off some of their heat to the adjacent air, making it warmer than the rest of the atmosphere. The warmed air is then buoyed upward, and the necessary updraft has begun. As with any thunderstorm, the proper combination of initial conditions of temperature and humidity are necessary or perhaps only a small cumulus cloud will result, if any cloud at all.

Frontal Storms

The other major category of thunderstorms, frontal thunderstorms, depends less directly on heating. The Midwest sees many of these. Frontal thunderstorms get their initial upward boost from the dynamic force of moving air masses. Frontal storms are divided into several classes: cold front, warm front, stationary, and prefront, or squall line. The collision of masses of air at different temperatures usually results in updrafts, but not always thunderstorms.

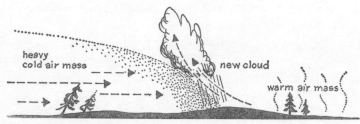

Fig. 21   Advancing cold air mass can wedge warm air upward to start an updraft at the cold front.

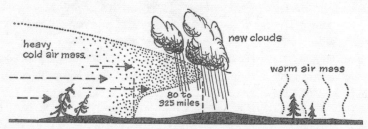

Fig. 22   Overrunning cold front may cause storms over a wide area.

The typical cold-front thunderstorm follows a prolonged warm, humid period. When a mass of heavy cold air moves in, it slides under the warm air and wedges it upward, starting a draft. If the lifting is fast enough and the moisture sufficient, a thunderstorm might start. Rain is a common result at a cold front. If the cold front is abrupt, a distinct "squall line" may appear. Sometimes the cool air moves in very fast, overrunning the warm air, producing rain or thunderstorms over a large area, perhaps 80 to 325 miles ahead of where the front meets the ground.

Warm fronts can also produce thunderstorms but here the warm air derives its uplift from sliding up and over the cool air mass in front of it. Wispy "mare's-tails" (cirrus clouds) created at high altitudes, serve notice of an approaching warm front. The warm "front" is usually gently sloped and its thunderstorms are usually scattered.

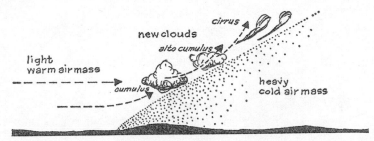

Fig. 23   Advancing warm air mass slides up over heavy cool air mass, producing new clouds ahead of the front.

Thunderstorms sometimes start when converging winds meet. The interaction of conflicting air masses may start updrafts through wavelike turbulence. Still other thunderstorms get their upward kick when moving air is deflected by a row of mountains.

Frontal storms move along with the general air movement, so once a frontal storm has formed, weathermen have a reasonable idea of where it will go. The heat thunderstorm is a bit more tricky. Since it is born in a relatively still air, there are no prevailing winds to force it in any particular direction. Consequently, its own activity may make it wander in a haphazard course. Heat thunderstorms formed over mountain ranges, however, tend to move along the ridge of the mountains, even when moderate winds are blowing in various directions at various levels. These storms rarely drift into mountain valleys.

The birth of a thunderstorm is so influenced by the vagaries of the atmosphere and topography that it is difficult to predict long in advance. The topographic features that tend to breed updrafts do not always produce thunderstorms. Colliding fronts do not always produce thunderstorms. Fronts do not always behave in a predictable fashion, sometimes moving in an erratic way. It is apparent that the birth of a thunderstorm at a given place at a given time is the result of a complex combination of circumstances and events. Have patience with your local weatherman!

Global Influences

Topography, local heating and local atmospheric conditions are only part of the picture. Global air circulation exerts an over-all influence on thunderstorms as it does on all aspects of the weather.

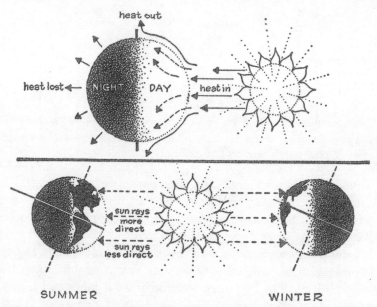

Fig. 24   Earth is a big "heat engine" with heat entering near the equator and leaving near the poles and on the night side. Seasonal differences are due to inclination of the earth's axis and to the earth's orbit around sun.

The sun and the rotation of the earth control the fundamental global pattern of atmospheric circulation. The skin of air surrounding the earth is two times thicker near the equator than near the poles, because of warmer temperature and less gravity at the equator. The tropical and subtropical regions of the earth, being closest to the sun and subject to more direct rays from the sun, absorb more heat than the temperate or polar areas of the earth. The net result is that the earth is a big heat engine, with heat entering near the equator and leaving at the poles. These temperature differences, combined with the earth's rotation, cause the air to circulate over the globe. If the earth had a smooth surface of only one material, the atmosphere

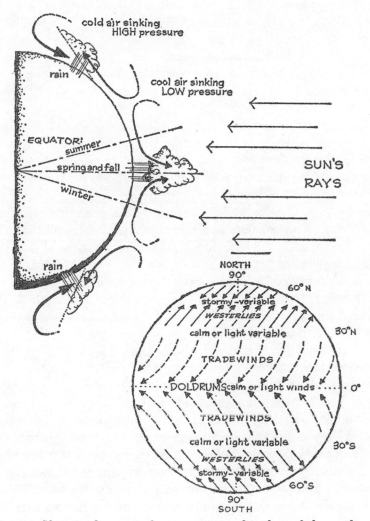

Fig. 25 If atmosphere were homogeneous and surface of the earth were one smooth material, global air circulations would be like this. Many factors modify this idealized circulation pattern.

would circulate as shown in Figure 25. But this ideal circulation of the atmosphere is tempered by the differing effects of the oceans and the land masses. The circulation of the seas, blocked here and there by continents, assumes a different course than that of the atmosphere. Water absorbs heat more slowly than land, and the water imparts some of its heat to the air lying next to it. The water surface also exerts friction on the moving air while it is modifying the air's temperature.

The earth is usually half covered with clouds. This causes some areas of the surface to be heated more slowly than others. These diverse factors combine with seasonal variations to produce the highly irregular and variable circulation of the atmosphere. When the irregularities of the global circulation are superimposed on the peculiar requirements of thunderstorm generation, we can understand why our weathermen have problems in predicting thunderstorms. But in spite of the complexities and the seemingly random appearance of thunderstorms, a global pattern of annual thunderstorms has emerged.

Weather stations all over the world keep track of thunderstorm activity in their own areas. Their method is simple. If thunder is heard anytime during a calendar day—it could be heard once or twenty times —it is recorded as one "thunderstorm day." For example, New York City has an average of 31 thunderstorm days per year. Unfortunately, this simple counting system does not precisely indicate thunderstorm activity. For one thing, thunder can only be heard for a limited distance. This is particularly significant near cities, where background noise masks the sound of thunder that might be heard if the station were in the country. Weather stations may be so far apart that a thunderstorm could slip unheard between them. But even with these imperfections, the system of counting thunderstorm days does give a reasonable picture of thunderstorm activity around the world. Very little data, however, has been obtained about the pattern over the oceans.

Around the Globe

There are few places in the world that have never been visited by a thunderstorm. But if you wish to escape the flash of lightning and the sound of thunder, you had better retreat to either the north or south pole. Thunder is almost never heard in the polar regions. Those frigid areas north of the Arctic Circle and south of the Antarctic Circle have thunderstorms about once every ten years. Thunderstorms are most frequent in the tropical and temperate zones. For example, parts of Panama, Indonesia, and Equatorial Africa can have up to 200 thunderstorm days per year. In the heart of Brazil, the town of Caruauri hears thunder 206 days of the year, while the residents of Kampala in Uganda (British East Africa) are bombarded on the average of 242 days each year.

The capitals of the major world powers all have about the same number of thunderstorm days per year. London and Peiping score 16, while Paris, Rome, and Moscow each hear thunder 21 days.

In the United States there is a wide variation of thunderstorms with location. Generally the South has more than the North and the East Coast has more than the West Coast. Seattle, Washington, for example, hears thunder five days a year, while at Eastport, Maine, there are 13 thunderstorm days. Los Angeles, on the Pacific, is fairly free of thunder and lightning, with an average of only three days per year, while Wilmington, North Carolina—at about the same latitude but on the Atlantic coast—hears thunder 46 days each year.

Florida has more thunderstorms than any other region of the United States. The prevailing wind, moving across the Gulf of Mexico and gaining moisture as it goes, finds the scattered lakes and sun-baked terrain of the Florida Peninsula a ripe environment for thunderstorm formation. Residents of Daytona Beach have the distinction of living in the most thundery city in the United States with an average of 93 days per year. Orlando and Fort Meyers tie for second place with an average of 91 per year. In 1958, Fort Meyers was champ, with 102 thunderstorm days. North of Florida, thunderstorm frequency decreases to 53 in Savannah, 38 in Norfolk, 31 in New York, and 20 in Boston.

The Pacific Coast is relatively quiet, with only two per year in Oakland and San Francisco. There is a marked increase in thunderstorms just east of the Rockies. The Great Plains states are greeted with thunder somewhat less frequently than Florida. A region of high thunderstorm frequency, second only to Florida, centers near Santa Fe, New Mexico, during the summer.

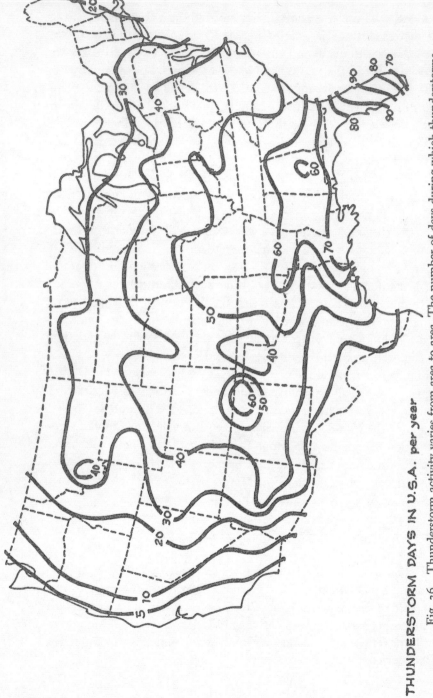

THUNDERSTORM DAYS IN U.S.A. per year

Fig. 26 Thunderstorm activity varies from area to area. The number of days during which thunderstorms occur is represented on this map as an "isokeraunic" line. For example, western portions of California have 5 thunderstorm days each year. U.S. Weather Bureau derived this map based upon records of 266 weather stations up through 1951.

Centers of thunderstorm activity shift from one area of the country to another during the year, generally moving southward with the sun during the winter. June, July, and August produce about half of the storms for the entire year in most parts of the United States. The summer increase is particularly marked in the Rocky Mountain area during July. The mountain type of summer storm is quite common there. The figures for thunderstorm days shown on the U.S. map are general averages. Within any area, the pattern may be quite different. For example, in California there are about three thunderstorm days in Los Angeles and one or two in San Francisco, but this rises to three or five in the Sacramento Valley and five or ten in the foothills, and may be on the order of 20 in the regions of altitude of 4000 or 5000 feet. The Gallatan forest, in the southwest corner of Montana near the Wyoming border, has an average of 44 thunderstorm days each year. This is more than double the average for that general area. Missoula, Montana, has twice as many thunderstorm periods as a point just 40 miles west, proof that topography plays an important part in summer mountain-thunderstorm formations.

ANNUAL AVERAGE THUNDERSTORM DAYS
FOR U.S. CITIES

ALABAMA	Birmingham	67
ALASKA	Juneau	0
ARIZONA	Phoenix	26
ARKANSAS	Little Rock	58
CALIFORNIA	Los Angeles	3
COLORADO	Denver	44
CONNECTICUT	Hartford	27
DELAWARE	Wilmington	33
FLORIDA	Miami	70
GEORGIA	Atlanta	50
HAWAII	Honolulu	6
IDAHO	Boise	18
ILLINOIS	Chicago	37
INDIANA	Indianapolis	42
IOWA	Des Moines	46
KANSAS	Wichita	54

KENTUCKY	Louisville	46
LOUISIANA	New Orleans	75
MAINE	Portland	27
MARYLAND	Baltimore	32
MASSACHUSETTS	Boston	20
MICHIGAN	Detroit	32
MINNESOTA	Minneapolis	39
MISSISSIPPI	Jackson	64
MISSOURI	St. Louis	49
MONTANA	Helena	31
NEBRASKA	Lincoln	47
NEVADA	Las Vegas	13
NEW HAMPSHIRE	Concord	24
NEW JERSEY	Trenton	35
NEW MEXICO	Albuquerque	47
NEW YORK	New York	31
NORTH CAROLINA	Raleigh	41
NORTH DAKOTA	Bismark	31
OHIO	Columbus	40
OKLAHOMA	Tulsa	58
OREGON	Portland	6
PENNSYLVANIA	Philadelphia	27
RHODE ISLAND	Providence	21
SOUTH CAROLINA	Charleston	56
SOUTH DAKOTA	Sioux Falls	46
TENNESSEE	Memphis	51
TEXAS	Houston	57
UTAH	Salt Lake City	35
VERMONT	Burlington	28
VIRGINIA	Norfolk	38
WASHINGTON	Seattle	5
WEST VIRGINIA	Charleston	47
WISCONSIN	Milwaukee	33
WYOMING	Cheyenne	46
DISTRICT OF COLUMBIA	Washington	35

Where there are thunderstorms, there is lightning. Knowing how many thunderstorms a year may occur in a particular area is of considerable importance to power-company engineers. They use thunderstorm-day data to help decide where the most comprehensive protective equipment must be installed. Federal, state, and private agencies responsible for preserving our nation's timberlands from forest fires also need to know the likelihood of thunderstorms. Airline and military pilots pay respectful attention to regions of frequent thunderstorms when planning a flight.

While predicting exactly when and where thunderstorms will occur is difficult, modern technology has developed means for tracking them once they start. Radar, which can bounce radio waves off the precipitation in a thunderhead, is an invaluable tool of weathermen today. Long-range radars easily detect approaching storms and permit advanced warning announcements. Another new technique, called "sferics locating," has been developed by the Defense Department. Lightning strokes generate an electromagnetic disturbance called *sferics*, or more simply "static," that can be received easily on specially designed radio receivers. The sferics produced by severe storms and squalls can be detected at great distances. The first comprehensive Sferics Locating System was installed at the Severe Weather Warning Center in Kansas City, Missouri, in 1959. It was developed by the Army's Signal Research and Development Laboratory and the Stavid Engineering Corporation, a division of the Lockheed Aircraft Corporation, and is manned by the Air Force's Air Weather Service. In conjunction with six remote stations—in Arkansas, Oklahoma, Illinois, Iowa, South Dakota, and Kansas—the central station at Kansas City detects and tracks severe thunderstorms as far as 1000 miles away. Each station detects the lightning discharges and simultaneously informs the central station of the time and direction. Special electronic devices plot the position of the discharge and display the information on a special map. The operator sees this as shown on Plate LIII. Ultimately the Sferics Locating System may monitor storms as far as 2000 miles from the central station, thereby providing coverage of the entire United States. The weatherman is finally getting a long-distance look at oncoming storms.

Thunderstorms plague airmen, drop hail that destroys valuable crops, and spit dangerous lightning. Lightning is destructive. Lightning is capricious. Lightning interferes with and threatens our lives.

Yet lightning is actually necessary to maintain the balance of nature. Scientists credit lightning with performing a vital role in keeping the earth in electrical harmony with the upper atmosphere.

6 ELECTRICITY IN THE AIR

The earth is like a big battery, continuously losing electrons to the atmosphere. Charles Coulomb, the French scientist, had shown in 1795 that air can conduct electricity away from charged bodies. Although air is admittedly a very poor conductor compared to a metal like copper, it can, nevertheless, conduct electricity. The German physicist F. Linss estimated in 1887 that the earth would lose almost all of its charge in less than an hour unless the supply were replenished. F. J. Scrase, scientist at England's Kew Observatory, computed in 1933 that the world could lose its charge in about 48 minutes. How, then, is the supply of electrons on the earth maintained?

C. T. R. Wilson, noted English physicist, suggested in 1920 that it is thunderstorms that feed electricity back to the earth. Most scientists today agree that the steady loss of electrons to the atmosphere is balanced by thousands of daily thunderstorms that pump electrons back to earth. All clouds modify the flow of electricity, but most of the replenishment is from thunderstorms. Approximately four out of every five lightning strokes that reach the ground transport electrons back to earth.

The fascinating give and take of electricity between the earth and the atmosphere has its origin in outer space. The sun and stars emit high-energy particles called cosmic rays. Cosmic rays collide with neutral particles of air, producing charged particles, called *ions*, that will conduct electricity. Cosmic rays reach and penetrate the envelope of air that surrounds our planet but most of their energy is spent before they reach the earth. The atmosphere fortunately shields us from this deadly radiation. However, in dissipating their energy as they pass through the upper layers of air, the cosmic particles crash into air molecules, knocking off an electron here and there, and creating ions.

Ions are merely atoms or molecules that are not in electrical balance. An atom of oxygen, for example, is normally in electrical harmony, with the total number of electrons being equal to the total number of protons. When an electron is knocked off, the oxygen atom is left with more protons than electrons and has a net positive charge. A particle of matter deprived of an electron is called a positive ion. If, on the other hand, an extra electron joins up with an atom or molecule a negative ion is born. An ionized molecule may acquire a cluster of a dozen other molecules—forming what is often called a "small" ion. When a small ion adheres to particles of matter such as sea spray, dust, or smoke, we have a "large" ion. An unattached electron is called a "free electron."

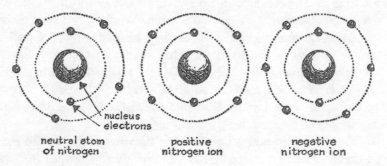

neutral atom   positive   negative
of nitrogen   nitrogen ion   nitrogen ion

Fig. 27 An ion is an atom or molecule whose normal complement of electrons has been changed.

Cosmic rays don't produce all the ions in the atmosphere. Processes here on earth aid ionization too. Radiation from the normal disintegration of radioactive materials, like radium or uranium, ionizes some of the air near the surface of the earth and accounts for most of the ions found near the ground. The radioactive debris of nuclear and thermonuclear explosions causes additional ionization. But the major creator of ions is cosmic radiation.

Our atmosphere has many ions—some oxygen ions, some nitrogen ions, etc.—besides the normally balanced atoms and molecules that compose the atmosphere. About 65,000 ions populate each cubic inch of air near the ground. This is infinitesimal compared to the billions of neutral molecules, but the presence of these ions makes it possible for the atmosphere to conduct electricity. It should be pointed out again that air is a poor conductor, but when we consider that the earth-atmosphere system is such a huge physical thing, even a little bit of conduction per piece of air adds up to a lot of electrical carrying ability.

Scientists have found that the population of ions, relative to the number of neutral particles present, increases as we go to higher altitudes. Far above the earth, at altitudes of 40 miles or so, the atmosphere consists of more ions than uncharged particles or neutral molecules. This region is called the *ionosphere*. There are ten times as many electrons at 180 miles up than there are at 70 miles up. So many ions and free electrons are present that the ionosphere is an excellent conductor of electricity.

Above the ionosphere lies the *exosphere* and a highly charged region of space now called the Van Allen radiation belts, after Dr. James Van Allen of the University of Iowa who directed some of the satellite and rocket experiments made by the United States during the International Geophysical Year. Highly charged particles have apparently become caught in these belts by the magnetic field of the earth. The radiation belts surround the globe and are most dense above the equator and weakest above the poles. The effect of these belts upon the electrical balance of our planet is not yet known. It seems, however, that the interchange of electricity between the earth and the atmosphere is controlled primarily by the umbrella of the ionosphere that encloses the electrical processes in which the thunderstorm plays a part.

J. A. Chalmers, physicist at England's University of Durham, has shown that the inside of the ionosphere is "uncharged," containing the same number of negative ions as positive ions. The earth, with its surplus of electrons, is about 300,000-volts negative with respect to the ionosphere. It is this voltage difference that powers the flow of electricity from the earth to the atmosphere. The ionosphere and the earth's surface are like the oppositely charged plates of a Leyden jar or condenser. The earth's surface is the negative plate and the ionosphere is the positive plate. The atmosphere, like the glass of a Leyden jar, is the insulator.

But this is an imperfect or "leaky" condenser because the air insulator, which separates the earth from the ionosphere, can conduct electricity. The 300,000-volt difference drives electrons from the earth toward the ionosphere. The rate of flow, called the *air-earth* or *ionic current*, has been calculated to be between 1400 and 1800 amperes. Because it originates from the entire surface of our planet, this current is too small for us to feel, amounting to only .000009 amperes for every square mile. Sensitive measurements have shown that this estimate is reasonably accurate.

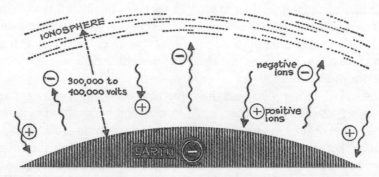

Fig. 28   A fair weather or "ionic" current flows between the earth and the ionosphere in cloudless areas over the earth.

Because there is a potential difference between the earth and the ionosphere, there is also a difference in potential between any two levels of the atmosphere, much as different pressures exist at different depths of the sea. When we walk about, our heads are at a different voltage than our feet. We don't feel it because the amount of current flowing through our bodies is negligible. Near the earth this voltage difference or *potential gradient* is about 150 volts per meter (39.37 inches) of height, so a six-foot man has his head at about 260 volts compared to his feet. When a good conductor, like a kite wire, is hoisted hundreds of feet above the ground, the voltage difference between the air and the end of the wire may be enough to produce a spark. See Figure 29.

The normal fair-weather potential gradient varies from month to month, reaching a maximum of 20 per cent above normal in January, when the earth is closest to the sun, and falling to about 20 per cent below normal by July, when the earth is farthest from the sun.

How do the electrons get from the earth up to the ionosphere?

Falling raindrops often drag positive ions back to earth and water moisture rising from the earth generally leaves electrons aloft when returning to earth as rain or snow. Precipitation, therefore, contributes to the loss of electrons from the earth. But the prime carrier of charge during fair weather is the atmosphere's ions. These ions transport

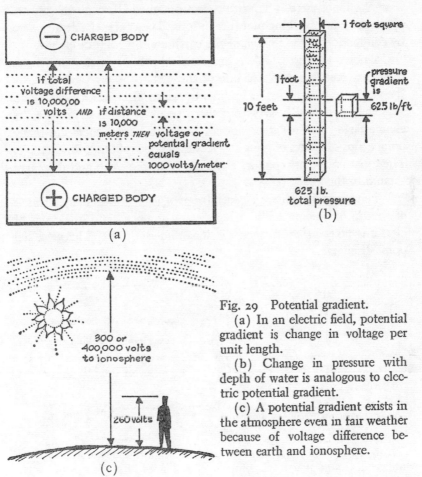

Fig. 29   Potential gradient.
(a) In an electric field, potential gradient is change in voltage per unit length.
(b) Change in pressure with depth of water is analogous to electric potential gradient.
(c) A potential gradient exists in the atmosphere even in fair weather because of voltage difference between earth and ionosphere.

electrons in two ways. Ions may pass an electron from one to another. And the ions themselves can actually move, carrying electrons along with them. All particles of a gas—be they atoms, molecules, or ions—are in continuous random motion. The warmer the gas, the more active the particles are. The ions—some positively charged, some negatively charged—are always banging around in the air. Some pick up and lose electrons and may be restored to an uncharged state, but new ones are always being formed by radiation or by collisions. The lighter, "small" ions are more mobile than heavier, "large" ions. The positive ions drift toward the earth and the negative ions migrate toward the ionosphere. The earth's electrons move through the atmosphere by riding on rising moisture or ions. They enter the atmosphere by conduction at the surface of the earth and by point discharge.

Unknown to most people is an electrical process often going on at their very feet. Franklin was one of the first to become intrigued by the ability of sharp electrical points to "draw electrical fire." He had seen that a charged body with a sharp point or rough edges loses its charge faster than a flat or smooth body. In nature there are many points: tips of blades of grass and leaves or edges of sand, for example. These natural points conduct electrons from the earth and discharge them into the air.

When ions collide in a concentrated area, such as the charged region of the tip of a point, additional ions are produced and a transfer of electrons takes place between the ions and the point. This is called point discharge.

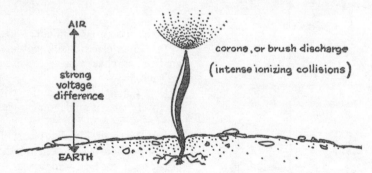

Fig. 30 The strong potential gradient beneath a thundercloud may cause intense discharge at natural points such as blades of grass, tips of leaves, etc. The electrons that are exchanged between the earth and the atmosphere pass through nature's points.

Electricity flow from a point is normally a quiet, invisible process, but if the potential gradient, or voltage difference, becomes sufficiently great, ion collisions yield enough energy to excite particles of air and make them luminous. This visible ionization is termed *corona*, or

brush discharge and can sometimes be seen in darkness as a bluish
glow. Another popular term is *St. Elmo's fire*. The kite experiment
of De Romas is an example of how atmospheric electricity can produce visible sparks or corona. The kite wire of De Romas reached up
into a region of air that was at a different potential or voltage than
the ground. Electrons at one region of the atmosphere were under
pressure to move to the other region. Since the kite wire was a better
conductor than the air, the electrons traveled along it. Intense point
discharge occurred at the ends of the wire and near the frazzled strands,
producing corona and light.

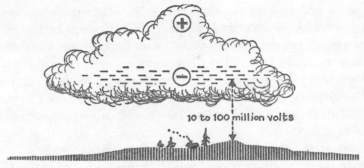

Fig. 31 The typical thundercloud has separated electrical charge so that
the upper regions are predominantly positive (deficiency of electrons)
and the base regions are negative (surplus of electrons).

The areas underneath thunderstorms experience more potent effects than those areas enjoying fair weather. C. T. R. Wilson had
found in 1917 that the rate at which electricity flowed from the earth
fluctuated widely when thunderstorms were near. It was this observation that led Wilson to suggest that it was the influence of thunderstorms over the globe that fed electrons back to the earth. Count-
less experiments since then have found that a thundercloud generally
has two regions of electrical charge. Near the base, the cloud is usually
negatively charged with a huge surplus of electrons. Higher up the
cloud is usually predominantly positively charged, with a deficiency of
electrons. The top of the cloud generally emits positive ions, while
the negatively charged cloud base produces the electrical effects observed on the ground. Sometimes charge is also stored in the clear
air immediately around the cloud.

The Charging of a Thundercloud

How the thundercloud separates the charges into different areas is a natural phenomenon that is not clearly understood. Many theories have been advanced to explain how the thundercloud gets its charge. Men have been trying, since Franklin wrote his thoughts on the subject, to come up with a satisfactory explanation of how cloud electrification comes about. But the scientific community of today, more than 200 years later, still is divided into many fields of view. C. E. Bruce, scientist of the Electrical Research Association Laboratory in England, writing about thunderstorms in the December 1959 issue of the *Journal of the Franklin Institute,* called attention to a letter of 1755 where Benjamin Franklin said, "I wish I could give you any satisfaction on clouds. I am still at a loss about the manner in which they become charged with electricity; no hypothesis I have yet formed perfectly satisfying to me." Bruce commented that Franklin's last sentence "might, and indeed can still be found in any exhaustive discussion of the subject."

Most of the theories point to the upward-driving energy of the thundercloud as being a prime agent in the separation of charge. The violent turbulence in the updraft of a cumulonimbus may produce collision and rubbing of air, water, ice, ions, or other particles, causing some pieces to become charged opposite to others. After collision the bigger particles are apt to be negative and smaller particles positive. Gravity and the action of updrafts may help to separate the charge. The late Professor P. E. Shaw of England's Nottingham University has shown that rubbing two pieces of the same material can produce a different electrical charge on each piece. Bruce has pointed out that this can even happen with wind-blown dust, powder, or even dry ice. He cited the production of lightning in the smoke of volcanoes as an illustration of how electrical fields might be produced after particles become charged by friction and then separated into different areas by the action of gravity.

G. C. Simpson suggested in 1927 that the breaking up of raindrops might result in charge separation. His theory says that the charging of drops, like peeling off a wool sweater on a dry day, leaves one drop charged one way, and the other the opposite. As the droplets of moisture coalesce with others, the drops grow to the size where the updraft can no longer support them. They then fall against the updraft and collide with the smaller ones still on the way up. S. E. Reynolds has suggested that collisions between small ice crystals and graupel (soft hail) may separate the charge.

Other theories are based on the idea that fair-weather electricity initiates the separation of charges in a thundercloud. The German scientists Elster and Geitel hypothesized in 1913 that raindrops became polarized by induction, with the bottom nearest the ground charged positively and the top charged negatively. As the big drops fall, the smaller droplets still moving up collide with the bottoms of these big drops and give up electrons, leaving the big drops increasingly negative as they go down and the small ones getting increasingly positive on the way up. Wilson felt, as did Elster and Geitel, that the normal fair-weather currents help set the stage by polarizing moisture droplets in a cloud, and theorized that the moving ions in an updraft selectively capture electrons from falling raindrops. Many, like G. Grenet of France, believe that charge separation depends on normally charged ions being carried aloft in the updraft.

Ross Gunn, recently retired scientist of the U.S. Weather Bureau, made extensive studies of clouds, droplets, and charge separation of clouds. His research included more than two dozen airplane flights into thunderclouds, as well as controlled experiments using the Weather Bureau's artificial cloud chamber. Gunn concluded that induction does play an important role and that moisture droplets or ice crystals are essential to the process. While it is possible that electrified drops and droplets may play an important role in the production of lightning, there are growing objections to the idea that falling precipitation causes electrification. C. B. Moore and Bernard Vonnegut of Arthur D. Little, Inc., question this and note that electric fields in and around the clouds are found before any precipitation is detectable by radar. They believe that charged particles or ions, carried by the convective movement of the cloud, may be responsible for cloud electrification. They suspect that perhaps lightning is the cause rather than the result of the heavy precipitation that accompanies it.

While scientists disagree on the origin and mechanism of the charging of a thundercloud, they generally do agree that a thundercloud has two major charge areas: negative charge spread through the lower

portion of the cloud and centered near the base and a positively
charged area midway up. Sometimes a weak, positively charged pocket
is also found near the base.

Electrons Come Back

Because of this charge separation, thunderclouds feed electrons
back to earth. They drive electrons to the earth in two ways: through
point discharge and by actual lightning strokes. Even though the earth
is negatively charged, the thundercloud base has a much more intense
negative charge than the area of earth below it. Wilson's measurements proved this.

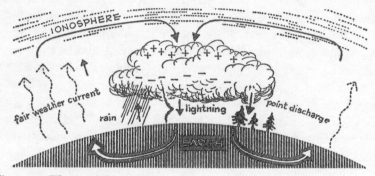

Fig. 32a   The earth loses electrons through the fair-weather ionic current
and through the precipitation cycle. Lightning and point discharge restore
electrons to earth. Arrows show movement of electrons in maintaining
earth's electrical balance.

	From Earth	To Earth
Fair weather ionic current	90	0
Precipitation	30	0
Point discharge	0	100
Lightning	0	20

Fig. 32b   Balance sheet estimated by H. Israël of Germany shows yearly
electricity transfer for entire globe, measured in Coulombs per square kilometer. (One Coulomb is equal to 6,242,000,000,000,000,000 electrons.)

As a result, the normal atmospheric electricity situation is reversed
underneath a thundercloud. Instead of the sky being positive with

respect to the earth, the "sky" (cloud base) is strongly negative with respect to the earth. The base of a thundercloud may be many millions of volts negative with respect to the earth.

This voltage forces the flow of electrons through nature's points to reverse direction when a thunderstorm is near and instead of electrons being driven off the negative earth toward the positive ionosphere, the electrons in the air under the thundercloud find themselves being pushed toward earth. The normal potential gradient of 150 volts per meter is replaced by an opposite potential gradient of perhaps 10,000 volts per meter.

B. F. J. Schonland actually measured the current of point discharge from a tree in South Africa in 1927. He insulated a small tree from the ground and connected it to earth with a galvanometer. He found that electrons flowed from earth in fair weather, but when a thundercloud was overhead, the current changed direction and electrons

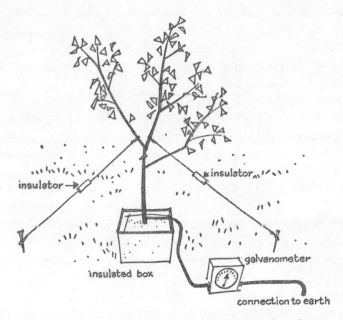

Fig. 33 B. F. J. Schonland's tree experiment showed that electrons leave the air, enter points on trees, and flow to earth when thunderclouds are overhead. Dr. Schonland also found that electrons pass from the earth, through the tree, and out into the air during fair weather, but with less magnitude.

flowed to earth. During thunderstorms, the flow of electricity *to* earth is considerably greater than the flow *from* earth during fair weather.

Point discharge may produce visible and audible corona under the influence of a thundercloud. The sharp spire of a church or the point of a lightning rod may appear to be crowned with a bluish glow. If the thundercloud is particularly heavily charged, even leaves and blades of grass may glow at the tips because of the intense ionization activity there. The biblical "burning bush" that was not consumed may well have been displaying a brush discharge. The term "discharge," while commonly used, is somewhat misleading since electrons are actually moving from ions in the air into, and not from, the points.

Even parts of the body can take part in brush discharge, as John G. Anderson, one of the General Electric engineers on duty at the Empire State Building, demonstrated a few years ago. The Empire State Building is a good conductor, since its main structural members are steel. The top of the building is therefore at almost the same potential as the ground. But the air near the top of the building is at a considerably different potential than that near the ground. Therefore a strong potential difference is found between the top of the building and the air next to it. When a thunderstorm is near, this difference is particularly marked. On a summer afternoon in 1947 Mr. Anderson, standing in the building, extended his arm out the window. The strong voltage difference then existed between his fingers and the air. Intense local ionization occurred, producing a distinct hissing sound and a perceptible glow from his finger tips. He was unharmed because the current flow was small.

The preponderant supply of negative electricity at the base of a thundercloud tends to repel the electrons on the surface of the ground directly below the cloud. The earth under the cloud becomes less negative (positive with respect to the cloud) because many of the surface electrons have fled from the influence of the cloud. Electrons leave the air and enter the many natural points. But usually the points cannot draw enough electrons to equalize the difference between the cloud and the ground beneath. The electrons in the cloud look to the positive area on the ground. They yearn to get there, but the air is too poor a conductor to let them flow. As the cloud matures, the negative charge builds up and soon the pressure becomes too great. The insulative effect of the air is ruptured and an avalanche of electrons passes between the cloud and the ground: lightning.

Scientists estimate that the earth is struck by lightning on the average of 100 times every second. This is only a part of all the lightning in the atmosphere. Lightning also passes between, within, and above clouds. D. M. Fuquay, a meteorologist with the U.S. Forest Service, found that of 2610 lightning flashes observed during three storms over the Northern Rockies in 1958, 548 strokes, or 21 per cent, struck the ground. In arid regions the bases of thunderclouds are higher than in moist or cold areas, so lightning finds it easier to flash from one cloud charge center to another than to go all the way to the ground. In these regions the percentage of flashes reaching the ground is less than 20 per cent.

The strokes that do reach the earth usually bring down negative charge. English scientist T. W. Wormell showed that 84 per cent of lightning strokes to earth bring down electrons. This has been confirmed by utility-company engineers whose measurements of several thousand lightning strokes indicated that about 90 per cent of all earth-cloud lightning strokes are of negative polarity.

The lightning flash is a huge spark that packs a huge electrical wallop into a brief instant. A typical lightning stroke lasts less than a half second and may release about 250 kilowatt-hours of energy, enough electrical energy to operate a 100-watt light bulb continuously for more than three months. The brilliant flash is so brief that you may miss seeing it if you blink your eyes. And yet, brief as it is, the lightning flash represents a complicated series of events.

Briefly here is what happens: the lightning flash starts when a blob of electrons from the cloud gropes toward earth, in a succession of steps, pulsing forward with an additional step every 50 millionths of a second, creating a faintly luminous trail called the *initial* or *stepped*

Fig. 34 Lightning does not always bring electrons to earth. Possible flashes include: (1) Negative charge center to ground (this is the most common cloud-to-ground type), (2) Negative charge center to small positive charge pocket, (3) Negative charge center to main positive charge center in cloud, (4) Earth to small positive charge pocket (this is most common of the so-called positive cloud-to-ground strokes), (5) Earth to main positive charge region, (6) Main positive charge center to upper air. Sometimes a stroke from the cloud may dissipate into clear air before reaching the ground or another cloud.

leader. As the leader nears the ground its effect may be felt on the ground. Electrons are often "sucked" from the air near the surface, creating an ionized *streamer* that rises from earth to meet the advancing leader. When the two join, the ionized path from cloud to ground is completed and a final leader blazes a faint trail to earth, charging the air around the path with electrons. Immediately a deluge of electrons pours from this channel of charge, creating the brilliant *main* or *return stroke* that produces most of the light we see. (The term "return stroke" is somewhat misleading, for, as we shall see later, while the light moves upward the charge moves downward!) Many additional flashes composed of leaders and return strokes may follow this same path, but the entire series of events happens so fast that your eye sees only a single flash.

Even now, many of the details of this sequence are still in the theory stage of understanding. But most of the basic facts are known. The motion of the leader and the main or return stroke may appear to move in different directions, but lightning is not an alternating current. The electrical charge transferred in a lightning flash moves in only one direction. Let us take a closer look at the mechanism of the lightning discharge.

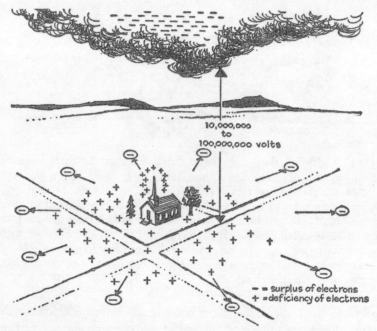

Fig. 35   Before a lightning strike the cloud base is generally very negatively charged with respect to the earth below. Many electrons on the ground are repelled away from below the cloud.

Just before the lightning flash, the ground below the cloud is deficient in electrons. Repelled by the army of electrons in the cloud base, many of the free electrons on the ground are pushed away. The result is that the ground beneath the cloud base is positively charged. As the cloud moves, the positively charged region below moves like its shadow. Tall objects, such as trees and church steeples, are closest to the cloud and are affected most. Tall objects are even more positively charged than the ground upon which they stand. Pointed objects, as we described earlier, may be crowned with corona as intense ionization occurs under the influence of the strong potential between cloud and ground.

The air between the cloud and the ground acts as an insulator and prevents the cloud charge from getting to the ground. But as the cloud charge builds up, the pressure becomes too great. In their eagerness to get to the ground, electrons probe for an easy path. They are accelerated by the strong potential between the cloud and the ground. A few may collide with air molecules with sufficient impact to cause ionization of the air at one place. (If electrons move fast enough they reach a critical speed—about 90 miles per second—above which speed a chain reaction of ionization occurs. Many neutral air particles are split into positive ions and free electrons.) As soon as the air is ionized, it becomes a good conductor. Other electrons from the cloud give up their futile attempt to pierce the insulation elsewhere, and instead they follow down this newly created ionized path. As more electrons plunge down the path, they create additional ionization as they go. The ionized path is pushed farther toward the ground. But the downward motion reaches an inherent speed limit because some of the electrons are held back by their own positive-ion progeny left behind.

If there were a movie camera fast enough to catch it, the lightning flash would show up as a series of still photographs like those shown in Figure 36. The channel twists and turns as it goes because minor variations in the content and conductivity of the air make it easier for the electrons to forge ahead one way rather than the other and the electrons pick the best path of the instant. The channel moves closer to the ground. When it reaches to within perhaps a few hundred feet of the surface, *streamers* may rise to meet the oncoming channel. The cloud had exerted influence on the ground before the lightning flash started, but the channel brings the charge closer to the earth and greatly intensifies the effect. Under this influence, air near the ground may become ionized, electrons drain from the air to earth, and one or more streamers start upward. At perhaps 50 or 150 feet from the ground the descending leader channel meets the highest upward streamer. Now a conducting path between the cloud and the ground is complete. A final shot of electrons passes down the complete path, then electrons are drained from the path, starting at the bottom. Electrons are rapidly "sucked" from the channel—and like sand falling

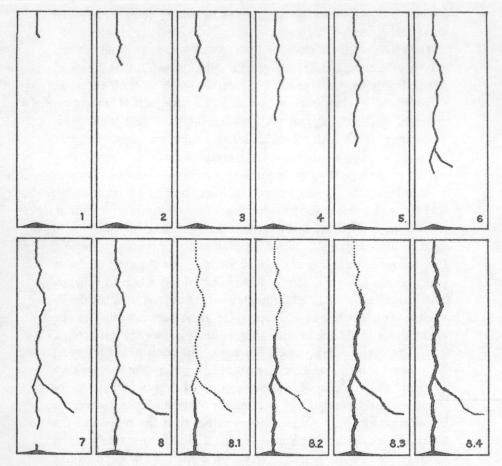

Fig. 36 How a single-stroke lightning flash might appear to a superfast movie camera. Picture frames 1 through 8 show advance of initial leader and cover a total of about .005 second. Frames 8.1 through 8.4 show fast return stroke and cover a total of only .0001 second.

out of a hole in a can full of sand, the action moves up. The upward activity proceeds much faster than the original downward leader, and we have what is called the *return stroke*. Establishing the leader channel may take five-thousandths of a second but the return stroke which appears to move upward, may take only one-fiftieth of that.

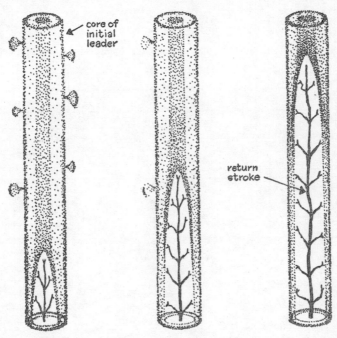

core of
initial
leader

return
stroke

Fig. 37   The main, return stroke of a lightning flash moves upward by draining charge out from the bottom of the ionized channel previously created by the downward leader.

Karl McEachron, the late General Electric engineer, reported that for about 80 per cent of the Empire State Building lightning strokes, the step-leader mechanism was initiated by the building rather than by the cloud. It seems that for extraordinarily tall objects, the initial stepping channel may start on the object, work its way upward (in the same manner as the normal stroke comes downward) but then a final smooth leader still comes from the cloud and the return stroke moves upward as normal. Apparently only the initial stepping direction is different.

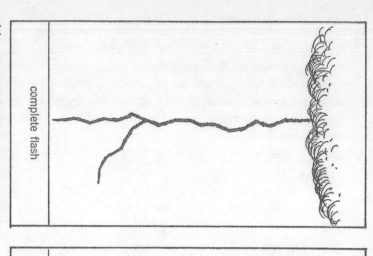

complete flash

(a) AS SEEN BY STILL CAMERA

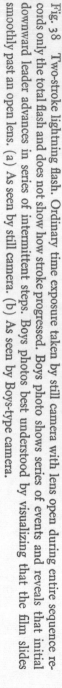

initial stepped leader mechanism

bright step

streamer

1st stroke

return stroke

subsequent leader

2nd stroke

return stroke

(b) AS SEEN BY BOYS TYPE CAMERA

Fig. 38   Two-stroke lightning flash. Ordinary time exposure taken by still camera with lens open during entire sequence records only the total flash and does not show how stroke progressed. Boys photo shows series of events and reveals that initial downward leader advances in series of intermittent steps. Boys photos best understood by visualizing that the film slides smoothly past an open lens. (a) As seen by still camera. (b) As seen by Boys-type camera.

A time exposure of a lightning flash made with an ordinary camera records just about the same things as your eye sees.

Special cameras have made it possible for scientists to dissect the lightning stroke. Dr. B. F. J. Schonland, using a modified Boys camera, spent years photographing and analyzing lightning strokes in South Africa and over the last thirty years has developed an explanation of the sequence of the lightning stroke that most scientists accept today. Figure 38b shows schematically how a lightning flash would appear on the film of a Boys-type camera. The principle is simple. Unlike a movie camera, which takes a series of still pictures with the shutter opening and closing at regular intervals, the Boys camera has its lens open all during the filming and, in effect, merely slides the film past the lens. In an actual Boys camera the lens is made to rotate past the film, but the principle is the same. It was Schonland's Boys camera that revealed that the initial leader process does not move downward in a smoothly continuous motion. It actually "steps," pausing at regular intervals before continuing farther. This stepping process is like driving a nail with a hammer. Each successive blow drives the nail farther down the same path. Each successive step moves 33 to 330 feet and 150 feet is typical.

Boys photos show that the lowermost portion, called the *bright step*, is brighter than the channel above it and that each step advances about the same distance each time. The stepping distance is usually the same length as the bright portion of the leader channel. There is no "smear" between steps, even though the film is sliding past the lens, evidence that a stepping, rather than a smooth motion is involved. When the stepping is complete and the leader has met the rising streamer, the initial leader channel is complete. The return stroke takes this ionized route and moves upward in a smooth continuous motion, losing speed as it goes. Usually the process is repeated a short interval later and with one, two, or three additional return strokes.

Figure 38b shows a flash made up of two "strokes." Successive strokes usually follow the same path as the first. After a brief time delay (perhaps .07 second) a subsequent leader, called a *dart leader*, reaches for the ground. Stepping is usually not necessary since the dart leader need not penetrate virgin air and can follow the ionized path of the previous stroke. Branching is usually not involved on

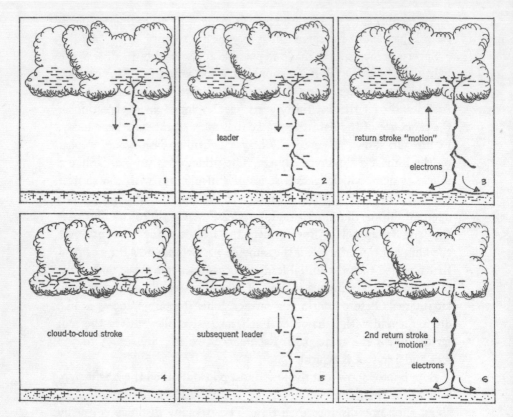

Fig. 39   More than one stroke of lightning may use the same channel, with subsequent strokes possibly coming from different electrified regions in the cloud.

subsequent trips. Any subsequent return stroke is similar to the first return stroke, moving upward along the channel made by the leader.

Figure 39 shows how more than one main stroke might be produced in a single flash. Repetitive strokes are generally believed to come from different cloud regions. A cloud may have its charge distributed over a large area or may be next to another charged cloud that has not yet produced a lightning stroke. As discussed previously, the leader reaches for the ground, makes contact, and then the main return stroke moves upward. This drains the charge from the area around the channel and from the cloud itself. Once the first return stroke is completed, the charged cloud region that fed the stroke is left relatively uncharged compared to some other region of the cloud or another cloud. A lightning stroke may then occur within the clouds as an untapped charge center finds it easier to flash over to the now uncharged cloud than to fight its way to the ground. Upon reaching the original cloud charge center, the new group of electrons finds the ionized path that was previously used and heads for the ground with a swift dart leader and then a main return stroke.

Lightning flashes are frequently made up of more than one main stroke and some scientists have reported flashes made up of 40 separate strokes. D. J. Malan, an associate of Dr. Schonland, has suggested that these high numbers may have been a result of misinterpretation of data and that the maximum number of strokes ever recorded in a lightning flash may be only 14. In any event, multistroke lightning is common, but it happens so fast that it appears as a single flash.

Many scientists believe that the stepping process cannot take place without a *pilot streamer* from the cloud which prepares an ionized channel before any stepping takes place in the initial leader. The stepped leader, it is said, is superimposed on this slow pilot streamer, which is periodically helped on its way by the stepped leader. Photographs of natural lightning have not revealed the pilot streamer, but measurements of potential gradient changes, and occurrence of a pilot streamer in laboratory lightning, appear to confirm its existence.

Much of what occurs during a lightning stroke is invisible to photographic film. We know, for example, that lightning generates static or a radio noise which is a form of energy wave at a wave length that films cannot record. Most cameras have a very narrow range of sensitivity, limited both by the lens and by the film, and usually record only those wave lengths that are visible to the eye. Normal camera lenses absorb electromagnetic emanations of long wave lengths like heat. Glass lenses cannot focus radio waves or high-frequency wave lengths like cosmic or X rays. Mr. S. B. Griscom, a Westinghouse engineer, theorized in 1958 that the stepping process of the initial downward leader is due to a series of corona bursts that is invisible to the eye or the camera. Figure 40 shows how this process might operate.

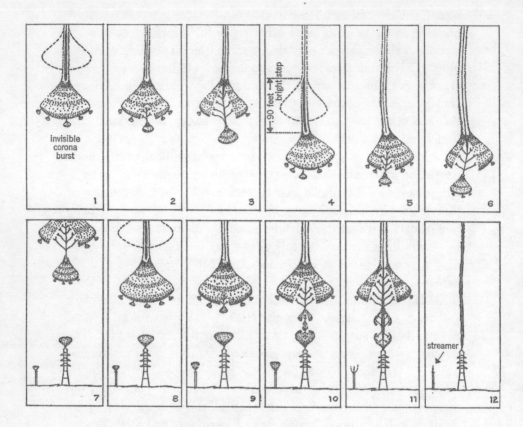

Fig. 40   Griscom's theory explains stepping action as series of invisible corona bursts (1–6). Burst collapses as electrons are withdrawn to feed new burst. Burst theory shows how a streamer may start from the ground, only to collapse when lightning stroke contacts some other target (7–12).

The heavy line indicates the bright step of the initial leader. A surge of electrons, fed from the cloud, races down the channel. When it meets the end of the path, it flares out into an invisible pestle-shaped burst. The burst is fairly uniform, with all electrons racing forward at about the same speed. Some, however, may encounter less resistance than others and break out into the lead, leaving an ionized path behind them. Nearby electrons find this easy path, give up their fight to penetrate virgin air, and start to follow the most advanced path. Then more electrons are drawn into this easy route. The corona burst collapses completely when all the electrons have joined into the new route and the freshly ionized path, originally started by just a few electrons, grows backward to the point where the burst began. Bright illumination results and the step is completed when a new surge of electrons comes down the main path into the new route to feed a new burst. The process is repeated over and over again, with each step covering a typical distance of perhaps 150 feet every 50 millionths of a second.

Griscom's theory helps to show how a streamer can come up from the ground. Figure 40 shows two elevated objects: a transmission-line tower and a pole, both of which are made of metal for this illustration. As the downcoming leader steps nearer and nearer to the ground, a similar burst may be initiated from the elevated objects or points. These bursts, of course, are not outward bursts of electrons, but rather withdrawals of electrons from the air. Both the rod and the tower "suck" electrons from the air, under the strong influence of the approaching leader. Each upward "burst" is attempting to reach up and join the approaching leader, but actual contact of the downward burst with the upward burst is first made above the tower, because of its greater height. As soon as the cloud-to-tower path is complete, the electrons in the downward burst rapidly drain into the tower, the influence on the short pole is reduced and its upward burst collapses. The ions here recombine and, as electrons are restored, light is produced. A photograph would show an incomplete streamer, similar to that shown on Plate XXXVI.

The initial dumping of charge into the tower at the instant of completion of the path is what Griscom has called the "lightning prestrike" and has said causes extremely high currents, but of very brief duration, to pass through the tower. Then the main return stroke occurs, starting at the tower and racing up the channel. The brilliant return stroke, of course, draws electrons from the ionized area around the initial leader channel, and appears to move upward, even though electrons are being brought to earth.

Before 1959, direct measurements of lightning strokes to objects on the ground had not revealed the "prestrike," but some lightning arresters had failed to do their job, even though the measured current, voltage, and timing of measured lightning strokes were well below those which the arrester was designed to withstand. Griscom suggests that the prestrike happens so much faster than the ability of the traditional instruments to respond that the prestrike really exists but that we haven't yet been quick enough to catch it.

Lightning, then, is made up of a series of events, but it is all over in a flash. Some parts of the sequence are brilliant, some are faint, and some may be invisible. The downward-reaching leader is only faintly luminous while the powerful "return stroke" is brilliant. It is during the "return stroke" that charges are brought to earth, but the charges had already left the cloud and were "stored" in the air around the downward leader channel.

What are the statistics on this dramatic phenomena? For sheer speed, lightning is hard to beat. The typical downward, stepped leader advances at an average speed of 243 miles per second, and the main return stroke starts upward at an average speed of 61,400 miles per second. The voltage between the low charge center of the cloud and the ground may be in the order of 10 or 100 million volts. The amount of electricity brought to earth in a typical lightning flash is about 25 coulombs (or 156 billion, billion electrons), although General Electric engineers on the Empire State Building recorded one flash that brought down eight times as much.

Half of the strokes measured have less than 10,000 amperes, but 30,000 amperes is typical and currents as high as 345,000 amperes have been recorded—enough to simultaneously light 414,000 ordinary 100-watt light bulbs. But the flash is so brief, that those light bulbs would not burn very long. A typical flash, from start of downward leader to finish of return strokes, is completed in a fraction of a second: the current in a single return stroke lasts from about .00005 to .01 second. The peak currents occur during the early part of the return stroke, when it is drawing from the freshest part of the ionized trail created by the leader. A lightning flash is usually 1000 to 9000 feet long. A radar photo, shown on Plate XLV, indicated a flash 100 miles long, but this may have been a series of cloud-to-cloud flashes, like a row of falling dominoes. The diameter of a main stroke is estimated to be about six inches.

The total power or energy in a lightning flash varies, depending upon the magnitude and duration of the stroke. For a 30,000-ampere stroke under 125 million volts, a peak of 3750 million kilowatts may be developed (far more than the combined peak capacity of every electrical power plant in the United States). But since the stroke is so brief, only about 250 kilowatt hours of energy are involved. You pay about three cents for each kilowatt hour of electricity you consume in your home, so the lightning flash described represents about $7.50 worth of electricity. The key to lightning's destructiveness is that the power is released in such a short interval of time: 250 kilowatt hours of energy is enough to lift the S.S. *United States* six feet into the air.

No two lightning strokes are identical, since the cloud's charge and altitude, and the air's temperature, pressure, and resistance all vary. For general purposes, however, we can divide lightning into two general categories—"hot" and "cold" lightning. Cold lightning is of very short duration but with high current: it has explosive effects upon the things it strikes. Hot lightning has low currents of long time duration and is more apt to burn the things it hits. A comparison of these two classes of lightning is shown in Figure 41.

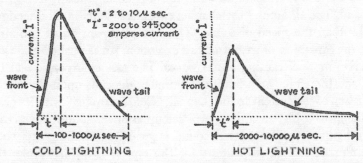

Fig. 41 "Cold" lightning is a lightning flash whose main, return stroke is of intense current but of short duration. "Hot" lightning involves lesser currents but of longer duration. Hot lightning is apt to start fires while cold lightning generally has mechanical or explosive effects.

Most of the energy of the lightning flash is dissipated into the air. Perhaps 75 per cent of the energy is dissipated as heat. This raises the temperature of the lightning channel to about 15,000° C.

Thunder is an explosion that occurs along the length of the lightning channel. Lightning's flood of electrons dissociates, ionizes, and heats the air in the path with a violent suddenness. The result is a sharp increase of temperature and pressure, causing the air to suddenly expand. The air around the channel expands radially in all directions, faster than the speed of sound. This abrupt expansion of the air is like the expansion of gases from an explosion. Air is pushed aside and set into motion, causing sound waves. The rate of expansion of the air, and therefore the intensity of thunder, depends upon the rate of variation of the current in the channel. "Cold lightning," with its faster build-up to a higher current, will set up stronger sound waves than "hot lightning." The greatest sound is generated at the place where the current change is greatest: for the typical lightning stroke this occurs near the ground during the return stroke. The sound is loudest at the base of the stroke and also occurs earlier, since the stroke starts there. But the stroke moves upward at a speed of 61,400 miles per second, so for practical purposes we can say that the thunder is generated along the entire length of the channel simultaneously.

The rumbling of thunder is partially due to the varying distance between the listener and the different portions of the lightning stroke.

Fig. 42   Rumbling of thunder is primarily due to differing distance between you and the lightning channel. These simplified charts show how the path and location of the stroke affects what you hear. For practical purposes light takes no time to reach you, but sound takes one second to travel 1090 feet.

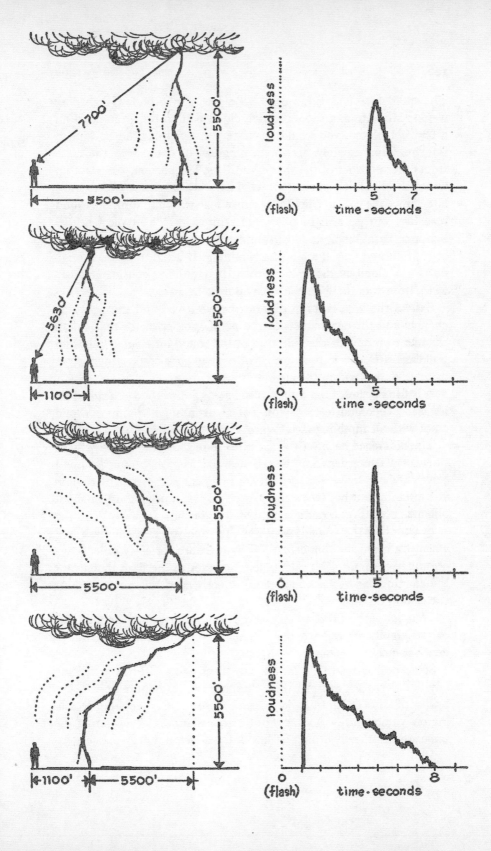

The speed of sound is normally 1090 feet per second. If lightning were to strike from a 5000-foot-high cloud base to the ground within a few feet of you, you would hear the thunder from the bottom of the stroke immediately, and then, progressively later, hear the noise from other portions of the stroke, until the last portion, 5000 feet up where the lightning originated, would be heard almost five seconds later. Since the path of a lightning stroke may twist and turn, the sound reaching your ear will be of irregular intensity. The typical nearby lightning flash, then, produces thunder which you hear first as a loud crash, followed by a diminishing rumbling. If a lightning flash originates in a cloud overhead, but strikes the ground at considerable distance from you, the loud crash may not be heard first.

Besides the differences in distance between you and the lightning channel and the crookedness of the path, another factor that causes thunder to rumble is the reflection of the sound off clouds, hills, and buildings. Rumble is also caused, of course, by successive discharges or other flashes within the clouds.

A lightning flash from a low-altitude cloud directly overhead, striking a few thousand feet away on a clear plain, might produce a loud crack without rumbling (see Figure 42).

The difference between the speed of sound and the speed of light provides a convenient way to tell how far away lightning is. Light travels 186,000 miles in a second: for practical purposes light reaches you instantaneously. Since sound travels 1090 feet per second, or about one mile every five seconds, you can determine how far away lightning is by counting the seconds between the time you saw the flash and when you heard the thunder. Allow five seconds for every mile. Some error may creep into this calculation, however. If the flash that struck the ground has also been in a cloud directly overhead, you may hear the cloud portion first.

Thunder can be heard easily seven miles away, and if conditions or topography are right, it may be heard 15 or 18 miles. It is rarely heard at greater distances.

Some nearby lightning flashes have been seen without producing any thunder. Back in April 1885, during a twenty minute period, five brilliant flashes of lightning were seen to strike the 555-foot-tall Washington Monument without any noticeable sound. And yet during the same storm other lightning flashes did produce noise. A possible explanation for the lack of thunder is that the lightning strokes were of low current, long duration, and heated the air up so slowly that explosive heating of air was avoided.

On other occasions thunder has been heard without noticeable lightning. A. D. Zamorskiy reported in a Soviet meteorology journal that he had heard deafening thunder near Leningrad while a clear sunlit sky covered a wide region overhead in July 1954. He saw no lightning. The thunder, which was heard as a loud dry crack without any rumbling, seemed, on the basis of intensity of the sound, to be less than a kilometer away, but the nearest thunderclouds were about eight kilometers away to the south and only small scattered cumulus clouds dotted the clear sky overhead. The storm did not reach the area for another 43 minutes. Zamorskiy speculated that the discharge had truly come from the distant storm and that the bright sunshine may have blanked out the view of the stroke, since the storm was approaching from the south at the time, in line with the sun. The lack of rumbling may be because the observer was deafened temporarily by the crash and he was unable to detect the rumbling of the distant portions of the channel.

The small flickering branches of lightning generate a high-frequency crackling-like buzz, rather than the familiar powerful thunderclap, because they are relatively weak channels compared with the main stroke. Since these branchings are usually made during the initial stepping process, they precede the main stroke by a minute fraction of time, and may sometimes be heard just before the main clap of thunder.

Why does lightning produce light? The origin of light is still subject to much discussion but the light of lightning is believed to be produced by ionization rather than by heating. A neon sign glows when the neon gas, in a glass tube at very low pressure, is ionized by high voltage electricity from a transformer. When a gas is ionized, the individual molecules and atoms are disturbed. Not only can an electron be added or removed, but also an electron may be moved from one "shell" to another within an atom. This involves a change of energy. When the air is ionized by an advancing lightning stroke, some of the ions have undergone energy changes as the electron complements of the atoms are rearranged. Energy is absorbed when an electron moves farther away from an atom nucleus. When the disturbing forces are removed, the electron may jump back to the lesser energy level and release energy as it goes. The generally accepted theory of why lightning produces light is that the recombination of ions back to their original undisturbed state produces energy sufficient to release high energy photons—in short, light.

Types of Lightning

No two lightning flashes are identical.

The most common type is popularly known as *streak lightning*, and is the one shown in the diagrams. In spite of the tendency of artists to draw it as a zigzag, lightning's path is not a zigzag, but a winding, twisting, sinuous shape. Some strokes may involve considerable branching, which looks like a map rendition of a river with its tributaries. Sometimes two branches may simultaneously reach the ground, creating what is popularly called *forked lightning*.

Ribbon lightning is a term applied to a minor variation of streak lightning which looks like what would be obtained if a camera were moved sideways while photographing a stroke. It is possible for the ionized path of the lightning stroke to be blown sideways with the

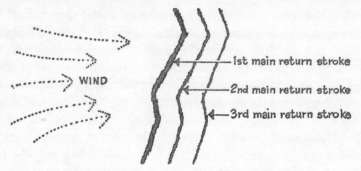

Fig. 43   Wind may shift the ionized lightning channel between subsequent main strokes, giving the appearance of "ribbon" lightning.

wind during a multiple stroke flash. A 30-mile-per-hour wind would move air laterally 44 feet in one second. The second stroke of a two-stroke flash of lightning may follow the first stroke by perhaps .07 second, so that the subsequent stroke could be displaced 3 feet from the first if the air were moving in a 30-mile-per-hour wind.

Bead or *chain lightning* is lightning that starts as a continuous

streak, but seems to dissolve into bright pockets of light when disappearing. The author saw this phenomenon in 1952 over Ohio during
an airplane flight through a thunderstorm when a horizontal cloud-
to-cloud stroke, off the left wing tip, appeared to dissolve into a series
of more or less evenly spaced dashes of light. It seems probable that
this phenomenon is partly due to a temporary effect upon the eye.
Professor O. J. Ferguson of the University of Nebraska, writing in the
Journal of the Franklin Institute, reported seeing "chain" lightning
during a spring evening thunderstorm over Lincoln, Nebraska, in 1914.
He saw what appeared to be a typical flash of streak lightning strike
vertically downward from a cloud elevation of about 45 degrees. He
noticed that when the flash died away "it took probably a full second
to disappear; it broke up, seemingly, into detached portions, short
and numerous. In fact, it gave a beadlike effect, and it would be very
easy for one to have retained the latter impression and to have called
the stroke bead lightning." But Professor Ferguson explained the
phenomenon by suggesting that "each bead probably represents the
'end on' view of the irregular portions of the lightning path, and that
they remained luminous during the subsequent lesser discharges, while
the intermediate sections became nonluminous, because viewed from
the side." It would seem that the end-on portions being brighter than
the other portions would affect the retina of the eye more intensely
and, because of the persistence of vision, would "last" longer.

Heat lightning is merely lightning too far away for the thunder to
be heard or the individual stroke itself to be actually seen. The light
from an ordinary lightning flash can be reflected or diffused by clouds,
giving the impression of a broad area of flashing light. Heat lightning
is usually seen close to the horizon, far in the distance. As Kipling
describes it, "lightning . . . dancing on the horizon to a broken tune
played by far-off thunder."

A close relative of heat lightning is *sheet lightning*. An intracloud
lightning flash, obscured from view by clouds, appears to light up a
large cloud area simultaneously, giving the impression of a "sheet" of
light. Unlike heat lightning, which is "silent" because it is far away,
sheet lightning can produce thunder. Sometimes "sheet" lightning
is silent. Although not much is known of the electrical processes within
the thunderhead, it is possible that many small currents, flowing in
broad regions in a cloud, can produce light without thunder.

Ball Lightning

The most controversial form of lightning is *ball lightning*. Some scientists do not believe that ball lightning exists. It is generally described as a luminous ball—ranging in color from red to orange, yellow, blue, or white—that may be as much as twenty inches in diameter. It may appear to float across a floor, glide down a tree, or wander through the sky. Some lightning balls have been said to disappear quietly while others evaporate with a loud bang. A lightning ball supposedly lasts from several seconds to several minutes and usually occurs with or slightly after a nearby lightning stroke.

Many of the published reports contain insufficient information for proper evaluation. Most observers fail to recall important and significant details. W. J. Humphreys, a physicist and U.S. Weather Bureau meteorologist, collected data on 280 reported sightings and concluded in 1936 that not a single case was truly a "ball" of lightning that moved slowly as a luminous globular mass. B. F. J. Schonland commented in his book *Flight of the Thunderbolts* that "most of the reported cases are extremely likely to have been caused by optical illusion, since the retina of the eye, when dazzled by a nearby flash seen out of the corner of the eye, retains a residual image of the nature of a luminous ball of light."

A typical news report of a "ball of fire" shows why many scientists find the phenomenon difficult to believe. For example, here is a June 27, 1891, report from a newspaper in Cedar Rapids, Iowa: "During a severe electrical storm here this evening lightning struck the ice house of Taylor and Davis, consuming it, causing a loss of $1,000. Balls of fire darted into several business houses, and in one a barber was seriously shocked." This hardly substantiates the existence of the lightning ball. Another news item, this one from Chicago in September 1894, attributes to a lightning ball damage that was probably caused by an ordinary lightning stroke: "Rev. Dr. E. C. Towne reports that during last night's thunder storm a large ball of fire fell in a vacant lot near the business portion of the suburb of Austin. A hole several feet in diameter and of considerable depth was torn in the ground, and the earth for 20 feet around was seared and cracked. The fall of the fire ball was accompanied by a terrific peal of thunder and vivid lightning."

Some of the reports relate most unusual phenomena. Martin Rodewald reports in a German meteorology journal in 1954 that a Mrs. Else Schmidt of Plochingen, recalls that "it was either 1913 or 1914 when I saw a very odd lightning in Posen." She claims to have seen in the sky "a lightning which rotated inwardly like a spiral, something like a vertical disc. It seemed to me that a fire ball moved along the spiral path in whose center it became extinguished." She estimated that the diameter of the spiral was about equal to the distance from the horizon to 10 or 12 degrees.

The author has not seen a lightning ball, but a friend who is considered a competent witness has. Mr. E. Markow, a graduate engineer, relates an experience with ball lightning in the summer of 1943. It was a hot muggy day, and thunder was becoming quite loud at about 5 P.M. when he was upstairs taking a shower in his frame house. A brief downpour had just passed, and he had opened the windows at both ends of the hall. He had finished his shower, heard a peal of thunder and was about to step into the hall when he saw a bluish ball, about 12 to 18 inches in diameter, float through the screened window at the end of the hall and start to come toward him. Startled, he stepped back, and the ball, seeming to move at about the speed of a gentle breeze, drifted by, about waist high. As the glowing ball went by, he felt no heat, but did smell ozone. The ball proceeded down the 30-foot hall in about 3 or 4 seconds, and passed out through the screened window at the other end, where it dropped out of sight without any noise. The observer in this case is an experienced engineer, who by his very training is objective, and since both his eyes and nose detected this ball, the author believes that this was not an optical illusion.

During the summer of 1937 several technical observers on duty at 500 Fifth Avenue, during the Empire State Building lightning program, saw what might be interpreted as ball lightning, not once, but four times. One of the engineers, now the chief technical executive of a large electric power company, saw a bluish luminescence slowly descend the 38-foot tower of the Empire State Building after four of the ten or eleven strokes that hit the tower that evening. Fearing that his colleagues might regard him as another lightning-ball "quack," he was hesitant to speak about what he had seen, but decided to mention it anyway. Surprisingly, several of the others admitted seeing the same thing. These observations were omitted from the technical reports since they did not appear on the recording cameras nor on the oscillograph records.

Balls of lightning have also been sighted in and around aircraft. In 1938 the pilot of a BOAC flying boat en route to Iraq in rain clouds at 8500 feet reported that a ball of lightning entered the cabin, where it burst with a resounding bang. A few minutes later another fireball entered through an open window in the cockpit, burning off the pilot's eyebrows and some of his hair before bouncing into the rear cabin where it disappeared in an explosion.

E. Golde, writing in *Nature Magazine,* reports that J. Durward, Deputy Director of the Meteorological Office in England encountered a lightning ball in 1934 while driving along the bank of Loch Tummel. It had started to rain and slight thunder and lightning were observed. Durward's twelve-year-old son "was opening the iron gates, and found one difficult to open. Mr. Durward, while walking the short distance from the motor-car to the gate to assist his son, saw among the pine trees on his left what looked like a ball of fire about 12 inches in diameter moving towards them. It struck the iron gate-post farthest from the latch. There was no noise, but the boy, who had his hand on the latch, gave a yell; for the next few hours he was unable to lower his arm."

Some scientists conclude that ball lightning is not an optical illusion and have attempted to explain what causes it. Sightings are rare, and few scientists competent to analyze them have ever seen a lightning ball. But the characteristics seem to be generally consistent, which has led to some theoretical analysis.

Dr. T. E. Allibone, noted for his work in analysis of sparks, suggests that lightning balls have their origin at the place where the downward leader of a lightning stroke joins a streamer rising from the ground. Some think that the lightning ball is a blob of recombining ions and electrons, the rate of recombination determining its brilliance. T. H. Neugebauer points out that a concentration of electrons and positive ions (a plasma) can be relatively stable at high temperatures and that it is conceivable that this is the content of a lightning ball. If original temperatures and concentrations are low, the ball would diminish in both stability and density and disappear silently as it cools. Rapid decrease in electron density could trigger an explosive dimunition. Temperatures could be high enough to produce luminosity. Such a mass might travel by the action of a breeze or by the earth's magnetic field. Uneven cooling or electron density could polarize the mass and the earth's magnetism could move it along, much as a current-carrying rotor of an electric motor is made to move in the magnetic field of the stator. Others suggest that a chemical reaction, such as the decomposition of ozone, is initiated by the lightning flash and then maintains the ball by the heat of the reaction.

Still another theory has been advanced by P. L. Kapitza, the famous Soviet physicist. The glowing cloud of ionized gas produced by a nuclear explosion is similar to a lightning ball, but it is much briefer than most lightning balls reported. Kapitza believes that there must be some nonchemical, nonnuclear process that feeds energy to a lightning ball if its long life is to be explained. Since lightning balls are usually floating and not in contact with a conductor, the energy must be from an absorption of intense radio or electromagnetic waves coming from some place outside of the ball. The source of this energy, says Kapitza, may be from a lightning stroke and the most favorable place for the appearance of a lightning ball is where the "radio" waves generated from a lightning stroke reach their maximum intensity at points of resonance for the waves. This would occur parallel to the surface of the earth and may account for the horizontal motion of lightning balls. Hallways and chimneys would then act as wave guides during the motion of the ball and the ball would be separated from a surface by a distance about equal to the radius of the ball. Kapitza believes that it is quite possible for several balls to be created at separated intervals at the same time.

Someday ball lightning may be reproduced in the laboratory. Then and only then will we have a satisfactory explanation.

PART THREE

LIGHTNING IN ACTION

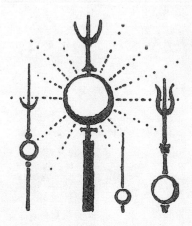

9 EARTH, MOUNTAIN, AND SEA

What happens when lightning hits the ground?

The primary objective of a cloud-ground stroke of lightning is to equalize the potential difference between the cloud and the ground. To do this, the electrons of the bolt must spread out in all directions as soon as they reach the surface of the earth. The earth and its soil are a better conductor of electricity than air, and wet ground is a far better conductor than dry ground. When lightning hits the ground, the flood of electrons spreads out radially in all directions, much like the wave from a stone dropped in a pond.

Lightning will penetrate below the surface to reach a good wet conducting layer of soil. In the process of burrowing down, lightning can produce strange effects due to heating. As the air of the lightning channel expands when it is heated, so does the air trapped in the soil expand when lightning passes through it. Sometimes dirt is thrown about near the surface when lightning strikes soft dirt. Lightning is believed to have blasted a small crater in the middle of a flat Illinois cornfield in April 1959. A few days after a severe thunderclap had broken four windows in a farmhouse, a hole was discovered three-fourths of a mile away. This unusual crater was from seven to twelve feet across and a foot deep. Lightning may dig a furrow-like trench too. Cases have been reported where lightning came down a tree and dug a six-inch-deep trench while traveling to reach a water pipe of a house near the tree.

On other occasions, lightning may leave a strange trail of holes in the ground. Mr. J. C. Jensen of Nebraska Wesleyan University reported an example in 1936 of how lightning will grope downward to reach a good conducting layer. The lightning may follow several paths, much like the roots of a tree. Jensen, writing in *Science* magazine, described a hole that was found in a field a few miles from Dodge, Nebraska, in June, 1935. Discovered a few days after a thunderstorm that produced a particularly severe explosive noise, the crater was found with an eight-inch hole at the center. Dirt had been thrown a distance of about three feet and piled about six inches above the general grade. Omaha Police Commissioner Frank Meyers and two professors excavated the site, digging carefully around the hole in order to follow its course. They found that it descended almost vertically for eight feet, generally maintaining an eight-inch diameter. The path diverged a bit from the vertical and became slightly smaller for another seven feet down. The diameter tapered to four inches at a point fifteen feet below the surface and the hole split up into several branches of two-inch holes, which disappeared after spreading out about four feet in very moist soil. Mr. Jensen reported that "The clay showed signs of fusion at a number of points, and the inside of the hole had a corrugated appearance, as though moist clay had been forced violently back by high pressure."

It was fortunate that the storm from which the burrowing thunderbolt had come did not also bring rain, or this unique hole might have been filled in and gone unnoticed. Although this type of lightning hole is rare, it does show how deep into the earth lightning current can go before being dissipated.

Fulgurites

The Dodge, Nebraska, lightning hole had a shape that is similar to what is popularly called "petrified lightning." If lightning strikes sand of the proper composition, the high temperature of the stroke may fuse the sand and convert it to silica glass. "Petrified lightning" is a permanent record of the path of lightning in earth, and is called a *fulgurite*, after *fulgur*, the Latin word for lightning. Fulgurites are hollow, glass-lined tubes with sand adhering to the outside. Although easily produced in the laboratory in an electric furnace, silica glass is very rare in nature. The glass lining of a fulgurite is naturally produced silica glass,* formed from the fusion of quartzose sand at a temperature of about 1800° centigrade.

---

* The geological name for this natural silica glass is lechatelierite, in honor of the French chemist Henry Le Chatelier.

Most people have never seen a fulgurite and if they have they might not have recognized it for what it was. A fulgurite is a curious glassy tube that usually takes the shape of the roots of a tree (Figure 44). In effect it gives a picture of the forklike routes taken by lightning after striking sand. One of the largest ever found was discovered in South Amboy, New Jersey. When scientists dug the sand away from around

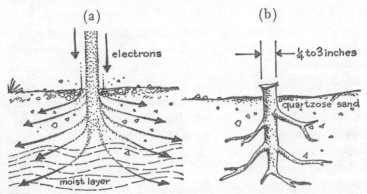

Fig. 44   (a) When lightning strikes the earth, electrons flow outward in all directions. (b) Petrified lightning or fulgurite is sometimes made when lightning strikes and fuses certain types of sand. Formed on beaches or shores, a fulgurite is usually covered with shifting sand and goes undiscovered. Eroding sand may expose a fulgurite. See Plate XLII.

the fulgurite, it broke so that the largest single piece was only six inches long; however, when put together, this Jersey fulgurite was almost nine feet long. It was virtually a straight tapering tube with only a few branches coming off the main stem. It was three inches in diameter near the surface of the ground and tapered down to about three-sixteenths-of-an-inch diameter at the lowest recovered piece. The thickness of the tube wall was on the order of a thirty-second of an inch.

Fulgurites have been found in all parts of the United States as far south as Florida and Mississippi and as far north as Waterville, Maine. Next time you are at a beach after a thunderstorm, look around, perhaps you will be lucky enough to find a fulgurite. You can recognize it as an approximately circular section of tube that would go down into the ground. A fulgurite is quite brittle. Dig around it carefully so that it can be removed with a minimum of breakage. Fulgurites vary in color, depending upon the type of sand from which they were formed. They are usually tan or black, but an almost translucent, white fulgurite was found in Pensacola, Florida. The inside tends to be lustrous and somewhat irregular and the outside is rough sand which adheres to the fused areas. The glassy portion usually includes tiny bubbles which are formed by moisture trapped when the fulgurite cools suddenly after the lightning has passed.

Fulgurites are produced not only in sand but also on rocks. Pieces of rock may be consolidated and fused together or the surface of a rock may be converted to a lustrous glassy material when struck by lightning. William Hallock, a Professor at New York University, reported an incident in August 1900 of a rock fulgurite formed near Lake Champlain, New York. Lightning struck a mountain, splitting an old pine tree. Observers went to the scene and found, near the pine, a large rock which had been split into fifty to a hundred pieces. "A white incrustation was apparent on the rock as if white paint had either been splattered about or had been spread over as a rough branching, straggling line. This incrustation went as far down as a foot into some of the large cracks of the large rocks." Besides the Lake Champlain rock fulgurite, others have been found near mountain summits in the Caucasus, in Toluca, Mexico, and on Mount Thielson, Oregon.

Good specimens of fulgurite are almost as rare as gold. They are rare because most people wouldn't recognize one if they saw one. Beach fulgurites are quickly rendered invisible by shifting sands, but they sometimes are seen to protrude from sand as sand is eroded away. The fine fulgurite specimen shown in Plate XLII was obtained from a prospector in California, in the early 1940's. While ferreting around Indio, in Riverside County, California, a grizzled prospector came across a fulgurite. He didn't know what the peculiar thing was, but he suspected some geologist would be interested in it. He sold it to a rock dealer in Hollywood who in turn forwarded it to geologists at Stanford University. The prospector, however, refused to tell exactly where he had found it.

Perhaps the finest fulgurite on display is at the Academy of Natural Sciences in Philadelphia. This fulgurite was discovered on Santa Rosa Island, near Fort Walton, Florida, in October 1940 by Miss Josephine de N. Henry. She dug it up and carefully tagged each of 500 pieces, which were later reassembled with dental cement. Its maximum diameter is two inches, and the lowest part was four and a half feet underground, where it reached the water table and branched out. A photo of this fulgurite is shown in Plate XLIV.

Scorched Grass

Lightning sometimes leaves strange patterns when striking a grassy area. In 1942 a young New York caddy at the Old Westbury Club had just finished for the day and was returning to the clubhouse when lightning struck at the eighteenth hole. He looked back and saw that the bamboo pin had been splintered by the bolt and was scattered about the green. Walking back to the scene, he found that some of the grass had turned brown. The pattern of affected grass looked very much like a klydonogram (Lichtenberg figure). The same phenomenon, reported on several other occasions, is shown in Plate XIII.

Folklore in some mining communities has it that lightning is "attracted" to one mountain in preference to another because of the presence of iron ore. If an area of high soil resistivity (poor conductivity) has an underground water course or narrow geological concentration of good conducting soil, it is possible that lightning may choose to follow that as a path of least resistance. This could result in a localized concentration of lightning discharges, much as the Empire State Building in New York City is struck more frequently than other buildings. Gustav Hellmann, a German meteorologist, studied lightning-strike incidents and reported in the 1890's that loam soil was struck 22 times, sand 9 times, clay 7 times, and chalk just once. What percentage of each type of soil was exposed is not known. It is possible that for the area studied, more loam exists than the other types. It is doubtful that geological conditions could affect lightning patterns over a large area. Topographical features play a more important role in determining exactly where lightning may strike.

Mountains

The easiest path to the ground is through a high conducting object. As might be expected, mountain peaks are generally struck more frequently than plains if the same number of thunderstorms occur in each area.

High terrain brings the earth potential closer to the thunderclouds.

Since the earth is a conductor, the high land is at the same voltage with respect to the cloud as lower terrain. But since the voltage difference spans a shorter distance, the potential gradient (rate of change of voltage with distance) is more intense and lightning is more easily initiated. The lower air pressure at high altitudes also facilitates the lightning discharge.

One indication of the lightning hazard at altitudes is the rate at which forest fires are started by lightning. In the Northern Rockies, lightning starts twice as many fires per unit area of ground at altitudes between 6000 and 7000 feet as it does at 2000 to 3000 feet.

But the top of a mountain is not always the most vulnerable area to lightning. In some areas, depending upon the general air movements, thunderstorms may follow valleys and lightning may lash out at the side of a mountain. This tendency is more pronounced with warm-air-type storms. On the other hand, the frontal storms, generally driven eastward by the general air circulation, may unleash lightning at mountain peaks. The relative hazard of one mountaintop compared to another depends upon local topography and circulation.

Fig. 45 Effect of terrain altitude (same storm frequency): (a) Infrequent, high-voltage lightning, high current. (b) Frequent, low-voltage, low-current lightning. (c) May be no lightning if mountain protrudes into charge center of cloud.

Extremely tall mountains are struck only rarely. This seeming contradiction is explained when we realize that if a mountain is tall enough, it will protrude into the clouds and be in actual contact with the negative charge center of the thunderhead (Figure 45). Charge can then drain directly to earth through the mountain without involving a "spark." The rare occasion when a very high mountain gets hit is when a discharge may come from the upper, positive charge center of the cloud or from another cloud.

Engineers who studied lightning strokes to power lines in the Rocky Mountains found that the intensity of the current in lightning strokes decreased with altitude. In 1937–41, L. M. Robertson, W. W. Lewis and C. M. Foust studied the Shoshone-Denver transmission line of the Public Service Company of Colorado. The power line climbs 150 miles through the heart of the Rocky Mountains, starting at an altitude of 6000 feet, and ending at 5280 feet in Denver. It crosses the Continental Divide three times, and at one point reaches an altitude of 13,500 feet. During the four years of study, the line was hit by lightning 145 times, with currents ranging from 2000 to 96,800 amperes. In general, the lightning currents were lower for the higher altitude sections of the line and indicated "that there may be no lightning strokes if the ground level is above an altitude of 18,000 feet."

A somewhat conflicting finding was reported a few years later by General Electric engineers C. M. Foust and B. C. Maine, and C. Lee of the Cerro de Pasco Corporation. They tested the effectiveness of lightning protective devices for a transmission line high up in a rocky and treeless terrain of a rich mining district of the Andes mountains of Peru. Here a transmission line of the Cerro de Pasco Corporation reaches a peak altitude of 14,650 feet at a point about 150 miles from Lima. Lightning in this general area is severe and frequent. In five years twenty-two strokes were recorded on the Cielo Punta peak, ranging from 7100 to 119,300 amperes.

It appears possible that in spite of the high altitude of the Peru measurements, the great magnitude of some of the strokes can be attributed to the severity of the Andes thunderstorms, which are both high and severe due to unusual turbulence resulting from conflicting air movements sweeping over the Andes Mountains.

Water As a Target

Can lightning strike water? It can and does. Water is a better conductor than dry or rocky soil and when lightning hits water, its electric currents easily spread out in all directions until the charge is dissipated. These currents can shock or kill swimmers or fish. After lightning hit Saranac Lake in 1932 fishermen picked up almost a hundred stunned fish.

United States Navy scientists captured on film a rare coincidence of lightning striking the splash of a depth-bomb explosion in 1957. The Naval Ordnance Laboratory was conducting tests with depth charges in Chesapeake Bay on a stormy day in June when a multiple stroke of lightning hit the plume of water from an underwater blast. Instruments showed that the first stroke hit when the plume had reached 235 feet into the air, 1.61 seconds after detonation. Plate XXXIX shows the third stroke striking when the water plume was 290 feet high. This unusually rare photo was one frame of a 35-millimeter movie-camera record of the depth-bomb tests.

PLATE I. Lightning over Huntington, New York.

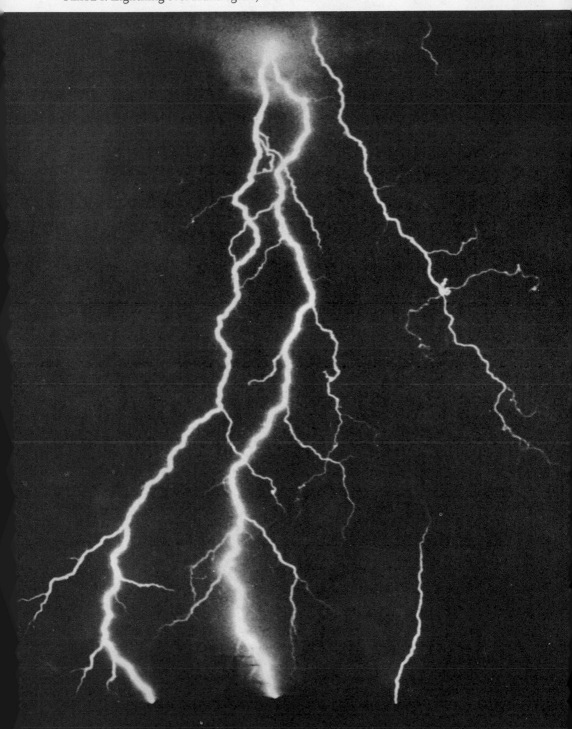

PLATE II. Navaho sand painting shows Slayer of Enemy Gods holding lightning in his hand. (See Chapter 1)

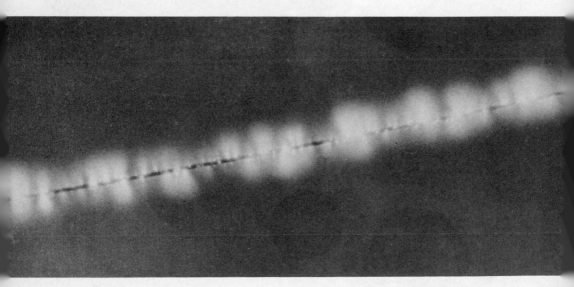

PLATE III. Photo of corona on high voltage transmission line shows how De Roma's kite string may have looked. (See Chapter 3)

PLATE IV. Professor Richmann is killed when lightning strikes his experimental rod in 1753. (See Chapter 2)

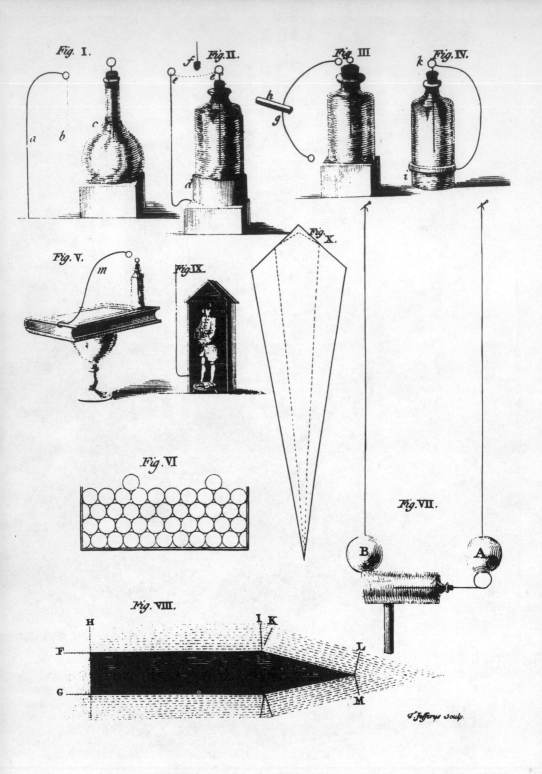

PLATE V. Diagrams used by Franklin to illustrate his 1751 book about electricity. (See Chapter 2)

PLATE VI. Mason Chamberlain's portrait of Benjamin Franklin includes bell arrangement for detecting electrified clouds. (See Chapter 3)

PLATE VII. Steinmetz working at Camp Mohawk. Lightning later struck tree by window and splintered his work table. (See Chapter 3)

PLATE VIII. Steinmetz shows Edison first artificial lightning generator. (See Chapter 3)

PLATE IX. General Electric's high-voltage laboratory can produce artificial lightning strokes fifty feet long. (See Chapter 3)

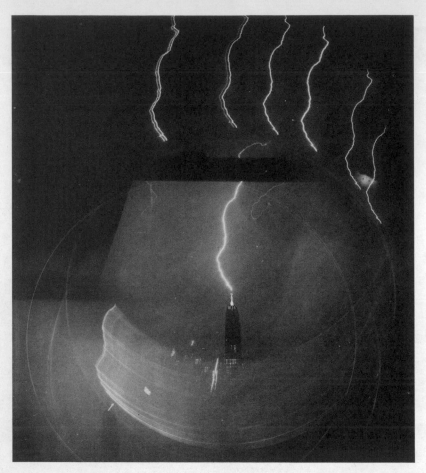

PLATE X. This Boys camera photo of bolt striking Empire State Building in 1937 proves that a flash is composed of several strokes. Oscillograph record (below) plots magnitude of current. (See Chapter 3)

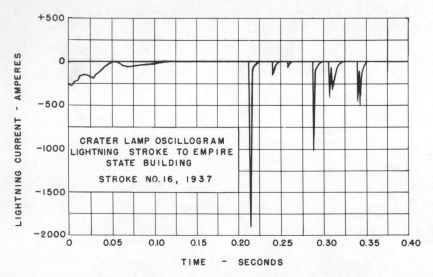

PLATE XI. Photographer John Stroud captured this view of lightning between clouds from a Comet jet liner flying at 34,000 feet north of Rome
on a July evening in 1960. (See Chapter 7)

NEGATIVE FIGURES   POSITIVE FIGURES   NEGATIVE FIGURES   POSITIVE FIGURES

Abrupt Wave Fronts   **5-Microsecond Fronts**

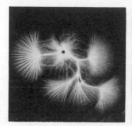
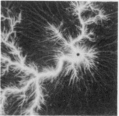

200-Microsecond Fronts   **Beyond the Calibration Range**

PLATE XII. Electrical surges through sensitized film produce these klydono-grams (Lichtenberg figures). Shape tells polarity and size tells magnitude of the current. (See Chapter 3)

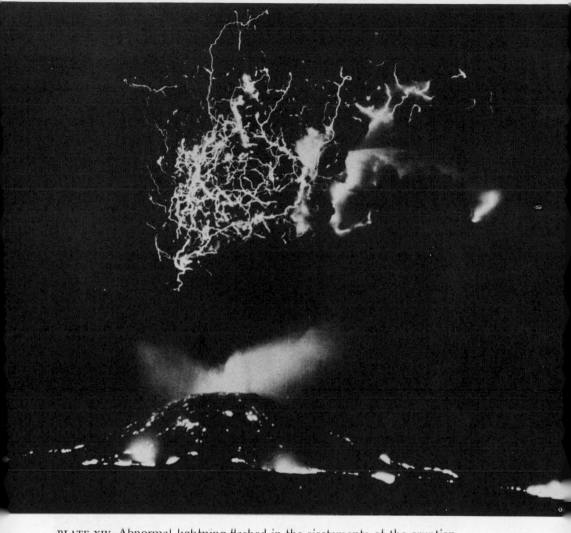

PLATE XIV. Abnormal lightning flashed in the ejectamenta of the eruption of Mount Vesuvius in 1944.

PLATE XIII. Lightning made this klydonogram of scorched grass on a golf course. (See Chapter 10)

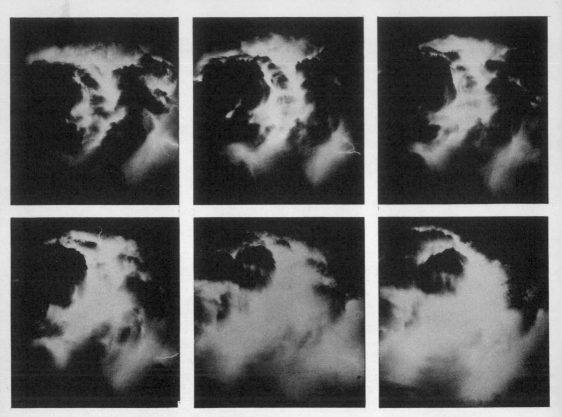

PLATE XV. One hundred ten seconds in the life of a boiling cumulonimbus. (See Chapter 4)

PLATE XVI. Lightning within the thunderhead illuminated these night photos.

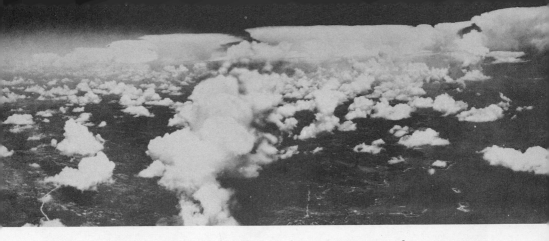

PLATE XVII. View from 18,000 feet of a line of thunderstorms nearly 140 miles long. (See Chapter 5)

PLATE XVIII. Navy dirigible *Shenandoah* was wrenched apart by a thunder squall in 1925. (See Chapter 16)

PLATE XIX. Trees are favorite lightning targets. (See Chapter 11)

PLATE XX. Explosive heating caused by lightning's currents often shatters trees. (See Chapter 11)

PLATE XXI. This mountaintop forest fire is one of thousands started each year by lightning in valuable timberlands. (See Chapter 11)

PLATE XXII. Cows electrocuted by ground currents radiating from tree struck by lightning. (See Chapter 14)

PLATE XXIII. Lightning blasted the top off this giant sequoia generations ago. (See Chapter 11)

PLATE XXIV. Fire scars are caused by burning debris on forest floor.

PLATE XXV. Debris dropped from top of sequoia hit by lightning smashed a small shed.

PLATE XXVI. Laboratory lightning explodes a utility pole during test.

PLATE XXVII. Actual utility pole splintered by real lightning.

PLATE XXVIII. Home in White Plains, New York, after lightning struck in 1936. (See Chapter 12)

PLATE XXIX. Tests show that metal automobile body shields occupant from electrical harm. (See Chapter 14)

PLATE XXX. Power line intercepts lightning in laboratory model test. (See Chapter 12)

PLATE XXXI. Model shows how an overhead ground wire diverts lightning from building. (See Chapter 12)

PLATE XXXII. Test with ½-inch-high "lightning rod" demonstrates cone of protection principle. "Lightning" strikes either the "rod" or some distance away. (See Chapter 12)

Target Made by Lightning. ½-Inch Needle at Center
r = radius, h = height of needle at center

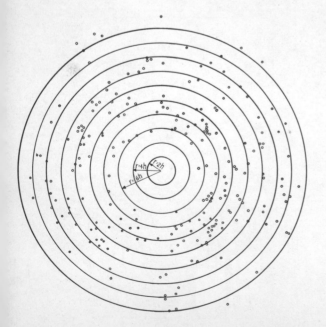

PLATE XXXIII. Hay-filled model barn is unharmed when artificial lightning strikes the grounded rod. (See Chapters 12 and 13)

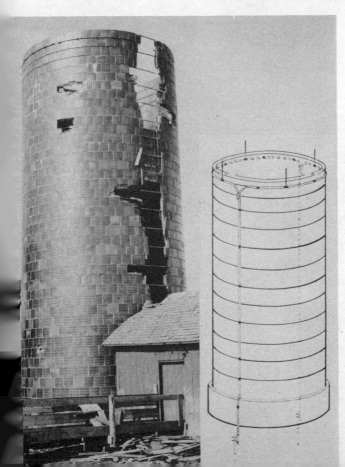

PLATE XXXIV. Stroke ripped tile from this silo. Inset shows conductor system that could have prevented this damage. (See Chapter 13)

PLATE XXXV. Pointed conductor at very high voltage ionizes the air around the tip. (See Chapter 6)

PLATE XXXVI. Lightning strikes a New Jersey beach. Incomplete streamers rise from the ground near the main lightning channel. (See Chapter 7)

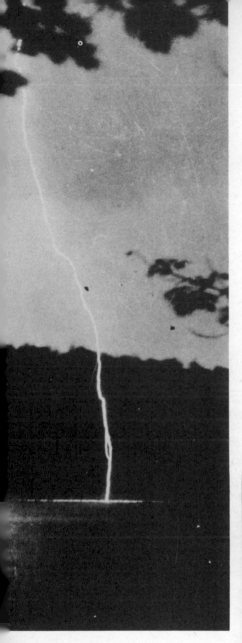

PLATE XXXVII. Stroke to lake causes illumination of water.

PLATE XXXVIII. Model boat subjected to laboratory lightning. Note lightning path after entering water. (See Chapter 15)

PLATE XXXIX. During a routine test of a depth bomb, lightning strikes the rising plume of water in this rare Navy photograph. (See Chapter 10)

PLATE XL. Bridge in Columbus, Ohio, was damaged when lightning set off a gas explosion. (See Chapter 17)

PLATE XLI. A lightning stroke triggered explosions that destroyed Navy ammunition depot in New Jersey in 1926. (See Chapter 12)

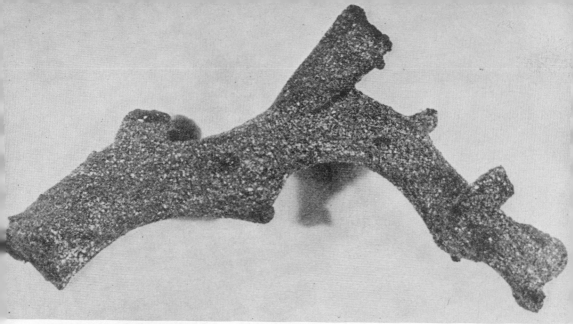

PLATE XLII, *above*. "Petrified lightning," or fulgurite, is made of sand fused by lightning. (See Chapter 10)

PLATE XLIII, *left*. Inside of a fulgurite is glossy.

PLATE XLIV, *below*. Fulgurite found in Florida went four feet into ground.

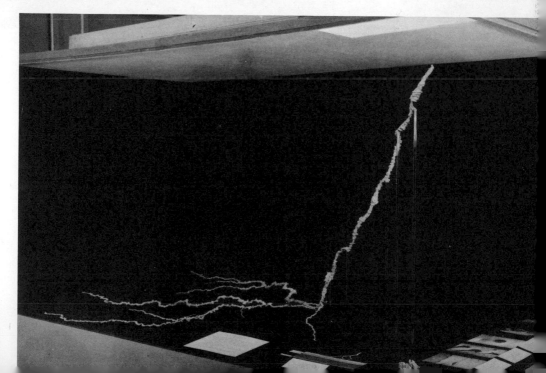

PLATE XLV. Photo of the scope of a radar in Missouri shows a radar echo of a lightning discharge that may have been 100 miles long. (See Chapter 7)

PLATE XLVI. Mobile observation station used in Project Skyfire. (See Chapter 18)

PLATE XLVII. Generator makes silver-iodide smoke of Skyfire cloud-modification tests. (See Chapter 18)

PLATE XLVIII. Lightning nipped piece from fabric-covered elevator of this Air Force transport plane. (See Chapter 16)

PLATE XLIX. Three-inch-wide hole burned in wing tip of all-metal airplane.

PLATE L. Fourteen-inch hole in airplane radome made by lightning.

PLATE LI. Model tests show where lightning may strike a proposed airplane design. (See Chapter 16)

PLATE LII. Actual WF-2 plane has three-foot lightning rod and buried metal conductor straps to protect huge saucer-like plastic radome. (See Chapter 16)

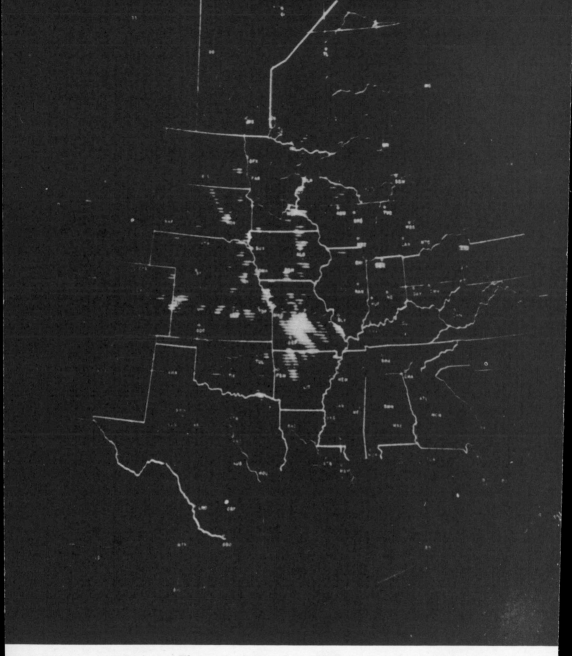

PLATE LIII. Electronic device plots courses of thunderstorms by tracking spherics (static) produced by lightning. (See Chapter 5)

11 FORESTS AND TREES

The favorite specific lightning target is the tree. Thrusting skyward, a tree—full of conducting moisture—offers lightning an easier route to ground than air. Thousands of trees are hit every day throughout the world. Forest fires are a common result.

The greatest single cause of forest fires in the Western United States is lightning. A long-term campaign to educate campers and tourists has helped reduce fire losses caused by man. In spite of ever increasing population and burgeoning tourism, the number of fires started by man has actually decreased. With all due respects to Smokey The Bear, it must be said that people can't prevent *all* the forest fires. In the United States each year about 7500 forest fires are started by lightning, causing a loss of $25 million. Nearly two million acres of valuable Western timberland went up in smoke from 1931 to 1953 because of lightning. This is an area bigger than the entire state of Delaware.

In the year 1957, more than 5 million acres of the interior of Alaska —an area the size of New Jersey—were destroyed in fires started by lightning.

In the twelve Western states of the United States more than 100,-000 forest fires were started by lightning between 1940 and 1956. About an equal number were caused by man. But in the Rocky Mountain states, more than two-thirds of all forest fires are ignited by thunderbolts.

Three million acres of timberland in the northern Rockies went up in smoke in 1910, but modern firefighters have prevented a similar conflagration in recent times. Today, up to 10,000 men work on fire control to protect an area of 90,600,000 acres of range and forest land in the northern Rockies. Fifteen federal, state, and private agencies spend over $7 million each year and have $45 million invested in fire-fighting equipment.

Lightning fires pose a severe challenge to the fire-fighting groups that protect our forests. Fire lookouts, on guard from towers at crucial locations sprinkled about the forests, can spot these fires better than visitors or personnel on other duties. But since lightning fires can start almost anywhere, they are difficult to fight and get under control. Unlike man-caused fires that usually start where people go—campsites, near highways, etc.—the lightning fire tends to be most common at high elevations which are away from roads and highways. In the northern Rockies region more than one-fifth of the lightning fires require more than four hours to get to, and one-tenth are so far from the firefighters that more than eight hours hard travel time is needed. This is in contrast with man-caused fires which can be reached in less than four hours 97 per cent of the time.

In spite of the difficulty in reaching a lightning fire, there is a compensating factor. Lightning fires are generally smaller than a man-caused fire. A study made by J. S. Barrows of the Forest Service of 30,000 fires on lands protected by various agencies showed that man-caused fires destroyed an average of 73 acres each compared to only 20 acres by lightning fires. Several factors help hold down the size of these lightning fires. For one thing, lightning is frequently accompanied by rain which helps quench the flames. In addition, lightning fires are detected faster even though they are apt to be farther away. A crash of thunder or a flash of lightning helps alert the lookouts and focuses attention and direction to the area where one starts. Lightning fires are started high up on mountains and burn downward, unlike the lowland, man-caused fires that convection carries upward.

Lightning fires are seasonal, varying with the thunderstorm activity. The winter months are peaceful, but lightning builds up to a peak in late July and early August.

Lightning fires also vary from year to year. For instance, in the northern Rockies in 1943, only 538 fires were set by lightning. But in 1940 six times as many were started in the same area, and in one hectic month, July 1940, nearly 2000 were started. One red-letter day, which most fire agencies would like to forget, is July 12, 1940. The day before had been peaceful: only eight lightning fires were started. But on the twelfth, the sky cut loose, spitting lightning that started no less than 335 fires in a single day!

Lightning fires generally follow a pattern as to hour of origin. The Barrows study showed that almost two-thirds of the lightning fires start in that part of the day between 2 and 10 P.M. In addition, lightning-fire frequency changes sharply with elevation. Generally the higher the terrain, the greater the number of fires caused by lightning. A region in the northern Rockies gives ample proof of the effect of elevation upon the likelihood of a lightning fire. Running from the Canadian border south through Idaho to the Salmon River is a belt of terrain with an elevation of from 5000 to 7000 feet. During the nine years ending in 1944 nearly 2400 lightning fires started there within a 2.5-million-acre area. In other words, 116 fires started for every million acres of land each year. This is in contrast to a lightning-fire ignition rate of 36 fires per million acres for all Western forests. The champion region is a 2200 acre tract of the Clearwater forest in Idaho. Here, on mountaintops just above 7000 feet, lightning starts fires at an ignition rate of 440 per million acres per year, almost twelve times as frequently as for all Western forests. At extreme altitudes (above 8000 or 10,000 feet), however, the vegetation tapers off, and above the timber-line lightning could strike all day without starting any fires.

The Tree

The moisture content of a tree is a measure of its electrical conductivity and hence its attractiveness to a wandering lightning bolt trying to get easily to ground. Since moisture conducts electricity, lightning would rather pass down a tree than go through virgin air.

Trees contain water in two forms: as water held in the cell walls of the wood itself and as free water contained in cell cavities. The *heart* of a mature tree is generally dormant and fairly dry, while the *sapwood* contains more moisture. The *cambium* lies directly beneath the bark and is composed of the outer rings. It is the live, growing part of the tree that holds the most water. A piece of wood containing 30 per cent moisture conducts electricity a million times better than oven-dried wood, and a waterlogged piece of wood conducts electricity best of all. Trees are better conductors in the summer than in winter. The running of sap in the spring increases the moisture content after a dormant, dry winter repose. In addition, warm wood passes electricity better than cold wood: the conductivity at 70° F. is twice as high as that at 48° F.

When struck by lightning, trees are not always set afire. Sometimes they are shattered or split, but frequently they merely lose some bark.

A common injury is a slight tearing of a two- to twelve-inch-wide strip of bark from an uppermost branch down the full length of the trunk to the base. Sometimes this path is a spiral track, that circles

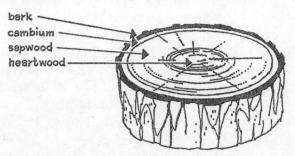

bark
cambium
sapwood
heartwood

Fig. 46   When lightning strikes a healthy tree, current usually travels in moist, conductive, cambium layer of wood just under the bark. Explosive heating of the moisture may result that strips bark from the tree and throws it considerable distance.

once or twice around the tree on the way down. The lightning current, seeking the path of least resistance, travels in the moist cambium layer of wood directly beneath the bark. The heavy surge of electricity is believed to heat this moisture, causing it to expand explosively and blast the bark from the tree. Pieces of bark can be thrown as far as several hundred feet.

In some cases, if the bark of the tree is thoroughly soaked with rain, much of the lightning current may pass down the outside of the tree with little damage. Even a waterproofed utility pole shows a moderate increase in conductivity after being exposed to rain. There is suspicion, but no confirmation, that smooth bark trees are protected by a continuous film of rain water on the bark that conducts the electricity to ground.

If the bark is dry when lightning hits, or if the sapwood of a tree contains much moisture, lightning may pass deep in the wood, causing it to explode and shatter the trunk. This happens more frequently to oak than beech trees, since oak heartwood has more moisture than beech.

The ability of a tree to survive a lightning stroke depends upon the magnitude of the stroke and the species of the tree. A survey made by the National Shade Tree Conference found that of the oaks hit by lightning, only 56 per cent recovered while 85 per cent of stricken elms survived. The Sitka spruce is known to suffer burns to its young, outer rings. These scars give false age readings when one is counting rings of a cut-down tree. Sometimes the upper branches of a tree, such as an evergreen, may be killed outright while the lower portions survive. On other occasions, a tree may suffer no visible damage, and yet ultimately die from damage to its sensitive roots.

A lightning strike on one tree may affect nearby vegetation. Lightning currents spreading out radially from the base of the tree may kill plants or roots of other trees. Trees react differently when struck and some types appear to be hit by lightning more often than others.

Tree Liability

Early civilizations revered the oak tree because they believed it to be a favorite target of Jove's thunderbolts. Oaks are commonly struck, but is this because they attract lightning, or is it because there are more oaks to be hit? Several studies have attempted to ascertain if some tree species are more susceptible to lightning than others.

Back in 1907 W. R. Fisher published a book on forest protection, in which he summarized the statistics of seven studies made in European forests. Together, the studies involved 3000 trees that had been struck by lightning. Not all investigators used the same scoring system, but it was clear that the most frequently struck types of trees were the poplar, pine, oak, and silver fir. Least struck were the beech and the ash. The relative number of times each of ten major species were mentioned is shown in Figure 47.

Unfortunately, the investigators did not tally how many of each species were standing, so it is impossible from this data to determine relative susceptibility. One study, however, made in 1899 by Lippe in Germany, did attempt to count both struck trees and unscathed trees. His investigation covered nearly 50,000 acres of German forests, and showed that although 70 per cent of the trees were beech, only 6 per

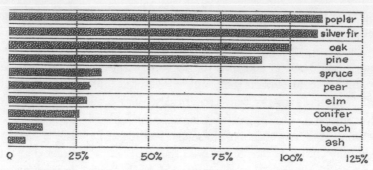

Fig. 47   Bar chart shows relative number of trees struck by lightning (oak used as reference of 100 per cent) based upon composite results of seven studies of 3000 damaged trees found in European forests. Poplar trees were struck many times more frequently than ash or beech trees.

cent of the trees actually hit were beech, while oaks made up only 11 per cent of the trees and yet accounted for 58 per cent of the casualties. From this Lippe concluded that an oak tree is 62 times as likely to be struck as a beech.

In 1946 a ten-year study of lightning damage to American trees was completed by the National Shade Tree Conference. Reports came in from 29 states on 420 trees that had been hit by lightning. Although 30 different types of tree were struck, the bulk of the reports, or 82 per cent, concerned just seven species. These were the oak, elm, poplar, tulip tree, pine, ash, and maple. The number of damaged trees found were:

Species	Number of Trees	% of Total Reported
Oak	130	30.96
Elm	76	18.06
Poplar	46	10.96
Tulip tree	28	6.67
Pine	27	6.43
Ash	22	5.24
Maple	18	4.29

The detailed casualty reports of these seven species were analyzed by A. Robert Thompson, forester with the National Park Service, to determine whether or not there actually exists a difference in susceptibility between species. He concluded that this particular data gave no justification for assuming that species is a major factor. Other elements, he found, have a more telling effect upon which trees will get hit by lightning. Exposure, or position relative to other tall objects and trees, is a big factor. An isolated tree, occupying an exposed position, is much more likely to be struck than the average tree in the midst of a forest. Less than a fifth of the trees struck were in a forest.

Almost all of the trees hit were either standing alone, or level with or above other trees in a group. For the seven major casualty types, 96 per cent were either alone, level with, or above trees in a group, and of these 84 per cent were the dominant species in the vicinity. Relative height and general dominance of species are the primary factors in which type of tree will be hit by lightning. If there are more oaks in an area, there is a good chance that more oaks will be hit than other types. Most trees hit are at least equal in height to their neighboring trees. When trees stand in a group, less than 8 per cent of the lower trees get struck.

Other factors contributing to the likelihood of attracting a lightning strike are soil on which the tree stands, bark type, and moisture content.

Some tree species have deep taproots, while others have very shallow roots. Extensive root structures may reach deep into electrically conductive soil. Tulip trees generally favor moist soil, while conifers tend to grow in stony, dry areas and have shallow roots. A thick, dry bark will act as an insulator and may impede the flow of electricity but may soak up considerable water during rain and increase its conductivity, and hence it "brings the ground up," electrically speaking, closer to the cloud.

When all these factors are examined, there are good reasons why more oak trees have been found to be hit by lightning than beech trees. The moisture content of a living oak is slightly more than for a beech, the oak tends to grow taller, and the oak likes moist soil.

Probably the most significant vulnerability factor is height. Most of the damaged trees counted in the Shade Tree Conference survey were between 40 and 90 feet high. Only 8.3 per cent were shorter than 40 feet. Those taller than 90 feet accounted for only 9.6 per cent of the casualties, but this is probably due to the fact that not many trees grow taller than 90 feet anyway.

If height is so significant, why is it that the towering sequoias have been able to live so long? Some of these trees are over 300 feet tall and almost 4000 years old.

Sequoias and Lightning

The biggest and perhaps oldest living thing, the sequoia tree is a unique native of the Western United States. There are two types of sequoias: the *redwood* (*Sequoia sempervirens*) and the *big tree* (*Sequoia gigantea*), both of which are a breed of conifer with dark, red-brown, and fibrous bark. The *redwood* is the tallest tree in the world —many tower above 300 feet. The biggest specimen, growing south of Eureka, California, is 20 feet in diameter and stands 364 feet tall, equal to a 36-story skyscraper. The *big tree*, or *giant sequoia*, is the bulkiest living thing, and only slightly shorter than the redwood. Most massive of all big trees is the "General Sherman" which weighs in at more than four million pounds and measures 36 feet in diameter and 272 feet tall.

Redwoods have a prodigious thirst for water. The ideal climate for redwoods is the coastal area of southern Oregon and northern California. Redwoods thrive here because of the 50- to 60-inch annual rainfall, warm days, cool nights, and relative freedom from freezing. Redwoods are rarely found outside this area. These unique climate requirements of the redwood happen to be in an area that is relatively free from thunderstorms. Living in an area of infrequent thunderstorm activity and growing on relatively low ground, the redwood is not bothered by lightning. Many are taller than 300 feet and have lived 400 to 2000 years.

The giant sequoia or big tree, however, grows where lightning is more of a problem. Outside of a few small members which have been transplanted, virtually all of the world's giant sequoias are found in an area of only 15,000 acres. The giant sequoia apparently requires less water than its lowland cousin, and it seems to thrive in the cool altitudes of the westerly slopes of California's Sierra Nevada. Giant sequoias stand majestically in distinct groves at altitudes ranging from 5000 to 8400 feet. Some are almost 4000 years old.

Thunderstorm activity in the Sierra Nevada is more frequent than along the California coast. This may help explain why the big tree,

although older, is not as tall as the redwood. Walter Fry, first superintendent of Sequoia National Park, lived near the sequoias for nearly
fifty years and has stated: "Scarcely any mature Big Tree has escaped
a Jovial bolt. A tree which for thousands of years towers above the
forest canopy must eventually be struck by lightning." Even if the
climate were suitable, it is doubtful if either the redwood or big tree
could grow so tall in the thundery Daytona area of Florida.

Lightning is the big tree's greatest enemy. The giant sequoia is
virtually immune to fungus, disease, or insect attack. The absence of
resin combined with the insulating capabilities of its bark—sometimes
two feet thick—makes it resistant to forest fires. A single fire could
not kill a big tree. For heat to reach and damage the living tissues
beneath the insulating bark, weeks of burning would be needed. When
lightning strikes a big tree, it may ignite its crown. This in itself may
not kill the tree, but flaming brands falling to the base may ignite
debris on the forest floor that may kill or scar younger trees. The
gaping black scars and hollows on some of the big trees were probably
caused by the heat of falling limbs from a crown fire started by lightning.

If the trunk survives heat from debris falling at the base, a big tree
can usually survive a crown fire. Perhaps the best examples are the two
most famous big trees. Both the General Sherman, which was already
a mature tree when Christ was born, and the General Grant (sometimes called the "nation's Christmas tree") are believed to have had
their tops blasted off by lightning generations ago. It is possible that
the General Grant was more than 400 feet tall when hit by lightning.
Today both of these awesome vegetables are more than 260 feet tall
and both have their first branch starting 130 feet in the air. General
Sherman's first branch is larger than the tallest American elm and is
almost seven feet in diameter and about 150 feet long.

Today the giant sequoia has man helping it prolong its life. All
but a few of the big trees are contained in either the Yosemite or
Sequoia and Kings Canyon National Parks where forest rangers help
douse fires. Most of the lightning fires cannot be doused immediately,
however, for the flames often burn at a height beyond the reach of
water pumps. Often the best that can be done is to prevent the fire
from spreading to other trees. On March 23, 1959, lightning struck
near the top of a 200-foot big tree. Firemen brought powerful water

pumps into play, but the stream of water splattered before reaching the burning part of the tree. Park personnel had to be content to extinguish falling debris. One branch, weighing several tons, crushed a woodshed and destroyed a supply of linen for the nearby public lodge. It wasn't until the fire had burned to within 100 feet of the ground that a large limb was pulled off with a cable to split open the shell so that firemen could pump water into the smoldering fire inside the tree. All told, two dozen men helped fight the fire, which burned for eight days.

Though better than air, the big tree is a relatively poor electrical conductor as woods go. The big tree has no taproot. It likes mineral soil and its vast root system spreads several hundred feet and may cover two or three acres, rarely going deeper than six feet. The shallow root system, combined with a heavy, nonresinous sap, makes the big tree a relatively poor electrical conductor. The big tree is usually shattered by lightning, and no cases are known where the lightning current contented itself to pass just under the bark.

Sometimes a big tree gets blasted by lightning without fire ensuing. Walter Fry, in his book *Big Trees,* states he once saw lightning cut a 300-foot sequoia in half by blasting out a 20-foot section. The remainder of the trunk was split almost to the ground. "Never shall I forget that sight. For when lightning hit the tree we could see clear daylight through the opening of the cut, and broken chunks of tree scattering everywhere; and while the two split portions of the tree gaped wide apart, the cut-off top of the tree was for a moment poised erect in the air above. . . . Then it dropped straight downward between the two open slabs which clamped tightly upon it." The cut-off portion died, but the damaged trunk has put out new growth and lives on.

The wood of a giant sequoia is brittle, and its cell structure allows it to be split both across and lengthwise when it is felled. Walter Fry saw a 300-foot-tall sequoia shattered by lightning in August 1895. Twelve feet in diameter, the tree was partly obscured by a cloud when lightning struck, enveloping about fifty feet of the trunk in fire. "Such wreckage of a tree I have never seen before or since. The upper part was sprawled down the canyon. About fifty feet of the lower trunk . . . was crushed to kindling and heaped in one circular sloping pile about 50 feet across and 20 feet in depth at the center. This tree looked as though it had been passed through a gigantic rock crusher and the product symmetrically piled."

Today there are less than 20,000 giant sequoias that are more than ten feet in diameter. Most of these huddle together in groves, some in high canyons and draws, and some in exposed ridge tops. Lightning seems to have decreed that the big tree will grow no taller than 300 feet. But these giants have survived almost as long as recorded history, and the breed will probably continue to survive. Even the venerable General Sherman is still dropping seeds today.

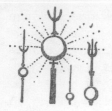

The tree is Nature's lightning rod. It "attracts" lightning by providing an easier path to earth than the air around it. A tall tree protects smaller trees nearby by diverting the lightning. Even the ancients noticed that tall objects are struck by lightning more often than adjacent shorter objects. As the National Shade Tree Conference survey showed, a tall tree provides protection for shorter neighbors by shielding them from lightning strokes. This principle of nature is put to work in the lightning rod.

The lightning rod—or more appropriately, lightning conductor—is a device intended to divert lightning from an object by offering an easier path to the ground. No object can be guaranteed absolute protection from lightning unless it is completely surrounded by a grounded, conducting shield: even the Empire State Building, whose towering mast and continuous steel skeleton offers lightning an easy path to earth, has been struck on the side by lightning. But for practical purposes, the likelihood of an object being damaged can be reduced to a near impossibility by the proper arrangement of a system of conducting wires, rods, or cables.

Lightning rods do not prevent lightning, nor do they, as Franklin at one time supposed, quietly drain the charge from a thundercloud. The only purpose of a lightning-rod system is to give protection in the event that lightning does come near.

When applied to a building, a lightning-protection system is composed of three elements: elevated metal tips or terminals that are tall enough and so placed to intercept strokes that might hit the building; continuous metallic conductors that lead downward from the tips to the ground; and grounding rods or buried plates that make a good electrical connection with the earth. The tips are usually placed on the chimney and roof of the building. The conductors are insulated from the building and are of sufficient size to handle the currents of lightning strokes. The ground connections are made to metal rods driven deep into the ground or to metal plates buried deep in a moist layer of earth.

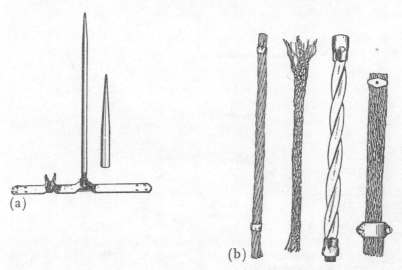

(a)

(b)

Fig. 48 (a) Tips or air terminals of lightning-protection system are usually pointed rods of brass or copper. (b) Conductors are usually copper or galvanized steel cable. COURTESY OF U.S. DEPARTMENT OF AGRICULTURE

The tip lures lightning that might otherwise blast through the non-conducting portions of the structure. The conductor leads the lightning current safely to earth. We have seen that when lightning passes through wood, the wood may be shattered, splintered, or exploded. The tiny pockets of air and moisture in brick, masonry, and lumber also expand explosively when lightning passes through them. On the other hand, a good conductor, like a metal rod or cable, easily passes heavy currents if it is large enough. If the conductors are too small, of course, they may melt when the heavy surge of lightning electricity comes along, just as a fuse melts when it is overloaded.

Lightning can severely damage wooden buildings. Large buildings like the Empire State, of course, are unaffected by lightning passing through their heavy steel frames. The typical private dwelling, made primarily of wood, can be severely damaged by lightning. Frame build-

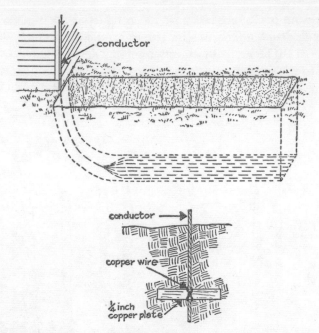

Fig. 49   Down conductors can be grounded by laying copper cable in deep trench or by connecting to buried copper plate. COURTESY OF U.S. DE-PARTMENT OF AGRICULTURE

ings can be damaged when struck by short-duration "cold" lightning, or set afire when hit by long-duration "hot" lightning.

Lightning starts as many fires in buildings as faulty heating systems and chimney fires. "Misuse of electricity" and "matches and smoking" are the only two causes of fire that outrank lightning in modern America. The Committee on Statistics and Origins of Losses of the National Board of Fire Underwriters studied all insurance claims for the 1948–57 period and found that lightning started the fires in 10.9 per cent of the claims and caused 6.1 per cent of the total damage. Lightning accounted for more than a quarter of a million claims, and $213 million in property losses. It is interesting to see that the lightning claims (10.9 per cent) account for a greater percentage of all the fire-insurance claims than the lightning losses (6.1 per cent). This may be due to two factors. Lightning is frequently accompanied by rain and the rain helps reduce any resulting fires. An ordinary fire may smoulder and spread without the property owner being aware of it. Lightning, on the other hand, usually announces its presence with a loud bang, which serves as a built-in fire alarm.

A "cold" lightning bolt can severely damage a house. In one classic example of this type of incident, lightning almost totally demolished a two-story home. It happened in June 1936 in White Plains, New York. The entire end wall of the building was blasted away, and part of the front of the house disappeared (see Plate XXVIII). The home-owner was killed and his wife thrown from her bed. More usually the cold-bolt damage is not so spectacular. Holes may be ripped in a roof or chimneys may be shattered by lightning. A more typical cold-light-ning incident occurred in October 1959, when lightning ripped a 10-foot section from the 110-foot steeple of the Freeport Methodist Church on Long Island. The gold cross atop the spire was knocked down and damage was estimated at between $10,000 and $15,000. The tallest object in town, the steeple had been unmolested by light-ning for the previous seventy-five years.

The entire ceiling of two bedrooms came down when lightning hit the home of Mrs. R. Durham in Ogden, Utah, in September 1959. The stroke apparently jumped to her roof after coming down a nearby cottonwood tree. Before it disappeared in the ground, the wandering bolt stripped a two-foot-wide swath of plaster and wallpaper from the walls, throwing debris throughout the house and shattering windows and screens on the back porch. Mrs. Durham was knocked across the kitchen while she clung to the telephone, suffering cuts, burns, and bruises. Several homes half a block away had windows broken by the blast.

Tall chimneys frequently are hit by lightning. Lightning cracked the 22-year-old chimney of the Clifford Scott High School in East Orange, New Jersey, in July 1959, loosening brick and mortar from top to bottom. The chimney had to be replaced. Most tall industrial chimneys are now equipped with lightning rods.

Building fires are started with an appalling frequency throughout the United States, as newspaper items attest. A brother and sister died in a blaze started by lightning at their home in Ragsdale, Indiana, in the fall of 1959. Lightning turned a highway garage into a raging inferno, destroying dump trucks and road equipment in Nyack, New York, that same season. A single storm over Huntington, New York, in September 1959, set two house fires within a few blocks of each other. The National Fire Protection Association estimates that lightning started 45,200 building fires in the United States in the year 1956 alone.

Lightning Probability

A good lightning-rod system can protect a building with a high degree of certainty. But since the cost of an installation may amount to several hundred dollars for a typical house, the owner must weigh the odds. What are the chances of his home being hit? Good estimates can now be made on the likelihood of an object receiving a stroke of lightning. The Weather Bureau tabulation of thunderstorm days, while not telling how many lightning bolts will hit the ground, does give an indication of the frequency of lightning in a given area. There is variation from year to year and local topography may cause additional variations, but the number of thunderstorm days in your area is a good starting point for an estimate of the probability of lightning strike.

Edward Beck, when Manager of the Lightning Arrester Engineering Department of Westinghouse in 1949, computed the probability of lightning hitting an isolated mast or tower on the basis of height. His data, in graph form as in Figure 50, shows the effect of height on the likelihood of a strike to an isolated mast or tower standing on level terrain in a region of 30 thunderstorm days per year. This shows that for objects up to 600 feet tall, the probability is directly related to height: an object 500 feet tall will probably be hit twice as often as an object 250 feet tall. The graph also shows that the probability increases faster than the height for objects higher than 600 feet.

A 500-foot-tall mast (on level terrain of 30 thunderstorm days per year) will probably be hit two times each year, on the average. For areas where the thunderstorm-day count is different, this same object would be hit at a rate in proportion to the number of thunderstorm days. For example, if it were located on level terrain where there were 60 thunderstorm days per year, this tower would be hit twice as frequently, or 4 times each year. On the other hand, if it were located where there were only 15 thunderstorm days, it would be hit half as much, or once each year.

The graph shows that a mast or tower just 50 feet high, standing in an exposed, level area near New York, where the number of thunderstorm days is 30, may be hit 0.2 times a year, or once every five years.

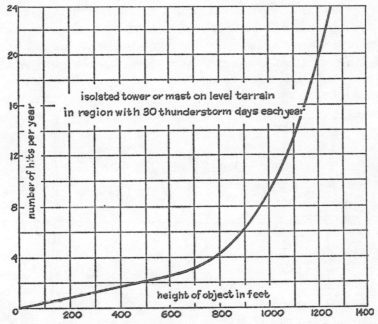

Fig. 50   Chart shows that tall objects are more susceptible to being struck than short objects. Graph based upon Westinghouse data.

Beck also concluded that the area of an object, such as the roof on a building, also has a bearing upon how many strikes may be expected. Although not as definite as the data for masts and towers, statistical evidence shows that a building 100 feet wide, 100 feet deep, and 30 feet high standing in open country will be struck on the average of about once every ten or fifteen years. The taller a building is, the less important is the area consideration; the building can be considered as a mast. Since buildings rarely stand alone in flat country, all these figures must be viewed as approximate guides. A building standing on high, exposed ground is in a much more hazardous position than one on a flat plain. On the other hand, the hazard is reduced (but not eliminated) if taller objects stand nearby.

Cone of Protection

That a tall object will "draw" strokes away from shorter objects is beyond doubt. General experience and laboratory tests indicate that a tall conductor will divert to itself all lightning strokes that might otherwise strike a circular area whose ground radius is equal to or slightly greater than the height of the conductor. This phenomenon is often called the "cone of protection."

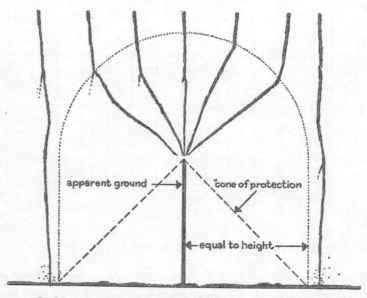

Fig. 51 Lightning takes the shortest, easiest route. A tall conductor attracts and intercepts lightning bolts that would otherwise strike within a circular area around its base whose radius is equal to the height of the conductor. The top of the rod is, as far as the approaching lightning is concerned, as good as the ground, so lightning takes the shortest route.

Several theories have been advanced to explain why this should be so, but probably the best explanation of why a conductor provides a cone of protection is the "shortest-route" theory. Imagine that you are the lightning bolt. You desire to get to the ground, and you want to do this as easily as possible. As you approach the earth from a cloud, you notice a conducting rod protruding from the surface of the

ground. The top of the rod is electrically connected to the ground, and
as far as you are concerned, the top of the rod *is* the ground. It would
be a lot easier for you to follow the rod than to fight your way through
air to reach the ground. You will take the shortest route to "ground."
If the real ground is closer to you than the rod, you'll go to the real
ground. If the rod tip is closer to you, you will go to it. Your choice
of route becomes a simple geometry problem. Figure 51 shows that
any vertical stroke will find that the rod is the shortest route to ground
if that stroke is within the limits of an area whose radius around the
base of the rod is equal to the height of the rod.

It has long been debated as to whether or not the top of a lightning
rod should be pointed. Franklin, who was impressed by a pointed
conductor's ability to draw or discharge electricity, firmly advocated
that rods should be pointed. Others disagreed with Franklin. Some of
Franklin's contemporaries, while acknowledging the wisdom of add-
ing conductors to a structure, believed that having a point atop the
rod was either futile or sure to cause trouble. One of the most elo-
quent critics of Franklin was Benjamin Wilson, a Fellow in the Royal
Society, who, incidentally, was otherwise such a great admirer of
Franklin that he had personally painted a portrait of him in 1759.
Their classic scientific debate grew out of the British government's
concern over lightning protection for ammunition depots.

In 1769 one hundred tons of gunpowder that was stored in the
vaults of the Church of St. Nazaire in Brescia, Italy, was exploded
when lightning struck the spire. Several thousand people were killed
and the city was leveled. As a result, the British government implored
the Royal Society to devise some means of protecting their powder
magazines at Purfleet. A committee that included Franklin, Henry
Cavendish, and Wilson studied the problem and proposed that lightning conductors be installed at Purfleet as soon as practicable. The
majority report recommended that the conductors have sharp points.
A minority, however, led by Wilson, vigorously dissented "in that part
only which recommends, that each conductor should terminate in a
point."

Wilson's report, issued in August 1772, explained, "My reason for
dissenting is, that such conductors are, in my opinion, less safe than
those which are not pointed. Every point, as such, I consider as solic-
iting the lightning; and, by that means not only contributing to

increase the quantity of every actual discharge, but also frequently occasioning a discharge where it might not otherwise have happened.

"It is with regret that I find myself obliged to differ from one who has so much merit in electrical enquiries as Dr. Franklin. But I trust no man of candor will be offended with my entertaining my own thoughts; especially in a matter of so much consequence."

He noted Franklin's own observation that points invite, or bring down and collect lightning. Wilson felt "using points, ought, in my opinion—cease because a greater quantity of lightning than we have yet experienced, may chance to attack us." He called attention to the blunt conducting system that had been installed on the new Eddystone Lighthouse and said "After twelve years, it had not been hit by lightning, even though a former building at the same rock had been set on fire."

To bolster his argument that points are unnecessary, Wilson used the example of metal-clad buildings and quoted Franklin's own words: "Buildings, that have their roofs covered with lead, or other metal, and spouts of metal continued from the roof into the ground to carry off the water are never hurt by lightning; as whenever it falls on such a building, it passes in the metals and not in the walls."

Edward H. De Laval supported Wilson on the issue of the futility of trying to drain a cloud of its charge and wrote "the quantity of lightning, which can be drawn from large thunderclouds by means of conductors, is so very small a part of the whole contained in them, that any attempt to exhaust them must be looked upon as altogether vain."

In spite of the dissention in the committee, pointed conductors were installed on the powder magazines at Purfleet. King George III also had a pointed-rod system put on his palace.

A short time later lightning struck at Purfleet, causing slight damage. Almost immediately, the king became embroiled in the debate about points by ordering them removed from Purfleet and from his palace, and substituting blunt rods. He applied pressure on the Royal Society to rescind the majority report and support Wilson. The President of the Society, an admirer of Franklin, refused to do so, on the grounds that he "could not reverse the laws and operations of Nature." Franklin, who had not sought any profit from his invention in any way, was unmoved. "The King's [action] is, therefore a matter of small importance to me."

Franklin's idea that the point would have a significant effect on draining the cloud has little foundation. Wilson's fear that a point would increase the hazard was also wrong. B. F. J. Schonland, like many other scientists of today, commented in his book *Flight of the Thunderbolts* that "on the scale which prevails in Nature the blunt top of any rod is equivalent to a needle point and no advantage is to be expected from sharpening it." Soviet scientist V. I. Arabadzhi and Westinghouse engineer Sam Griscom have each shown, however, that the effective height of the rod is increased somewhat by using a sharp point. In effect, the point serves to "extend" the rod farther skyward.

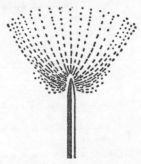

Fig. 52   Ionized air can conduct electricity, so when a high potential gradient causes ionization of the air around the tip of a lightning rod, the height of the rod is, in effect, increased and the rod therefore protects a greater area.

When a strongly charged thundercloud is overhead, ionization or corona may occur near the tip of a lightning rod. Lightning views this ionized area as a good conducting path better than the nonionized air nearby and almost as good as the rod itself. A sharp point facilitates ionization, so the "height" of the rod is "increased" when the point tip is sharp instead of blunt. The size of the ionized area depends upon the intensity of the electric field around the tip of the rod.

Scientists have long known that an electric charge on a pointed body tends to concentrate at the point. The charges in a lightning rod concentrate in the point, accentuating the difference in voltage between the cloud and the rod. If the charge at the point is sufficiently intense with respect to the air around the point, corona or ionization may

occur. The likelihood of producing corona on the tip of a lightning
rod depends upon three major factors: the potential gradient of the
air (caused by the presence of the thundercloud), the height of the
rod above the ground, and the sharpness of the point.

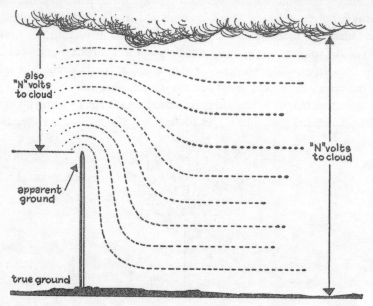

Fig. 53   An elevated conductor distorts the potential gradient of the air
around it by raising the "ground" at one point. The result is an intensified
potential gradient around the tip of the rod.

Since the rod is connected to the earth, it is at the same voltage as
the earth. Even a tall rod will be at the same potential as the earth if
the rod is a good conductor of electricity. But the air is at a different
potential at different heights, changing from a large cloud-air difference (near the ground) to no difference (in the cloud itself). A
tall rod protrudes into air at a different voltage than the air near the
ground, so a voltage difference does exist between the rod and the
air, with the greatest difference at the highest part of the tip. Laboratory demonstrations prove that air can be ionized when a sufficient
voltage difference is compressed into a small physical distance. This
is the condition at the top of a lightning rod. The tip is at one voltage
(same as ground), the air is at another, and this difference is increased

as the rod is made taller. A sharp point will "compress" this difference into a very small area, thereby triggering corona.

The ionized region of air around the point of an elevated conductor is relatively small if influenced only by the thundercloud: the corona envelope around the tip may extend for just a few inches. However, just before a nearby lightning stroke reaches the ground, the ionized area increases significantly, and may reach for a distance away from the tip equal to the height of the rod itself. An approaching lightning stroke sends out a strong electric field around itself: this causes the potential gradient of the air to increase manyfold, aiding ionization at the point. Therefore, just before the lightning stroke hits, the ionization is so extensive that the effective height of the rod may be nearly doubled and an upward streamer may form. When this effective increase in height is applied to the "shortest-route" concept, we can see why a pointed lightning rod can provide protection to an area whose radius is more than the height of the rod. A general rule for the size of the "cone of protection" for a pointed conductor is that the apex of the cone is 120°, or 60° on each side of the vertical. For every 10 feet of rod height, the radius of the circle protected on the ground is 17 feet. More conservative scientists discount the effect of tip ionization and assume that the circle radius is equal to the height of the rod. This is a 90° cone—45° on each side of the vertical.

The need for a sharp point is not so important if the rod is very tall, since the ionization at the tip is facilitated by the large difference in potential at the tip compared to the air. Sharply pointed rods are usually used for rod systems on homes, since very tall rods might be considered unsightly.

A lightning rod is truly a lightning "attracter"—but its reach is limited to a distance equal to one or two heights away. It will not, for example, attract a lightning bolt that approaches the ground a mile away. Its purpose is to divert the stroke from something that might be damaged by a high surge of electricity. The heavy down-lead conductors carry the lightning surge to earth.

Induced Effects

Some engineers are hesitant to install lightning rods on their homes for fear of the side effects of having a surge of electrons passing down the conductors attached to the houses. Electricity can produce harmful effects by induction even though the current does not flow through the damaged object itself. It is because of the hazard of induced effects that consideration must be given to what is inside the building. A lightning-protection system with a high point, a heavy down conductor, and a good connection will certainly chaperon a lightning stroke to earth. But it may not prevent induced harm to the contents.

A tragic example of what can happen when a lightning-conductor system is installed without full consideration of induced effects was the calamitous explosion in Lake Denmark, New Jersey, back in 1926. The case in point is the most expensive lightning stroke in America's history: before all the smoke had cleared away, sixteen people were killed and $70 million of property was destroyed.

Today the area is the site of the Naval Air Rocket Test Station, adjacent to the Army's Picatinny Arsenal, but when lightning struck on July 10, 1926, its target was a 456-acre reservation of about 200 magazines of the Navy's largest ammunition depot. Lightning singled out the Number 8 magazine, a small brick building with a tar-paper roof, terra-cotta gutters and sheet-iron doors. It contained depth charges and cast TNT aerial bombs. No. 8 had a network of lightning conductors that were grounded at each end of the building.

Lightning zipped earthward at 5:15 P.M. during a typical afternoon thunderstorm, starting a small fire that triggered a series of explosions that ended in catastrophe. Two vacationers were quoted the next day by the New York *Times*: "We were driving through the reservation near the gate. Everything was dead quiet and the storm seemed right on top of us. There was a tremendous clap of thunder, and right on top of it, so quick that we were completely stunned, there was a horribly terrific noise that shook the whole earth. A red ball of fire leaped to the sky and our windshield shattered and spilled in broken glass around us." Debris fell as far away as 22 miles, all buildings within 2700 feet were destroyed, and sixteen people died. Why did the rods fail to prevent this holocaust?

A Court of Inquiry, headed by Rear Admiral Robert E. Coontz, concluded, "The court, in the light of all the evidence, cannot conscientiously fix the responsibility for this disaster upon any human being." They found that "the fire in the . . . magazine was caused by lightning, either from a heavy direct stroke or by induced currents, despite the fact that the building was equipped with lightning protection in accordance with the best practice of the day." The Court recognized that a fire can be started by induced currents passing in or between metal objects when lightning currents surge close by, and recommended that cast bombs, depth charges, mines, and similar metal containers should, in the future, be segregated from other explosives and stores and that all metallic parts and their contents be grounded. Interconnection or bonding might have prevented this disaster.

The ordinary house, of course, is not faced with problems of induced charges in depth bombs or TNT containers, but large metallic objects or water pipes should be considered when installing a lightning-rod system. Conductors should be interconnected with the cold-water-supply pipes or lightning may jump from the conductor to the pipe and puncture the wall. Self-induction in the conductor is a problem. A rapidly changing current sets up an opposing electrical field that tends to resist the change by producing an opposing voltage. Lightning currents may rise at a rate of about 15,000 amperes in a millionth of a second. For a straight conductor with the usual cross section, this surging current can produce nearly 6000 volts per foot of wire. If the wire is 40 feet long, this voltage adds up to 240,000 volts —enough to jump an air gap of about a foot to a nearby conductor, such as a water pipe leading to ground. Proper location of a sufficient number of down conductors, combined with interconnection of all grounded objects, can prevent this. In addition, conductors should be as straight as possible. An electric current always sets up a magnetic field around it. If the conductor twists and turns, the magnetic field of one section may inhibit the magnetic field of another section and thereby choke or impede the free flow of current through the conductor.

One of the most important requirements of a lightning protection system is a good ground connection. A poorly grounded lightning rod may be worse than no rod at all. Lightning currents passing easily down a conductor, upon meeting unexpected resistance where the conductor enters the ground, may suddenly jump to an easier path, such as a water pipe or house wiring, and set fire to the structure in the process. Digging a deep hole for a good ground electrode is hard work and many installations have suffered from inadequate spade

work. Back in the last century, our country's sharpest salesmen ped-
dled lightning rods. Unfortunately, the salesmen did a better job of
selling than the installers did of installing, causing some rods to fail
when put to Nature's test. Unscrupulous salesmen were known as
"state liners," because they would skip over the state line just ahead
of the local police. Other homeowners who already had lightning rods
were sometimes cajoled into paying glib salesmen high fees for having
their rods "recharged." As a result of poor installation and super sales-
manship, lightning rods fell into disrepute in many areas. Even today,
the average citizen is skeptical of the value of lightning rods.

Do modern lightning rods protect a building? When properly installed, lightning rods can provide virtual immunity from direct lightning strokes. The Washington Monument was struck and damaged
before rods were installed in 1885. Since that time, it has been struck
innumerable times without injury. The Statue of Liberty has a rod
system, as well as Mount Vernon and the White House. In 1923 the
National Board of Fire Underwriters inaugurated a system for moni-
toring the installation of lightning protection systems through the Underwriters Laboratories. A Master Label is granted to a system that
meets a stringent set of requirements. Since the start of the Master
Label program, more than 240,000 labels have been awarded, and less
than one-tenth of 1 per cent have been reported damaged by lightning.
Investigators found that in the majority of damage cases the protection system was either in poor condition or the building had been
altered without appropriate updating of the system.

The appendix includes a list of national codes that define the detailed requirements of lightning-protection-system installations.

One interesting set of comparative statistics was reported by the
late Karl McEachron, long-time lightning researcher for General
Electric, in the May 1952 issue of the *Journal of the Franklin Institute*.
The Ordnance branch of the U.S. Army found that during the 1944–
48 period unprotected structures were hit 52 times, causing damage
exceeding $130,000. During the same period, rod-protected structures
absorbed 330 strikes with negligible damage.

Next time you are up in an airliner, look down at the ground and
make believe you are a lightning bolt: it is apparent that your house
is just a speck on the landscape, and the odds are fairly high against

your house being struck, but if you live in an area where lightning causes you to have sleepless nights, you probably ought to consider a rod system. If it doesn't bother you to have thunder crashing overhead and lightning flashing nearby, that's your choice. An informal poll of scientists and engineers who have studied lightning for years finds that these men are about equally divided as to whether or not they should have rods on their homes. If lightning really terrorizes you, a "Master Label" lightning-rod system can give you peace of mind by giving you almost 100 per cent protection from direct lightning strokes.

If you don't like the idea of having lightning conductors on your building, you can achieve good protection with the "overhead ground-line" system. Two tall masts are erected near each end of the building and a conductor is strung between them. The conductor is grounded at each mast by a separate wire, or if the masts are metal, the masts serve as the grounding conductor. If lightning approaches the building, the overhead ground intercepts the strokes and ushers the electricity to ground away from the building. That an overhead ground can intercept lightning strokes is clearly seen in Plate XXXI which shows a model tested in the laboratory by Westinghouse. Another method of providing protection from direct strokes that will avoid putting conductors on the building is to put conductors on nearby trees—if the trees are properly situated and tall enough to shield your home within their cones of protection. This is a geometry problem that you can

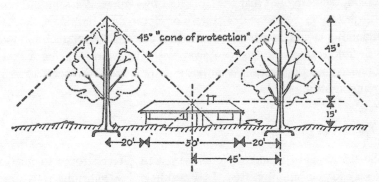

Fig. 54   Lightning conductors installed on tall trees can provide a cone of protection that shields this house from direct strokes. For the size building and tree spacing shown here, the trees should be at least 45 feet taller than the building, or a total height of at least 60 feet.

easily solve by drawing the trees and your home on a piece of paper. Draw a cone of protection from the tip of each tree that is to be equipped with a conductor as shown in Figure 54. For example, if you live in a ranch-type home that is 50 feet long and 15 feet high, and you have a 65-foot-tall tree within 20 feet of each end of your house, sketch it on a piece of paper and see if the entire building is enclosed within the two cones of protection. This example would work and is illustrated in the picture. You can see that if the trees were shorter or farther away from the house, or if the house were longer or higher, this arrangement would not work out.

Don't count on an ordinary tree near your home to act as a lightning rod and protect you. The tree is an imperfect conductor and, as we have seen in Chapter 11, lightning may shatter it and throw chunks of wood in all directions. If the tree is fairly close to your house and the tree is struck by lightning, you may experience a side flash. Lightning racing down the tree encounters resistance that may tempt it to leap from the tree across to your house and through the wall to where it can follow the easier route to ground through a water pipe or electrical BX cable. The flash may start a fire. To prevent possible side flash from any tall tree within 10 feet of your house, cut the tree down or equip it with a lightning conductor. Lightning conductors on trees are not unusual. Some trees have been outfitted with conductors even when side flash is not the problem. Valuable or historic trees may be protected from lightning damage: twenty-three trees at Mount Vernon, including ten that were planted by George Washington himself, are now protected with a system of elevated air terminals, flexible conducting cables, and buried grounding wires. Tree conductors must be flexible so that the tree can sway with the wind. Making a good ground connection is just as important for a tree conductor as it is for any lightning rod.

Loopholes in the Defense

So far we have concerned ourselves with direct strokes to nearby trees or to the building itself. In Franklin's day, lightning rods were all that was needed to assure safety when lightning struck. But it is no longer adequate to merely install conductors: the twentieth century has introduced loopholes in this defense. In this age of electricity,

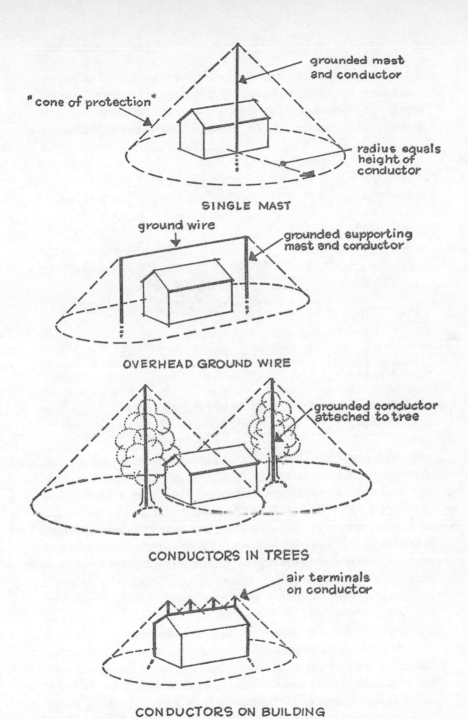

grounded mast and conductor

"cone of protection"

radius equals height of conductor

SINGLE MAST

ground wire

grounded supporting mast and conductor

OVERHEAD GROUND WIRE

grounded conductor attached to tree

CONDUCTORS IN TREES

air terminals on conductor

CONDUCTORS ON BUILDING

Fig. 55 Possible methods of installing lightning conductors to protect a building from direct strokes.

telephone, and television, lightning has a new route into your house—along wires that enter your house. Lightning may enter your home through your power lines, your telephone wires, or your television-antenna transmission lead-in. Fortunately, these avenues of entry can be blocked.

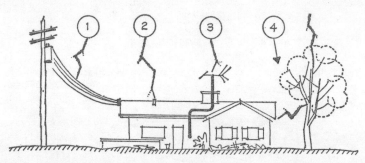

Fig. 56 How lightning could enter your home. (1) Strike or induced surge may follow utility lines into building. Arresters can divert these. (2) Direct stroke to building. Lightning rods can intercept these and lead them to ground. (3) Strike to TV or radio antenna. Good ground connection on mast and arrester on lead-in will keep these strokes out. (4) Side flash from nearby tree struck by lightning. Keep trees away from house or install conductors on house and trees.

To understand why lightning may enter your home through your electrical power lines, we must understand a bit about how the power companies protect their transmission networks from lightning. The typical power company sends out electricity over a transmission network of three or four types of arteries. For long distances, electricity is transmitted at very high voltages to keep currents low and therefore minimize resistance heating losses. At the power plant, giant transformers step the output voltage up to perhaps 69,000 to 138,000 volts for the main transmission line. In some regions 345,000 volts are used, and Westinghouse and the American Electric Power Company are experimenting with 750,000 volts for transmission at Apple Grove, West Virginia. As the transmission lines reach cities and communities, the voltage may be stepped down by other transformers to about 13,-000 volts, and then at smaller substations to perhaps 2300 volts. Just before it enters your home, the electricity is again reduced in voltage to a safer value. If you look out your window you will probably see a transformer attached to the utility pole in front of your house or just down the street. This gives 110 volts or two separate circuits totaling 220 volts. Just after the lines enter your house they meet your fuse box—your electrical safety valve.

About 10 per cent of the investment in a power-transmission network is for lightning protection equipment. This includes lightning arresters and overhead grounds. Main high-voltage transmission lines, whether carried by steel towers or wooden poles, are protected from direct lightning strokes by overhead ground lines. The overhead ground, which is sometimes called a *static line,* is a wire above the power lines that runs across the tops of all the poles. Grounded periodically, the static line serves as a continuous lightning rod, ready to intercept any lightning bolts that may approach the power lines. Depending upon the geometry of the pole support arms, one or two static lines may be used. The static line provides a "tent," rather than a "cone," of protection for objects below it. Most power engineers assume that the line shields anything within 45 degrees of a vertical line, but for good measure they usually position the static line so that no power line is outside of 30 degrees of a vertical plane through the line.

The static line is grounded at every metal tower by the tower itself or, where wooden poles are used, by a separate down-lead conductor. For high-voltage sections of networks, the static line is grounded at

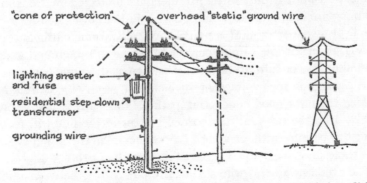

Fig. 57 Overhead ground wire or "static line" serves as continuous lightning rod to shield power lines from direct strokes. Wire is grounded with down conductors, on wooden poles, or by metal in structure of transmission tower. Fuses and arresters protect transformers from burnout if induced surges occur in power lines.

every tower while the lower-voltage circuits have every third or fourth pole grounded. The size of the down conductor wire is determined not so much by possible lightning currents as by simple requirements for mechanical strength in handling and installation. You can see these grounding wires coming down the poles. They may be covered with a strip of semicircular wood to prevent children or vandals from breaking the wire. Engineers use the wire itself as the grounding electrode, merely driving it 10 or 15 feet into the ground. If the soil is dry or has poor electrical characteristics, the wire may have to be driven 60 or 70 feet into the soil. If the soil is a particularly poor conductor, all grounds are interconnected by a buried wire called a *counterpoise*, which assures that all poles are at the same ground potential. If a heavy lightning stroke, or several strokes, hits the static line, having all grounding wires at the same potential prevents the lightning from converging upon and overloading a single ground wire whose resistance is lower than the others. The counterpoise reduces the chances of lightning vaporizing a ground wire and flashing over to the power lines themselves.

The overhead static line protects the power lines from direct hits by lightning. But it cannot prevent surges in the power lines that may be caused by induction. Any long conductor may have currents induced in it by a nearby lightning stroke (see Figure 10b). These induced-current surges might be large enough to overload a transformer and burn it out, so transformers are protected by fuses and lightning arresters to guard against surges in the power lines.

A lightning arrester must act quickly when lightning currents come its way. It must allow surplus current to escape to the ground and it must also close or turn off the circuit as soon as the surge has passed. The passage of high-voltage or high-current electricity ionizes air, making the air a good conducting path. If this path is not severed quickly after the surge, all the normal current in the line will follow along this path to earth, creating a "short circuit" in the power system that could drain all the power in the lines to the earth.

The overhead ground wire shields the power lines between utility poles but it does not shelter the wires that lead to your house from the utility pole. The chances of lightning striking these wires is quite remote, since they are usually lower than the utility poles or the nearby trees. But the possibility does exist. A surge of electricity can be induced in these wires even if lightning doesn't strike them, so the home must be protected from these abnormal currents. What happens when a surge, either from a lightning hit or an induced effect, occurs in the power lines between the pole and your house?

The surge has two alternatives. It can trigger the arrester in the transformer and escape to ground that way, or it can come toward your house. Chances are that it will do both. If you have the normal 110/220-volt supply system, three wires come to your house from the transformer. The three wires are usually packed into a common cable, but insulated from each other. One is at +110 volts, one is at −110 volts and the third wire is a common neutral ground wire. The neutral wire is grounded at your house, either by an electrode driven into the ground outside of the building or by a heavy copper wire inside the house connected to the water pipe coming from the street water main. If an abnormal voltage builds up in the hot supply wires, it may rupture the insulation and arc across to the neutral ground wire and escape to earth. Some excess, however, would enter your home before this could happen. Your house fuses would probably blow, but while the fuses were melting, part of the surge would get through to the wires within your house. This overvoltage, flitting throughout your household wiring system, could easily burn out motors in a freezer or a refrigerator, wreak general havoc, and possibly start a fire. How can this be prevented? The effective, and surprisingly inexpensive, solution is to install a lightning arrester on the power lines at the point where they enter your house.

Household Arrester-Protector

The household arrester, called a "protector" by manufacturers, has two functions: to divert and to arrest. Its primary function is to divert a surge by allowing it to escape to ground. Performing like a spark gap, the protector permits high-voltage electricity to leap a tempting gap to a well-grounded conductor. Its other main function is to interrupt or arrest leaping currents after the surge has passed. Arresters can repeat their performance over and over again without wearing out.

The protector is about the size of a baseball and costs just a few dollars. Installation is extra. Sometimes the power company provides the protector but generally the property owner has to purchase it. A licensed electrician can supply and install it for you.

Excessive voltages cannot be completely eliminated by an arrester, but they can be held to values below the breakdown levels of the insulation on the wires. If the protector blew off steam every time the

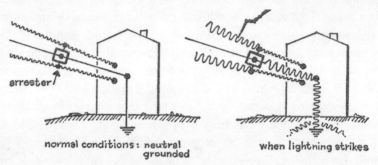

normal conditions: neutral grounded   when lightning strikes

Fig. 58   Arrester attached to power lines where they enter your home can protect wiring and appliances from heavy current caused by direct or induced strokes in power lines. Arrester diverts overload from the lines to the ground wire and into the earth.

voltage went slightly above normal, your lights would blink off and on with annoying regularity. Some tolerance is needed. If the voltage exceeds the tolerance, the arrester goes into action and lets the excess current pass off through a grounding wire to earth. Keep in mind that if lightning strikes, you may get some excess current in your household wires, even if the arrester functions perfectly. If Griscom's "lightning-prestrike" theory is correct, extremely brief surges of electricity may be produced by a lightning stroke that may sneak past before the arrester has time to act. For this reason, it would seem prudent to *avoid handling your appliances when lightning bombards your locality.*

The protector is still a wise investment, since it can bar the long-duration incendiary or "hot-lightning" strokes from entering your home through the power lines.

Telephone

Lightning is less likely to enter along your telephone wires than it is along power lines. Telephone wires are generally below the electric lines on the utility poles and are therefore shielded from direct strokes by the power lines. Induced surges may form in the telephone lines, however, so your home should be protected from lightning surges penetrating by way of the phone wires. Telephone companies usually provide lightning arresters where the wires enter the house. It is best to locate the protector outside of the building, but it is often attached just inside the house, perhaps in the basement. The normal currents and voltages in a telephone circuit are relatively low, so the telephone protector can act at a lower voltage than the one on your power lines. But even so, some surplus current can get through. Is it wise to use the telephone during an electrical storm?

People have been injured while using the telephone during a thunderstorm. In November 1959, the Seattle *Times* reported that a Lake Hills, Washington, housewife had her telephone knocked from her hand when lightning shattered a nearby tree. Her tongue was blistered and she received mild burns on her neck and shoulders. The woman was believed to have been sitting on the edge of her bed while talking on the phone when lightning struck a large fir tree next to a small office building and about 75 feet from her home. The protectors at both places, which were outside the buildings and grounded to water pipes, were damaged but there was no apparent damage to either the telephones or the inside wiring.

A month earlier a Wisconsin teenager was burned when lightning struck while she was using the telephone. The telephone is said to have been burned and shriveled. The Sparta *Herald* reported that the girl had just finished washing her hair and was sitting in a metal office chair. Her hair, which was still wet, was touching the back of the steel chair when a lightning surge is believed to have come through the telephone. She was burned on her ear, the side of her face, the back of the neck, and on her shoulders. The linoleum under the chair legs was also burned. Although temporarily impaired, her hearing in the burned ear was recovering at last report.

These incidents are two rare examples of what may happen when lightning is at work. A more common hazard with the telephone is acoustic shock rather than possible burns. Lightning nearby may produce a loud click in the telephone earpiece that may temporarily affect your hearing. The author has not found any reports about a fatality involving lightning and the telephone, but the possibilities cited suggest that *you should postpone calling the bridge club when lightning visits your neighborhood.*

TV Antennas

Another lightning avenue you should consider is your television antenna.

Some homeowners have a false sense of security, thinking that their TV antenna protects them from lightning. A television antenna is not a substitute for lightning rods, even when it is properly installed. A TV antenna with a good ground connection and a lightning arrester will protect the TV set and at the same time afford some protection to the building upon which it is mounted. But when we consider the size of the cone of protection provided by the TV mast, it is evident that the entire building is not shielded unless the TV mast is very tall.

Unfortunately, most television antennas don't provide any protection and, in fact, actually invite trouble because their ground connections are inadequate. The ground connection makes the mast intercept lightning strokes for the reason explained by the "shortest-route" theory of lightning rods. But once the lightning has struck, the surge of electricity meets too much resistance at the ground. As a result, the current "piles up", a high voltage is produced in the down conductor, and a side flash may occur. Lightning may leave the conductor and jump to a better-grounded conductor, such as a water pipe in the walls of the building. This may cause a fire in the wall where the lightning passes through. *Grounding of the antenna mast should not be given only casual attention.*

In one case in Huntington, New York, where a TV antenna had an inadequate ground, lightning became impatient with the grounding conductor and came down the chimney, jumped to the oil-burner exhaust stack, burned out all the wiring in the burner, and fused the stack switch control. At the other end of the cellar all the fuses in the fuse box were blown. The TV wires were unharmed. During the same storm that burned the Lake Hills housewife in Washington, lightning damaged the house of a neighbor a few doors away. Downspouts and shingles were torn from the house and nails from the wallboard flew into the room. The Seattle *Times* quoted the resident as saying "the lightning came through our television set and left a large, black mark on the floor."

If you have a professional install your lightning rods, he will usually attend to your TV problems as well as the roof conductors. However, even if you have no rods you should protect the TV set yourself. Lightning hazards require two areas of attention for the TV antenna. The metal mast should be well grounded and *the antenna lead-in should be equipped with a lightning arrester.*

The actual antenna components of the "antenna" are insulated from the mast, which is used as the means of support for the entire assembly. Generally the mast is the highest part of the antenna and is therefore a logical lightning target. To protect the lead-in and at the same time shield the parts of the building below the mast, it must be grounded with a heavy down conductor. (If the mast is supported by guy wires, these too should be grounded by conductors attached at the lowest point of the guys.)

Usually a No. 6 AWG bare wire (about 3/16 inches in diameter), made of either copper or aluminum, is recommended. The conductor should follow a path as straight as possible down the outside of the building where a good connection must be made to earth. The electrical ground electrode can be a rod or pipe driven deep into the ground or a buried metal plate. The fulgurite shown in Plate XLIV gives an idea how far into the earth lightning currents may spread before being dissipated and illustrates why a deep ground connection is needed.

The electrode should extend well below the permanent moisture level. The National Electrical Code suggests at least eight feet. Ground plates should have at least two square feet of surface area and to minimize corrosion problems, should be made of copper at least .06 inch thick.

If a pipe is used for the grounding electrode, it should be at least a ¾ O.D. copper pipe. If solid rods are used, a copper rod should be at least ½ inch in diameter. If iron or steel, the electrode should be at least ⅝ inch in diameter. Locate this grounding electrode at least six feet from any other ground serving a lightning rod system. If soil resistance is high, interconnect all ground electrodes and underground water pipes.

Be careful about the problem of corrosion when using aluminum conductors with iron or steel or copper ground electrodes. When the connection gets wet, a galvanic action may start that will corrode the material and destroy the connection. If you do use two different materials for the conductor and the electrode, use a special bimetallic connector where they meet.

If lightning hits a grounded antenna, most of the electricity will pass through the mast and conductor down to earth. However, some of the stroke may follow the antenna transmission line (lead-in), so it too must be protected from surges that might travel along it into your TV set. If the lead-in is the coaxial type with a braided metal outer covering, it will suffice to ground the covering to a good ground electrode. On the other hand, if the lead-in is the more common "twinlead" type, a lightning arrester must be used. The arrester should not be located up on the mast but instead at the point where the twinlead enters the building. Follow the manufacturer's instructions in connecting a down conductor to the arrester. This conductor should be, of course, connected to a good ground electrode.

Typical of what can happen when a mast is grounded but no arrester is used on the lead-in occurred on Long Island in the fall of 1959. Lightning struck the mast: most of the current passed down the grounding conductor to earth, but some seared along the twinlead. As it followed the twinlead, which had been looped around an aluminum downspout, the lightning cut the spout in two and then followed the twinlead into the basement, where the wire passed near a water pipe. At this point the current jumped to the water pipe. No major harm was done, other than singeing the shingles outside of the house. Innumerable other cases have not turned out so well: TV sets are frequently burned out or exploded by lightning. The arrester keeps all but a small fraction of the lightning out of the house. Your radio-TV dealer can supply you with a good arrester for a few dollars.

Lightning-Proof House?

The twentieth century has created additional lightning problems through our dependence upon wires. But it has also led to the development of a house with a built-in lightning conducting system.

National Homes Corporation, the nation's largest manufacturer of prefabricated homes, offers several models that are essentially immune

Fig. 59a   Typical lightning-rod system protects this barn.   COURTESY OF
U.S. DEPARTMENT OF AGRICULTURE

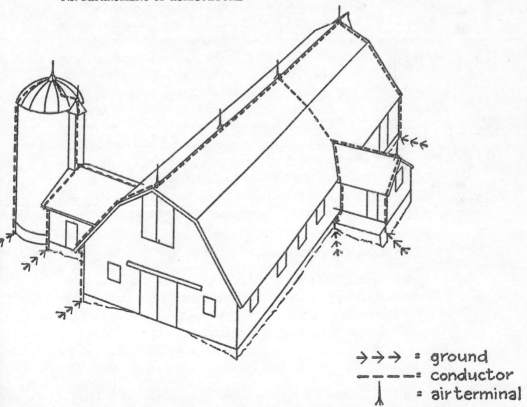

→ → → = ground
– – – – = conductor
ʎ = air terminal

Fig. 59b   All air terminals are interconnected. Numerous down conductors come down corners of building where they are grounded to the earth.
COURTESY OF U.S. DEPARTMENT OF AGRICULTURE

to a direct stroke of lightning. The roof, chimney, and walls of these houses are sheathed in aluminum. The chimney is electrically bonded to the roof, the aluminum of the roof (which is .028 inch thick) is bonded to the outside walls, and the outside walls are connected to the ground in two places—to a rod driven into the ground on one side and to the cold-water pipe on the opposite side. You could even improve this by grounding the building on all four sides. It is possible for a lightning stroke to burn a hole in thin aluminum, as will be discussed in a later chapter about aircraft, but the effect of this aluminum-skin construction is to surround the contents within a Faraday cage. Lightning striking the building would spread over the structure as the electrons try to get away from each other, staying on the outside because this is the place where they can get the most distance between each other. Induced effects inside would probably be negligible, since the lightning currents are spread equally all around.

Most of us, however, still live in old fashioned houses made of masonry and wood. We can achieve virtual immunity from lightning damage through judicious use of lightning conductors and lightning arresters. Lightning rods and conductors protect a building from direct hits and the arresters can keep powerful lightning surges from entering the building along wires. Installing lightning conductors is a complex and laborious job that requires particular attention to connectors and deep grounding electrodes and may cost several hundred dollars.* If you cannot afford to install lightning rods, you should at least properly ground your television antenna and attach an arrester on the lead-in. A few more dollars spent for a power-line protector is a small investment that could prevent damage to expensive appliances.

Lightning Protection and Insurance

Lightning protection systems are in wide use on dwellings in the Midwest and Great Plains regions of the United States, but in some areas lightning rods are rarely evident. Perhaps the major deterrent to more extensive use of lightning rods is the lack of financial incentive. Years ago, almost every fire-insurance company granted credit for lightning-protection systems, and lightning rods paid for themselves

---

* A list of manufacturers of lightning-protection equipment may be found in the appendix.

through savings on fire insurance. This is no longer the case in many
areas.

A prospective purchaser may often assume that because there is no
insurance saving this must mean that insurance companies have found
that lightning-protection systems are no good. This is not true. Underwriters privately admit that lightning rods make good sense, and
some insurance firms, such as Farmers Mutual of Nebraska, recommend the use of lightning rods and arresters. As recently as 1952,
Farmers Mutual advised: "You can stop nearly all lightning losses. The
thing you can easily do at small cost (less than $10.00) is to install an
arrester on your electric service wires. To increase your protection
lightning rods are also highly desirable."

The insurance situation in many states is similar to that in New
York, where most insurance companies allow a 15 per cent rate credit
if approved lightning-rod systems are installed on farm outbuildings
but do not grant credit for dwellings. If lightning rods do reduce fire
losses, why is it that some states do not grant rate reductions when
rods are installed on houses?

If you were to ask why the New York fire-insurance rate for a brick
house with a slate roof is no lower than the rate for a clapboard house
with asphalt shingles, the answer is the same: one basic fire-insurance
rate prevails for all dwellings, regardless of the type of construction
and irrespective of whether lightning rods are installed or not. For
many years New York insurance companies took all these factors into
account when determining the rate for a particular dwelling. However,
in an effort to simplify the rate schedule, dwelling fire-insurance rates
were overhauled in 1954 and one general rate was adopted. The rate
assumes that some homes will have rods and underwriters recognize
that those buildings with rods will be less susceptible to damage and
therefore the total insurance losses will be reduced. As a result, the
basic rate for all dwellings benefits from the rods that are on just some
of the buildings. The lack of allowance for an approved lightning-
protection system is not because the rods are ineffective, but rather
because insurers wanted simpler rates.

It is possible, although not presently contemplated, that fire-insurance rating bureaus of states like New York may reinstate the policy
of granting credit for lightning rods. In the meantime New Yorkers
who want to have rods installed must foot the whole bill. But be

philosophical: you are helping to keep someone else's fire-insurance rate down as well as increasing your own safety.

Since rates on policies vary widely from state to state, you should check with your local insurance agent for what credits may be available where you live.

13 FARMS, FENCES, AND FERTILIZER

The farmer faces more lightning hazards than the ordinary suburban homeowner. Farm buildings are generally more exposed than suburban homes and fires can be more disastrous because fire departments are few and far between. When a fire starts, the farmer cannot depend upon help arriving in a few minutes. Lightning is a major cause of building fires in rural areas. Authorities estimate that from 21 per cent to 37 per cent of all rural building fires are started by lightning.

In 1950 lightning struck a large farm building near Hinsdale, Illinois, and set fire to the hay-storage mow. Flames and smoke raced through the 300-foot-long structure, suffocating a stable hand and seventeen thoroughbred horses. The loss was estimated to be $400,000. In that same year, a two-story stone, wood-joisted barn near Phoenixville, Pennsylvania, burned when lightning struck the roof and ignited the hay mow. Another hay barn went up in flames near Knoxville, Tennessee, and a pile of charred ruins marked the remains of a $110,000 barn in Howell, Michigan, after a lightning fire. A lightning stroke to a building can bring grief to a farmer even without starting a fire. Lightning struck the water-supply pipe of an East Aurora, New York, barn in 1953. Nineteen cows, in contact with metal drinking stanchions, were killed instantly. None of these buildings had lightning-protection systems.

A modern farm is a complex of many buildings, interconnected with a network of water pipes, electric wires, and metal fencing. The buildings usually contain highly combustible materials like hay or straw. When we consider the many ways that lightning can enter a building, it is easy to see that a lightning strike to a building, a wire, or a fence can affect all the elements of the complex unless precautions are taken. To prevent a sizable loss of his investment, the farmer who lives in an area of frequent thunderstorms would be wise to consider a lightning-protection system.

Barns have special problems. Long metallic objects like door tracks and eave troughs can pick up strong induced charges from a nearby lightning stroke. The charge may flash to a grounded water pipe and set fire to hay or dry timber situated between the metallic object and the pipe. The Underwriters Laboratory recommends the interconnection of lightning rods, conductors, and grounds with ventilators, vent stacks, eave troughs, down pipes, hay-fork tracks, water pipes, door tracks, and telephone and electric service ground lines. Consideration should also be given to metal clotheslines and guy wires, metal posts, railings, and stanchions. It is apparent that providing a complete lightning-protection system for farm buildings is not a simple job for the average farm handyman.

If you are a farmer and are concerned about lightning, call in a few reliable lightning-rod installers and get estimates on how much the job will cost. Then check with your insurance agent to determine how much you might save on your fire insurance. A good lightning-protection system needs little maintenance and should last for at least twenty years. Consider this a "paid-up" policy. If the installation costs $640, when spread over the life of the rods, the cost amounts to $32 per year. If your buildings are insured for $40,000 and you are paying a base rate of perhaps $4 per thousand per year, your annual insurance bill is $160. If a credit of 10 per cent is granted for installing approved lightning rods, the annual insurance bill would drop $16, enough to pay half the cost of the installation. These numbers are purely hypothetical examples, of course. Depending upon the complexity of your buildings and the insurance-company policies for your area, the net cost to you for a lightning-protection system may be more or less than these sample numbers.

Don't assume that your barn is protected from lightning if it has a metal roof. A metal-clad roof didn't prevent the Knoxville, Tennessee, barn mentioned earlier from being destroyed by a lightning fire. A metal roof can provide protection from a direct hit if the pieces of metal are bonded to each other and if enough down conductors with adequate grounds are provided. For detailed information on the requirements of lightning reprotection for farm buildings, write for the booklets listed in the appendix.

Whether your farm buildings are protected or not, you should use common sense when you are working outdoors. It is sheer insanity to continue working in an open field if lightning is flashing nearby. Tractor drivers have been struck by lightning and farm hands have been killed or injured. More than two-thirds of all people killed by lightning were outdoors at the time. Sometimes a direct hit is not needed to cause a fatality, particularly when you are working near power equipment, since the blast of nearby thunder may startle you or momentarily confuse you. For example, lightning struck near a tractor driven by a farm hand in Sun Prairie, Wisconsin, in 1959. The man either fell or was knocked from the tractor into the path of a corn chopper. Your best bet is to stop work when the thunderclouds begin to roll in, and get inside a large building, preferably one with a system of lightning conductors.

Farm animals are frequent victims of lightning. The most comprehensive study of animal lightning casualties was made by Henry F. Kretzer during the five-year period ending in 1887. Kretzer, a lightning-rod manufacturer, tabulated statistics from news items in 192 American newspapers and found that during the five-year period lightning killed 1426 cattle, 1273 horses, 567 hogs, 610 chickens, 445 sheep, 273 mules, 29 dogs, and 8 cats.

Two particular behavior tendencies work against animals in thunderstorms. Herds of livestock may drift against fences or seek shelter from rain under a tree. Both habits can be fatal. Fortunately, the hazards can be reduced by the farmer. Metal fences deserve special attention.

Fences

Two years ago a twelve-year-old Alabama girl was electrocuted while grasping a metal fence during a thunderstorm. Numerous animals have been burned or killed during thunderstorms while leaning against metal fences.

A metal fence is a good electrical conductor and can carry electricity for great distances. To conserve posts some farmers nail wire fencing to convenient trees. If lightning strikes one of the trees, a good share of the lightning current may leave the tree trunk and travel outward in both directions along the fence. If the fence is continuous and insulated from the ground, the current may travel for several thousand feet. Lightning may also strike a fence directly, sending current surging for several miles. Often, however, currents move through a fence without the fence being struck at all. Current can be induced in a wire fence by the strong electric field around a bolt that strikes the ground nearby.

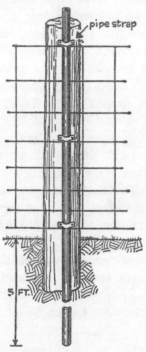

Fig. 60   Metal fences should be grounded every 150 to 300 feet to prevent currents from direct or induced strokes from traveling around the farm and injuring animals that may be leaning against the fence.   COURTESY OF U.S. DEPARTMENT OF AGRICULTURE

You can do two things to prevent current from traveling around your property on fence wires. You can ground the fence to let the currents escape to earth and you can interrupt the electrical continuity of the fence with insulators. A fence is not grounded if it is attached to wooden posts or steel posts set in concrete. A metal fence should be grounded at intervals of about 300 feet if the soil is moist, or about every 150 feet if the soil is dry, by using a metal post or by fastening the fence to pieces of ½- to ¾-inch galvanized steel rod or pipe driven five feet into the ground. If the rod is placed alongside a wooden fence post, use pipe straps to hold it tight to the post and make sure that it touches all of the fence wires. As an additional precaution, the rod should extend a few inches above the post to intercept lightning strokes before they hit the fence wire.

To prevent large induced currents from flowing through the full length of fence, use insulators in the fence wire every 500 feet. The U.S. Bureau of Standards recommends using a 24-inch piece of 2 x 2 wood for interrupting metallic continuity. If your fence is composed of several wires, make the break in all of them at the same place.

Some fences terminate against a building. Ground the fence here to prevent stray currents in the fence from flashing into the building.

In the Pasture

Lightning can affect a large area when it hits the ground, dumping floods of electrons that radiate outward along the ground from the point of impact like waves from a stone dropped in a pond. These radial currents produce a strong potential gradient along the ground that may amount to several thousand volts per foot—enough to produce a strong voltage difference between the feet of animals or people standing nearby. (The voltage depends on the resistance of the soil. Ohm's law says Voltage = Current x Resistance. For a given current the voltage is higher for dry soils with higher electrical resistance than for wet soils of low resistance.) A body offers less resistance than the ground, so some current—small, but fatal—may pass through the body —up one leg and down the other. This phenomenon explains why animals can be killed even if they are not struck directly by lightning.

A large area can be affected when lightning hits high-resistance soil. A flock of sheep were grazing in a rocky Utah pasture when lightning struck, killing more than 500 of the beasts.

The earth currents also explain why people and animals are killed without a mark while standing near trees that are hit by lightning. Fatal current may expand outward from the tree for several hundred feet. Seven cows at a Long Island dairy in August 1959, seeking shelter from a thundershower, were killed when lightning struck a large tree in a grove. One cow was 100 yards from the tree.

A lone tree in a pasture lures both livestock and lightning. A lightning conductor would protect the tree, but even deep ground electrodes might not completely eliminate the possibility of fatal ground currents. To prevent lightning from reducing the size of your herd, you have several choices. Cut the tree down and eliminate the problem or fence it off to keep the animals at a safe distance. An inexpensive solution is to avoid the problem when a thunderstorm threatens by pasturing your herd in less vulnerable areas or by bringing the animals into a protected barn.

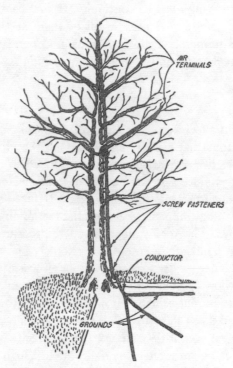

Fig. 61 Lightning conductor installed on a tree must be flexible and requires adequate grounding to properly protect the tree. COURTESY OF U.S. DEPARTMENT OF AGRICULTURE

Fertilizer from the Sky

In one way, lightning is a friend of the farmer: every schoolboy knows that plants need nitrogen to grow. Nitrogen gas makes up four-fifths of the air, but in the air it is useless to plants. Only when it is joined with other chemicals can it be utilized by plants. Lightning causes some of the nitrogen in the air to combine with some of the oxygen in the air, forming nitric-oxide gas. Laboratory demonstrations show that nitric oxide can be produced by passing ordinary air over an electric spark and quickly cooling the mixture. In nature, this gas becomes mixed with the atmosphere and is ultimately dissolved in precipitation and brought to earth as a nitrate. The nitrate is absorbed by the soil, where it nourishes trees, weeds, and food crops. Some scientists have estimated that lightning plays the major role in bringing useful nitrogen to the soil and have estimated that hundreds of millions of tons of nitrates are produced by lightning each year.

Recent rocket and satellite investigations have suggested, however, that nitric oxide is also produced at extreme altitudes from nitrogen and oxygen in our atmosphere by the action of extraterrestrial radiation. While this discovery indicates that lightning may have been overrated as a producer of fertilizer, lightning nevertheless does contribute to the nourishment of plants.

Some farmers believe that thunder kills unhatched chicks and makes milk turn sour. There is no good reason why fertile eggs should be affected by thunder—unless, of course, lightning knocks out the electric power to the incubator. As for turning milk sour, this is a matter of coincidence. Thunderstorms usually come on hot, humid afternoons, when milk may turn sour from accelerated bacterial growth. Clean milk, promptly chilled, will not turn sour just because there is thunder.

So far we have talked about the effect of lightning on natural targets and upon man's buildings and property. What about man himself?

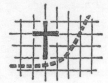

14 MAN IN THE OPEN AND ON THE MOVE

Your chances of being killed by lightning this year are approximately a million to one. During the period 1949 to 1958, an average of 180 people were killed by lightning each year in the United States. To put this in proper perspective, remember that more than 30,000 Americans are killed each year in automobile accidents. As a killer of man, lightning ranks near the bottom of the list, but to the families of the 180 people who are killed, lightning is understandably a terrible thing. Most of these tragedies could have been avoided had the victims been more familiar with lightning behavior and some victims might have survived if they had received prompt treatment.

Lightning is generally an "all-or-nothing" aggravator of humanity. Victims are either killed outright (without feeling what hit them) or merely stunned (and usually able to recover completely). Permanent injury is rare. In the next few pages you will learn how electrical currents affect humans and what treatment is needed when someone is injured by lightning.

First of all, what does it feel like to be "struck by lightning"? An elderly fruit farmer, who was knocked unconscious by lightning, said it felt as though he had been "hit by a giant hammer." He survived when lightning entered his packing-house barn in 1959 but a woman helper standing nearby was killed. The barn had no lightning rods and no arrester on the power lines. The woman and her four children had just finished packing pears for the farmer when a thunderstorm came up. The farmer went over by the open door to wait for the downpour to stop before heading back to the house. As the children tossed pears at each other, the woman came over and stood a few feet away from him. They stood there on the concrete floor as the rain pelted down just outside the door. He was wearing rubber boots.

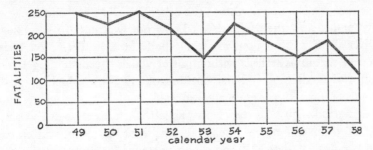

Fig. 62   Annual fatalities due to lightning in the United States. In 1958 only 104 Americans were killed by lightning, compared with 220 in 1954. DATA COURTESY OF U.S. NATIONAL OFFICE OF VITAL STATISTICS

She wore open-toe sandals. Suddenly, without a previous loud thunder, lightning split a big willow just down the road. Then it apparently flashed to the power lines, burning out the lights in a neighbor's house and damaging a hot-water heater. As this was going on a surge of electricity apparently entered the packing barn along the power lines, shattering a 2 x 4 in the loft. It charred its way along a ceiling beam above the heads of the two adults. The adults abruptly collapsed to the floor and the oldest girl was knocked unconscious. The girl quickly recovered and, seeing the two adults lying on the floor, ran for help. When help arrived, the woman was dead but the man was beginning to revive. Neither had any burns. Why only the woman was killed is not known.

The packer recalls that when he first regained consciousness, he had a sore shoulder and a tingling sensation in his fingers, as though they had been "asleep." What this farmer felt can be duplicated in the laboratory by sending a brief direct current through the body.

Just before Christmas in 1750 Benjamin Franklin absorbed a strong electric shock and vividly described his experience:

"Being about to kill a turkey by the shock from two large glass jars, containing as much electrical fire as forty common phials, I inadvertently took the whole through my own arms and body, by receiving the fire from the united top wires with one hand while the other held a chain connected with the outside of both jars. The company present (whose talking to me, and to one another, I suppose occasioned my inattention to what I was about) say that the flash was very great and the crack as loud as a pistol; yet, my senses being instantly gone,

I neither saw the one nor heard the other; nor did I feel the stroke on my hand. . . . I then felt what I know not well how to describe: a universal blow throughout my whole body from head to foot, which seemed within as well as without; after which the first thing I took notice of was a violent quick shaking of my body, which gradually remitting, my sense as gradually returned. . . . That part of my hand and fingers which held the chain was left white, as though the blood had been driven out, and remained so eight or ten minutes after, feeling like dead flesh; and I had a numbness in my arms and the back of my neck which continued till the next morning but wore off. . . . I am ashamed to have been guilty of so notorious a blunder; a match for that of the Irishman . . . who, being about to steal powder, made a hole in the cask with a hot iron."

Most of the people that have been killed or injured by lightning have not been "hit" directly by lightning. A direct stroke of lightning would produce severe burns. The majority of lightning victims are unmarked, having been killed or injured by relatively small currents that have passed through their bodies. Victims under trees, for example, do not receive the full lightning current. The current that passes through them is but a small portion of the lightning current that is spreading outward along the ground from the tree. Soil resistance can cause a voltage difference between the feet that may make current flow up one leg and down the other. It is also possible that currents may be induced in the body by the electromagnetic field of a nearby lightning stroke.

Although relatively little is known about the limit of man's ability to survive electrical shocks, human tolerance to electricity is very small: a fraction of an ampere of current lasting a second or so is enough to kill the average person by affecting the nervous system. Frequently, lightning victims are merely stunned or knocked unconscious. What is the best treatment for such victims?

Treatment for Lightning Shock

More than 100 years ago, the weekly *Long Islander* printed this item: "September 20, 1850 . . . Mr. Kitchen of Babylon, Illinois was struck by lightning, a few weeks since, and was left dead to all external appearance, but his wife took a bucket of cold water and poured it on his breast, when he revived and is now doing well. After this escape from destruction, let no one forget the efficacy of Cold water." Today, however, modern scientists recommend that the best way to revive someone who is "dead to all external appearance" is to apply artificial respiration immediately and call a doctor.

Electrical shock can make a person stop breathing. Both alternating current and a short pulse of direct current, such as might be produced by lightning, can cause temporary paralysis of the nerves that control the action of the lungs. If someone near you is knocked unconscious by lightning, check to see if he is still breathing. Even if he is not, he may recover if you act promptly. Start artificial respiration immediately. Most effective results can be obtained if you use the familiar "mouth-to-mouth" technique. Don't waste time going for help. The human brain can suffer irreparable damage in less than five minutes unless artificial respiration is applied. Most of the people who have survived severe electrical shocks had been given artificial respiration within three minutes of the incident. Continue the artificial respiration until the victim responds or until rigor mortis sets in. Be patient: sometimes it takes hours to restore a victim to natural breathing. The person may also be suffering from "shock" (trauma), so cover him to keep him warm and raise his feet slightly to stimulate blood flow to the brain.

The importance of prompt artificial respiration cannot be overemphasized. A Wisconsin farm youth who had been knocked unconscious by lightning in 1959 was revived by a fourteen-year-old girl who had learned how to perform artificial respiration at a swimming course. The youth recovered completely, except for a blanking out in his memory of the hour during which the incident occurred.

The injuries to lightning victims are frequently the result of involuntary contractions of their muscles, caused by electrical currents that give the nerves false orders. An electrical shock may make a person's arms or legs move violently, causing the person to bang into something or fall down.

Writers and storytellers have long used thunder and lightning to set a mood of impending doom. As a result, most adults associate thunderstorms with unpleasantness. When this conditioned response is combined with the physical effects of a thunderstorm—low barometer, brilliant lightning, and crashing noise—it is not surprising that many people become uneasy when thunderstorms approach.

Old wives' tales say that thunderstorms have killed people by frightening them to death. Thunderstorms have been blamed for burst blood vessels and heart failure as well. Other legends say people have been driven crazy by lightning and thunder. There is considerable doubt that these tales have any real basis in fact and it is possible that the ailments were improperly diagnosed. Lightning is certainly impressive, but permanent psychological effects are very rare.

A temporary reaction is more likely. When surrounded by a full-blown thunderstorm, some of us may find ourselves reflecting upon our own insignificance, compared with Nature's power, and making pledges for better behavior in the future. Charles Neider's *Autobiography of Mark Twain* quotes Twain on his thoughts during a night of his youth: "A prodigious storm of thunder and lightning, accompanied by a deluging rain that turned the streets and lanes into rivers, caused me to repent and resolve to lead a better life. I can remember those awful thunder-bursts and the white glare of the lightning yet and the wild lashing of the rain against the windowpanes. . . . With every glare of lightning I shriveled and shrank together in mortal terror, and in the interval of black darkness that followed I poured out my lamentings over my lost condition, and my supplications for just one more chance, with an energy and feeling of sincerity quite foreign to my nature. But in the morning I saw that it was a false alarm and concluded to resume business at the old stand and wait for another reminder."

In the Open

When man is unprotected by buildings and vehicles, lightning can be most dangerous since more than two-thirds of all reported lightning fatalities occur outdoors. Athletes, campers, beachgoers, and farmers seem to be most vulnerable. The man who is determined to finish his round of golf in spite of a crashing thunderstorm overhead, and people seeking "shelter" under a tree, seem to be the special targets of lightning.

A thunderstorm that visited the New York City area on August 25, 1951, took a toll of life that is typical. Reaching maturity over New

Jersey, the storm unleashed lightning that killed a golfer near Newark and a fisherman in a small metal skiff in Barnegat Bay, forty miles to the south. Over on Long Island, twenty miles to the east, it killed a young man at Sound Beach. The golfer was one of a foursome that ran for shelter underneath a tree when the storm broke. He was killed when lightning struck the tree, and his three companions were slightly injured. The fisherman died with a metal fishing rod in his hand. The lightning is said to have jumped from the rod to his jacket zipper. His companion was knocked unconscious but recovered after being hospitalized. The young man died in front of a small beach bungalow and his father-in-law, who had been standing nearby, suffered shock and burns on the left foot.

In Owensburg, Kentucky, three caddies died when lightning struck a tree under which they took shelter in July 1955. In June 1959 a caddy and four golfers were bowled over when lightning struck a tree near the sixth tee of a New Jersey golf course. One man was seriously injured. Another New Jersey golfer died when lightning struck a golf course two months later.

Swimming during thunderstorms is hazardous. As we saw in Chapter 9, lightning can hit water. The electrical currents, traveling outward in all directions, can pass through the body and possibly knock a swimmer unconscious. A nearby lightning bolt injured a man and his daughter while they were swimming near Allendale, New Jersey, in June 1953. Trees near beaches do not provide shelter. A storm that has just made a trip over flat water finds that the trees near the shore are inviting targets. During that same June 1953 storm, a woman scurried for shelter under a tree at a beach club on Long Island Sound, only to be killed when lightning struck the tree.

Five teenagers were hurt in July 1956 at Orchard Beach, New York, when lightning struck a tree under which they had taken shelter from a sudden storm. Three years later, in July 1959, at the same beach, four people died under identical circumstances. Then, one month following that, again at the same beach, a man was killed when lightning struck the beach. His infant daughter, whom he was carrying in his arms, was unhurt.

Athletes are vulnerable to lightning too. Fifteen cricket players in Pretoria, South Africa, were knocked down by lightning on February 2, 1959. Three weeks later, lightning hit a soccer field near Paulo de Farias in Brazil, killing two players and injuring seventeen others. In July 1949 lightning hit the diamond during a baseball game in Baker, Florida. The bolt dug a ditch 20 feet long in the infield, killed the shortstop and third baseman, fatally injured the second baseman, and hurt 50 people in a crowd of 300 spectators.

Lightning blasted into the crowd at England's Ascot race track on July 14, 1955. Two people were killed and 44 were injured when, according to the New York *Times*, "people were bowled over like nine-pins, some being lifted into the air."

One soldier was killed and eight others were hurt while on bivouac at Fort Dix. Two couples were hiking in the Mills Moraine area in Rocky Mountain National Park in August 1956 when lightning struck. One woman was killed outright. The other lady suffered burns and facial cuts but the men were merely knocked down and otherwise unhurt.

Use common sense if you are outdoors when a thunderstorm approaches. If you are on the golf course, get into the clubhouse, not under a tree. The electrical hazard near a tree is obvious. A secondary danger is that the tree may shatter and throw chunks of wood your way. If you are at the beach, get out of the water and into a large building.

If you are at a sporting event, get inside a large building.

If you are camping or hunting, and no building is available, get to low ground; stay away from tall trees. It won't make much difference whether you are standing or lying down, so don't feel you have to lie down in the mud! If you can't avoid trees, get in a grove of trees that are shorter than other nearby groves.

One of the safest places to be, of course, is in an all-metal car. The car, like a modern railroad train, shields its occupants from lightning currents.

Automobiles

Before the automobile, man's vehicles did not protect him from lightning. The lightning hazards faced by man in those days were not much different whether he was walking, riding on horseback, or sitting in a flimsy wooden wagon. For example, this article appeared in the September 1, 1854, *Long Islander*: "During the thunder-storm on

Friday evening last Mr. Moore and his family, while riding in a wagon near Jamaica (New York), were prostrated and injured by lightning. The electric fluid struck a tree just as they were passing it, and the shock stunned them. Neither of them were able to speak for fifteen minutes after the occurrence. They were taken to their homes by a gentleman who happened to be near the place at the time. The tree was split into fragments, and a piece of it was thrown with such violence against the horse's leg that the flesh was torn off. The animal was otherwise not seriously hurt."

Fortunately, today's family doesn't have to worry about being shocked by lightning while out in the family car. It is common knowledge that one of the safest places during a thunderstorm is inside an all-metal automobile. The passengers are protected not because the car has rubber tires, but because the car's metal body completely surrounds the occupants.

High-frequency electrical currents are known to travel on the outer surface of electrical conductors. This phenomenon may be called the *skin effect*. Although lightning current is not alternating in direction, it can be considered a "high-frequency" current because the current changes magnitude so quickly. If lightning strikes a metal car, the electricity travels easily from one area to another on the car body and there is little likelihood of sparks or current taking a short cut through the interior of the car and injuring the passengers. Convertibles, of course, do not provide this shield of immunity, although the metal

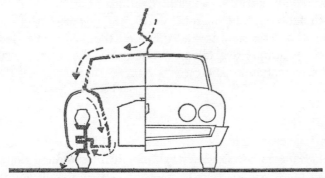

Fig. 63 Tests show that an all-metal car provides good protection to occupants. Current will pass on the metal body, through the springs, to the axles and wheels, and then jump past the rubber tires to the ground. See Plate XXIX.

bows that support the fabric top do serve, to a limited extent, as "overhead ground" wires.

Laboratory tests by Westinghouse, pictured on Plate XXIX, show that a lightning current spreads over the auto's entire body, passes through the springs, axles and bearings to the wheels, and then arcs past the tires to the ground. A passenger might feel a tingling of electricity if part of his body is touching metal of the car in more than one place. At the spot where the lightning hits the metal, the paint may become very hot and blister. So if a passenger is in contact with this spot, he could receive a local burn.

No reports are available to definitely establish that lightning has actually struck an automobile, and no fatalities or serious injuries have been attributed to lightning striking a car. A few years ago a motorist reported to General Electric engineers that he received minor electrical burns on his back when lightning struck his car. By the time the engineers learned of the incident, the car had been sold and could not be located. As a result the engineers were unable to inspect the car and see if there were any burns or magnetized areas on it. There is some doubt that cars have ever been struck.

Probably the greatest thunderstorm hazard in a car is not from being electrocuted or burned by lightning, but from the blinding flash or blast of thunder from a nearby bolt. At night a motorist may be temporarily blinded by lightning, lose control of his car, and go off the road into a tree or another car. Drivers have had serious accidents after becoming startled by a nearby lightning flash.

When lightning is bombarding nearby and you are out in your car, you should at least slow down. Pulling off the road isn't a bad idea, but don't park next to a tall tree. The best place to stop would be under an all-metal overpass.

Trains

On a June evening in 1893 the Air Line train of the Richmond and Danville Railroad was struck by lightning while trundling along at 25 miles per hour, near Gainesville, Georgia. The headlight and whistle were smashed, some car windows were broken by splintered wood, and several of the stoves in the passenger cars were demolished. No one was seriously injured.

Such a report would be rare today. The modern train, like the all-metal automobile, is one of the safer places to be during a thunderstorm. Railroad cars are now made of metal and provide a shield of protection that surrounds and protects the interior. From roof to track, there is a continuous conducting path for any lightning that may strike the car. The roof, sides, and floor of the car are made of metal and are firmly bonded to each other. The body sits on top of an all-metal suspension system of metal bolsters, springs, axles, and steel wheels. Wooden freight cars and cabooses, of course, do not shield people or animals inside.

The gandy dancers, men who maintain the railroad track bed, cannot have this lack of concern. The railroad track is essentially insulated from the ground by the wooden railroad ties. Electrified rail systems do have the track periodically connected to earth, but most railroad track is insulated from the ground for long distances. The track can have currents induced in it by a nearby lightning flash in the same way that currents are induced in long metal fences. Induced currents, or current from a direct stroke to the track or a train, can send strong currents through the rails, so walking on railroad tracks should be avoided when lightning is nearby.

The most frequent lightning problem for electrified trains is not a lightning stroke to the train, but loss of power because of disruption of service back at the powerhouse.

Cable cars and ski lifts have special problems. The long supporting metal cable can have currents induced in it or can take a direct stroke. Any person simultaneously touching both the ground and the cable is offering the current a tempting route to ground. People riding on the ski-lift chair may be subjected to harmful induced currents even though the chair hangs in the air below the cable and is not part of a complete electrical circuit. Sudden loss of power can be hazardous. On July 21, 1955, lightning struck on or near the power line of a cable car in the Alps near Salzburg, Austria. The stroke put the electrical equipment out of commission, causing the car to stop abruptly. Fifty passengers were spilled from the car onto a steep slope 100 feet below. Two were killed and thirteen seriously injured by the fall.

As we will see in the next chapter, of all man's surface vehicles, the boat or ship is most exposed to lightning. Sitting on top of essentially flat water, the vessel is usually the highest object around and therefore provides lightning with an inviting target.

Storms have plagued sailors since man floated his first raft. Whether he is an ocean-going professional or one of the millions of weekend pleasure boatmen, today's sailor is usually more concerned with winds and squalls than he is with lightning. Nevertheless, through history, lightning has taken a heavy toll of ships and sailors alike. Even now, we often read in our newspapers of cabin cruisers or sailboats that have been damaged or set on fire by lightning.

Legends tell us the story of Ceyx, king of Thessaly, who made a fateful voyage to consult the Oracle of Apollo. His wife, Halcyone, tried to discourage him from making the trip. She said that the winds en route were so violent that "they rushed together with such fury that fire flashes from the conflict." But Ceyx bid Halcyone farewell and departed in an oared sailboat. Halfway to its destination, the boat ran into an east gale. As the crew tried to reef the sail, the storm increased and lightning flashed all around them. The rumble of thunder mingled with the shouts of the crew, the rattles of the shrouds, and the splash of the waves. The rain fell in such torrents that it seemed as if the sky and the sea were one. The crewmen were frightened and Ceyx thought of his wife. Suddenly a stroke of lightning shattered the mast. The rudder broke, waves pummeled the ship, and the crew drowned. The body of Ceyx, as the story goes, eventually floated back to the bereaved Halcyone.

The early Greeks told of the strange powers of Castor and Pollux, the twin sons of Leda and Jupiter and brothers of Helen of Troy. Their special powers were revealed when they sailed with the Argonautic Expedition. During the voyage an unusually severe thunderstorm arose. Orpheus played his harp and prayed to the gods. As he did, "stars appeared at the heads of the brothers" and the storm dramati-

cally abated. Believed responsible for the calming of the storm, Castor
and Pollux were subsequently worshiped as patron deities of seamen
and voyagers. The basis for this legend may have been the appearance
of corona or St. Elmo's fire on the boys' hair.

Saint Elmo's fire is often seen by sailors. This display of corona
may play at the tips of masts and is sometimes accompanied by a
crackling or fizzing noise. It was described by a sailor with Columbus
as "a ghostly flame which danced among our sails and later stayed like
candlelights to burn brightly from the masts."

The name *Saint Elmo* is attributed to an Italian derivation from
the word Sant' Ermo or Saint Erasmus who was the patron saint of
Mediterranean sailors. The fire was believed to be a visible sign of his
presence and protection. However, this glow discharge is evidence of
a strong difference of electrical potential between the glowing object
and the atmosphere, so experienced sailors know that St. Elmo's
fire often precedes a stroke of lightning.

Lightning nearly killed the famous warrior Ulysses. The *Odyssey*
describes the wanderings of Ulysses on the way back from the Trojan
War. After forging past the whirlpools of Charybdis, Ulysses and his
crew rested on the Island of the Sun. When the weather cleared they
sailed from the island. But the weather soon changed and a violent
storm ensued. Lightning shattered the mast, causing it to fall and kill
the pilot. Out of control, the floundering vessel finally broke up in
the storm. Only Ulysses survived. He made a raft of the keel and the
mast and floated safely to Calypso's Island.

There is no record of the total damages incurred by sailing vessels
through the ages because of lightning. But the Royal Navy had a
particularly difficult time. The greatest sea power for several centuries,
the English probably lost more ships than any other nation. There
are many reports of ships being hit in the 1700's. Sometimes lightning
traveled down the masts and punched holes in the hull, causing the
ships to sink. When Franklin revealed the secret of the lightning rod
to the world, nautical men were quick to use his principles to protect
their ships. The obvious need was for some conducting route from
the high point of the ship to the water. Many theories that today seem
strange were proposed for minimizing the lightning hazard to the ships
of the Royal Navy.

A Dr. Watson of Payneshill, England, proposed in 1762 that "an

Fig. 64   Before the invention of the lightning rod, ships and boats had
no lightning protection and many vessels were sunk when lightning came
down the mast and punched a hole in the bottom of the hull.

electrical chain" made of quarter-inch copper links be hoisted from the
masthead and hung into the sea whenever a thunderstorm threatened.
This idea was tried with some success on the 370-ton sailing ship
Endeavour.

Captain James Cook commanded the *Endeavour* on the Pacific exploration expedition in 1768. He charted the coast of New Zealand
and Australia in 1770 and claimed them for England. Captain Cook
sailed north. Lightning struck while the ship was tied up at Batavia.
There the "electrical chain," as Captain Cook wrote, "which we had
just got up . . . conducted the lightning over the side of the Ship;

but though we escaped the Lightning, the Explosion shook us like an Earthquake; the chain at the same time appeared like a Line of Fire." A Dutch ship without a chain, "not more than Two Cable's Length" from the *Endeavour*, was hit and had its mainmast split and carried away and its gallant masts "shivered all to pieces." On the basis of this experience Captain Cook recommended that every ship "whatever be her destination" have chains of the same kind.

But chains were not the best solution. The appearance of the "Line of Fire" was due to lightning jumping the insufficient contact area between chain links. Some links became fused together after being struck. As John Simmons wrote in 1775: "Conductors that consist of different Pieces can never be so good as those which are made of one continued Piece of Metal." The poor contact between links so reduces the current-carrying capacity of the chain that side flashes can occur that could damage other equipment on board ship. Chains were also quite impractical. Frequently the ship's rigging was damaged by the heavy chain. When a storm approached, seamen had to climb the rigging, dragging the heavy chain with them while the other end dangled in the water. In heavy winds this was difficult at best. Climbing crewmen were especially vulnerable during this operation: three men aboard an American ship were killed by lightning while performing this task.

In spite of the use of chains the Royal Navy was still troubled by lightning. Sometimes the ability of its ships to participate in battle was affected. The HMS *Duke*, off Martinique in June 1793, was disabled in action by lightning while under fire from an enemy battery and in 1801 Sir J. B. Warren's fleet, which was in search of the enemy, had three of its six ships knocked out of commission by lightning. In July 1805 off Cape Finisterre, the HMS *Glory* had its main topmast shivered. The topgallant mast was destroyed and the mainmast disabled just before Sir Robert Calder encountered the combined fleets of France and Spain. Fortunately the carpenters of the fleet were able to patch up the *Glory* in time for the naval engagement.

No less than 35 sailing ships of the line, 13 frigates, and 10 sloops were disabled or greatly damaged by lightning in the years 1810 to 1815. As losses continued, it was suggested that a small thin metal rope be used instead of chain. The proponents of this scheme felt that it would be safer and cheaper. This method was used on the

HMS *Hazard* in 1841. An entry in the ship's log testifies to the ineffectiveness of the idea:

"Cape Po, Sarawak, Borneo, June 12, 1846. At anchor, A.M. 5:30. Lightning struck the ship, splitting and carrying away main top gallant and royal mast; the whole of the main top mast from the hounds to the lower cap; sprung after cross tree, split and carried away starboard trussel tree. The electrical fluid partly escaped down the conductor by main rigging over board. A part of the damaged top mast, on falling, went through the quarter deck into the gun room."

Sir William Snow Harris, formerly a doctor in Plymouth who had given up his successful medical practice to concentrate on electricity, believed that the best protection for a wooden ship was to make the masts themselves conductors by nailing copper strips from top to bottom and to connect these strips to copper plates on the bottom of the hull and keel.

In 1847 Sir William published the results of his study of 220 ships of the Royal Navy that had been hit by lightning. He noted that of these 220 ships, 87 were first line ships, 55 were frigates, and 78 were sloops. Almost invariably they were struck on the mast, with two-thirds of the strikes hitting the highest point of the ship. A few bolts struck lower points along the mast and four hit the ship hull itself. One ship was struck five times in a single hour. In nearly fifty cases the ships were set on fire. All told, ninety seamen were killed and almost two hundred were wounded.

In selling his viewpoint to the Admiralty, Sir William pointed out the successful experience of the HMS *Actaeon*, which had been outfitted with a mast conductor. The *Actaeon* fared much better than the HMS *Hazard*. Sir William reported on the experience of the *Actaeon's* carpenter, a Mr. May. "He was standing with his back against the pump winches, near the main mast, when there came a crash of thunder directly overhead, as if the ship's broadside had been fired. He says it was an awful sound, and attended by a loud whizzing noise; the ship fairly shook under it. He felt the pump gear against which he was leaning rumble; the cutlasses stowed about the main mast rattled in the stand; a momentary vivid flash seemed to strike the conductor, the effect of which in discharging the lightning was truly beautiful. The night was awfully dark, with a heavy sea; no damage or inconvenience was experienced; he examined the conductors as a carpenter of the ship after the squall, and found them quite perfect."

The technique advocated by Harris was eventually adopted officially by the Royal Navy. Significant reduction in ship losses resulted. Many merchant vessels, however, did not adopt mast conductors and losses continued.

The introduction of metal ships in the 1860's helped relieve the lightning problem at sea. An all-metal ship with a metal mast acts in its entirety as a lightning rod. Modern steel ships are rarely damaged by lightning. For example, U.S. Navy files for 1954–57 show that there wasn't a single report of material damage nor crew casualty attributed to lightning.

But smaller boats are still a problem, even though the loss of life on small boats in recent times has been remarkably low. Three fifteen-year-old girls were killed and a companion was stunned in August 1947 when lightning struck their small boat on the Seneca River near Syracuse. From 1950–57 the U.S. Coast Guard received reports of only one fatality due to lightning: on August 8, 1953, two men in a wooden pleasure motor boat were fishing in the Gulf of Mexico off Pensacola, Florida, when a bolt of lightning struck and instantly killed one of the two fishermen. Damage to the boat was set at $210.

Damage is common—and expensive. About one per cent of the fires on motor boats are caused by lightning. A typical example is a 52-foot motor boat that was moored at Pensacola Yacht Club pier in 1953. The boat's radio-telephone whip antenna was struck. The radio was destroyed and the lightning set fire to the adjacent woodwork and followed wiring to the other electrical equipment aboard the boat. Total damage amounted to $2500, in spite of the fact that the owner happened to be on board at the time and was able to extinguish the fire quickly. Virtually all electrical equipment—the generators, bilge pump, motors, relays, and meters were burned out. Radio antennas of motor boats are favorite targets for lightning.

Sailboat masts are frequently hit even though taller boats or objects are in the near vicinity. At Manhasset Bay, Long Island, an unoccupied Manhasset Bay One-Design boat that was tied up at its mooring one summer evening of 1954 was struck. The upper mast was shattered and the stainless-steel shroud lines had to be replaced. Fasteners in the hull were loosened and some seams of the hull were cracked. The boat did not have grounding precautions. Just three years later at the same location a sister Manhasset Bay One-Design boat was hit with similar results. A small sailboat at Eagle Mountain Lake in Texas took a severe beating from lightning in 1954. The bolt apparently struck the mast and zipped down the headstay, knocking out the stem. It passed down the shrouds and knocked a sizable hole in the starboard side of the hull and several fist-sized holes in the port side. All the holes were above the water line, so the boat did not sink. The sail, which had been stowed below deck, suffered five burn holes. This boat was not grounded: no metal from the rigging was in contact with the water. Although exact records are unavailable, it is safe to assume that the amount of damage to American pleasure boats is considerable.

To help reduce damages, the American Boat and Yacht Council has been working on a tentative set of recommendations to serve as a guide to boat owners. These, plus standards from the National Fire Protection Association and U.S. Navy practice, boil down to the few essential principles that follow.

Boat Protection

In general, suitable lightning protection can be provided by installing a continuous conductor, from a point at least six inches above the highest part of the vessel, down to a submerged metal "ground" plate. This conductor should follow the shortest route and should be as straight as possible. A metal mast may serve this purpose if it is properly grounded.

The cone of protection of a lightning rod depends upon height, so the protection system should be tailored to suit the dimensions of each particular boat. Radio antennas are usually satisfactory if they are not spirally wrapped, and if they are equipped with transmitting-type lightning arresters or with means for grounding during electrical storms.

With an all-steel boat there is little problem since all components of the hull are welded or riveted together. All standing rigging should also be grounded. The ship itself then serves as a great big lightning rod. Steel ships that have aluminum masts and superstructure are usually built so that the aluminum is not in direct contact with the steel. This is done, of course, to minimize the corrosion due to the electrical reactions of the contact of two different metals. In order to provide the necessary continuous path from the top of the mast to the water,

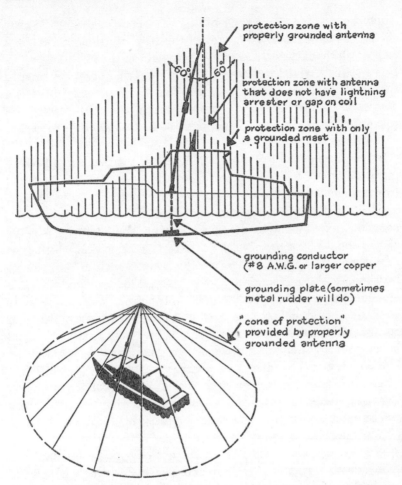

protection zone with
properly grounded antenna

60° 60°

protection zone with antenna
that does not have lightning
arrester or gap on coil

protection zone with only
a grounded mast

grounding conductor
(#8 A.W.G. or larger copper)

grounding plate (sometimes
metal rudder will do)

"cone of protection"
provided by properly
grounded antenna

Fig. 65   Nonmetal boats can be protected from damage by installing a
lightning-rod system or grounding a tall antenna. Illustration is based
upon recommendations of the National Fire Protection Association.

the mast should be connected by means of "jumpers" or heavy wires
which span the insulating material used to separate the mast from the
structure. The bolts or rivets which attach the superstructure to the
hull complete the path.

On wood- or plastic-hulled ships the problem is quite different. It
becomes necessary to put in a special grounding system to perform
the functions normally accomplished by a metal hull. A metal strip

should be attached to the mast and all metal components of the mast should be bonded to it. To the top of this strip, attach an air terminal or pointed conductor to serve as a high point on the lightning-protection system. A continuous electrical path from the top of the mast to the water should terminate at a grounding plate on the hull bottom. The exact size of this plate is the subject of some debate, but one square foot should suffice. Sometimes the metal rudder or propellers are satisfactory.

To cut down the possibility of induced side flashes, large isolated metal objects (both topside and below deck) should be connected to the grounding conductor. This ground system, of course, is independent of the electronic grounding system which merely provides a common ground for all electronic equipment. The internal grounding system should be a bare No. 8 (or larger) copper wire which runs throughout the ship. All large metallic objects such as rails, motor housings, shocks, and power-receptical cases are to be connected to this grounding system. Any metal object protruding through the topside structure should be bonded to the lightning conductor where it emerges and at its lowest inside point. Where the vessel has a metal hull and all large objects already make good electrical contact with the hull no additional bonding is necessary.

All radio antennas, whether used as lightning conductors or not, should be equipped with means for grounding during electrical storms and all radio transmitters and their antennas should be protected by transmitting-type lightning arresters.

Wooden or plastic sailboats should not only be outfitted with a conductor that extends at least six inches above the highest point of the boat but should also have provisions for grounding the metal shrouds and stays. These should be bonded to the main conductor and the lower ends of each stay should be grounded. This can be done with a metal cable that is dropped over the side and extends at least four feet into the water.

If you own a boat, common sense dictates that these inexpensive precautions be incorporated in your boat. They will minimize any damage if your boat is selected by a wandering bolt of lightning. The Appendix lists codes that will give you more details on how to install a lightning-protection system on your boat.

If a thunderstorm catches you at sea and you are unable to make it to shore before the fireworks start, observe the following simple rules:

1. Where practicable, stay below decks.

2. If your boat is not equipped with a protection system, or if it does have one but large metal objects in the boat such as the motor are not grounded to the system, stay away from these large objects. They may pick up a sizable induced charge, and if you are in the way, lightning may find you to be the path of least resistance.

3. If you do have a lightning-protection system, avoid simultaneous contact with more than one object connected to it. Don't make yourself a shortcut for any surge of lightning that may be going through the protection system.

Unlike wooden boats, metal airplanes are involved in less damaging accidents. But now that airplanes have better blind-flying navigation equipment, they venture aloft regardless of the weather. As a result the modern airliner, of all man's creations, contends with the greatest variety of lightning and the thunderstorm phenomena, as we will see in the next chapter.

One might think that the airplane faces the greatest lightning hazards of all. Up near or in the clouds a plane is exposed not only to cloud-ground strokes, but also cloud-to-cloud strokes.

Actually, the greatest hazard facing an airplane that flies through a thunderstorm is not lightning, but turbulence. Violent updrafts and downdrafts can severely strain the structure of an airplane, and have even torn off wings. Thunderstorm hail is also a problem. An airplane traveling at several hundred miles per hour can be battered by impact with hail. Lightning is one of the lesser problems that faces the pilot who strays into a thunderstorm. Lightning can damage a plane, confuse or blind its pilot, and disrupt its communications with the ground. But the Civil Aeronautics Board, which regulates the air-transportation industry in the United States, reports that no passenger-carrying U.S. airliner has ever crashed because of lightning.

Dirigibles

The problem of thunderstorms was probably the greatest single factor in the demise of the dirigible as a serious contender in transportation. The wallowing, floating ships in the sky could not cope with violent disturbances in the atmosphere. Huge in size and not so nimble as an airplane, the dirigible faded from the scene as an air transportation vehicle. Aircraft engineers may claim that the airplane eclipsed the dirigible because the dirigible was too slow, but many of the passengers who have ridden in the majestic *Graf Zeppelin* or the *Hindenburg* claim they would compromise speed for the luxury and comfort of travel in an airship. The dirigible might be flying the routes of air commerce today if it were not for weather problems.

During the First World War the Zeppelin played a prominent role in Germany's air might and people had great hopes for the future of the ships of the sky. But the French *Dixmunde* showed what tragedy could befall an airship that encountered a thunderstorm. This dirigible, filled with explosive hydrogen, was totally destroyed when lightning struck it in 1923.

Advocates of airships in the United States felt that this tragedy would not have occurred if the vessel had been filled with helium, which cannot burn, instead of hydrogen. The U.S. Navy had begun building the huge *Shenandoah* in 1919, America's first large dirigible and a copy of the German L-49 Zeppelin. Four years in the building, the *Shenandoah* was broken apart in just a few minutes by a thunderstorm in 1925.

The *Shenandoah* was the pride of the Navy and had a crew of almost four dozen men. She made her first flight in September 1923. After fifty-seven flights that covered 25,000 miles, the *Shenandoah* was scheduled to make a good-will flight to St. Louis and Minneapolis. The captain, Zachary Lansdowne, questioned the need for the trip but nevertheless planned it. He was not deterred when told of thunderstorms in northern Ohio, believing that he could get around them. The *Shenandoah* took off from Lakehurst, New Jersey, on September 2, 1925, and soon encountered a line squall over Noble County, Ohio. As lightning flashed nearby, the *Shenandoah* became trapped in the squall. A sudden updraft carried the ship upward from its 2500-foot cruise altitude to over 6000 feet. Almost immediately afterward, the ship was plunged earthward at 25 feet per second. A few minutes later the ship was carried up again and the violent lurching twisted, bent, and wrenched the *Shenandoah* apart. Cables snapped, frames broke, and the great ship separated into three parts. The three separate sections floated gradually to earth, but fourteen of the forty-three men aboard died.

The British also learned that sudden thunderstorm downdrafts can cause catastrophe to airships, when the 777-foot-long R-101 airship crashed in France, killing forty-eight of the fifty-four people aboard in 1930. The British then abandoned serious consideration of the dirigible as a long-range passenger transportation vehicle.

Another U.S. dirigible, the Navy's *Akron*, the 785-foot-long "Queen of the Skies," encountered thunderstorm turbulence a few miles off the New Jersey coast on a night flight in April 1933. Lieutenant Commander H. V. Wiley, one of the survivors, stated: "The lightning had become quite general and a few minutes after we left the coastline flashes of lightning were all around us and over us. Thunder was heard quickly after a flash and we knew we were entirely surrounded by thunderstorms. So far as I know the ship was not struck by lightning." Nevertheless, a sharp gust hit the ship, the tail hit the water, and the *Akron* broke up. Only three of the seventy-six men on board survived.

Thereafter only the Germans continued to promote air travel by airship. The success of the *Graf Zeppelin* prompted the development of the famous *Hindenburg,* the ultimate in airships. The *Hindenburg* measured 803 feet from stem to stern, almost 100 feet longer than the largest battleship then afloat. It was luxurious: its sumptuous dining room was the size of a six-car garage. The *Hindenburg* was filled with hydrogen, since the Germans had no helium supply and could obtain none from the United States. After a successful Transatlantic season in 1936, the *Hindenburg* crossed the Atlantic for its maiden flight of the 1937 season.

Thousands of spectators, news photographers, and reporters came out to greet the sky giant and its ninety-seven passengers and crew when it arrived at Lakehurst, New Jersey, on May 6. Some thunderstorms were in the area so the *Hindenburg's* skipper, Captain Max Pruss, cruised around until the storm passed. Only a drizzle marred the area when the *Hindenburg* came in, hovered 200 feet above the landing site, and began to lower its handling lines to men waiting on the ground. The crew dropped two of its 400-foot-long, 2-inch-diameter landing ropes which hit the wet sand in the mooring circle below. A few minutes later, just before the metal mooring cable had reached the ground, aghast spectators saw the stern of the ship burst into flames. Starting in the tail, the brilliant mass of hydrogen-fed fire soon engulfed the entire ship. The ship sank to the ground as it burned. Ground crewmen fled from the falling pyre, some passengers jumped clear, but thirty-six people were killed. Why did the *Hindenburg* catch fire?

Investigators concluded that a strong potential gradient existed in the air at the time. Like Franklin's kite string, the wet ropes could have served as a conductor and brought the ground potential up to the ship. With the top of the ship several hundred feet in the air, a brush discharge (corona or St. Elmo's fire) might easily have occurred there, igniting a combustible mixture of air and hydrogen from a leak. Some writers have suggested that the fire was due to sabotage. It seems more likely, however, that the correct cause is that determined by the investigating panel of the Department of Commerce: ". . . the ignition of a mixture of free hydrogen and air. Based upon the evidence, a leak at or in the vicinity of Cell 4 and 5 [just forward of the fins] caused a combustible mixture of hydrogen and air to form in the upper stern part of the ship in considerable quantity; the first appearance of an open flame was on the top of the ship and a relatively short distance forward of the upper vertical fin. The theory that a brush discharge ignited such mixture appears most probable." This was the end of airship passenger travel. Not a single dirigible has carried paying passengers since that tragic day at Lakehurst on May 6, 1937.

Airplanes and Turbulence

The MATS Flyer, magazine of the Military Air Transport Service of the U.S. Air Force, says that "Thunderstorms, like mothers-in-law, are best respected and avoided. The best advice on thunderstorm flying is DON'T DO IT." The main reason for staying away from thunderstorms, of course, is turbulence.

Airline buffs facetiously divide turbulence into three classes: light turbulence, which scares the passengers; moderate turbulence, which scares the stewardess; and severe turbulence, which scares the pilot. The commander of the Weather Reconnaissance Squadron, who has scouted through and measured typhoons and hurricanes, has said that a rough thunderstorm poses greater hazards to an airplane than a hurricane or typhoon. The air movement within a tropical storm is a fairly continuous whirling motion over an area of many miles, but the thunderstorm is a boiling caldron of air. Planes trying to fly through a thunderhead may meet strong up- and downdrafts just a few seconds apart. If an airplane encounters a sudden vertical draft, the jolt can be strong enough to strain or damage the airplane. Unusually severe thunderstorm turbulence strained an already fatigued wing attachment fitting of a twin-engine airliner over Minnesota in 1948. The fitting broke, the wing came off, and the wreckage fell to earth, killing all thirty-seven people aboard. This type of incident fortunately is rare. The worst that usually happens is typified by this case: A DC-7 over the Caribbean in 1958, in the span of just ten seconds, was first tossed down 1000 feet and then up 1700 feet by thunderstorm drafts. Pillows and magazines flew out of the racks. No passengers were injured, although the steward got a bump on the head.

Planes are rarely broken up by thunderstorms, but turbulence can lead to other calamities. Drafts can be most hazardous if the aircraft is near the ground. In 1954 a DC-3 transport entered a thunderstorm near Iowa at an altitude of about 400 or 500 feet and evidently sank to the ground in a downdraft. Twelve died.

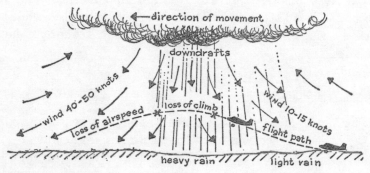

Fig. 66 Downdrafts from a thunderstorm can be hazardous to an airplane during a takeoff.

The seven crew members and thirty-eight passengers of a BOAC Argonaut noticed distant thunder and lightning before their plane taxied out for the takeoff from the Kano airport in Nigeria in June 1956. No difficulties were expected since other planes were landing and taking off without any trouble, so the captain started the takeoff run. The plane accelerated nicely down the runway and started to climb in a normal fashion. However, after reaching an altitude of 250 feet, the captain noticed that his airspeed was dropping off: the plane was slowing down and was no longer gaining altitude. Even though the four engines were functioning normally, the plane began to descend. It hit the ground, skidded for a few hundred feet, and burst into flames. The investigating board concluded that "The accident was the result of the loss of height and airspeed caused by the aircraft encountering, at approximately 250 feet after takeoff, an unpredictable thunderstorm cell which gave rise to a sudden reversal of wind direction, heavy rain, and possible downdraught condition." Two years later a DC-6B taking off from Salisbury airport in Southern Rhodesia met a similar fate. The airplane was totally destroyed and all sixty-three persons on board were killed. The verdict was the same as that for the Argonaut: "Uncontrollable loss of airspeed and height, due to a sudden squall accompanying the onset of a thunderstorm."

Thunderstorm turbulence can also contribute indirectly to an airplane crash. Most readers will recall the somber headlines that reported the crash of a Viscount airliner near Chase, Maryland, on May 12, 1959, that killed all four crew members and twenty-seven passengers. The pilot, a veteran of 22,260 hours in the air, inadvertently penetrated an area of extreme turbulence in the immediate vicinity of a severe thunderstorm, while flying at about 14,000 feet parallel to a line of cold-front thunderstorms. The Civil Aeronautics Board, in reporting on their investigation of the accident, pointed out that extreme turbulence may exist not only in a thunderstorm cell but up to five miles *around* it. After encountering the turbulence the captain had apparently followed the normal procedure of reducing his speed to alleviate the effect of the jolting drafts, but the Board concluded that the airplane must have gone steeply out of control in the turbulence and then pitched downward on an involuntary descent. The plane dove and, during the recovering pullout, a combination of excess speed and turbulence produced aerodynamic loads that exceeded the design strength of the aircraft.

Airborne Weather Radar

In the ill-fated Viscount was a weather radar, which was capable of detecting thunderstorms, but when the plane had taken off, the radar was not in operating condition. One beneficial outgrowth of this unfortunate accident was a new regulation issued by the Federal Aviation Agency. By January 1962 certified United States airliners cannot be legally dispatched—under poor visibility conditions when thunderstorms or other hazardous weather conditions are forecast along the planned route—unless the airplane has weather radar and the radar is operative. The airborne radar gives the pilot information about the air several hundred miles ahead by detecting areas of moisture concentration, precipitation, or hail. It can also reveal lightning.

Airborne radar reveals where moisture concentrations are located. A TV-like fluorescent tube shows the echoes from a high-frequency (short wave-length) pulsing radio signal that is bounced off these concentrations. The pilot uses the radar picture, together with his knowledge of weather, to plan his detours around storms. He knows that conflicting drafts may exist near precipitation, so he keeps away from the edge of the falling rain. If the radar scope shows that a thunderstorm is changing its shape rapidly, he knows that there is a probability of both turbulence and hail. At altitudes below 10,000 feet, hail may be within two miles of the storm echo, whereas at twice that height hail often spreads as far as six miles from the storm center. Pilots usually detour these storm centers by about five miles or more if below freezing altitude, and by ten miles or more if above freezing altitude. They avoid flying under an overhang of a thunderstorm because hail may be falling there.

Even with a weather radar, a plane may sometimes find itself engulfed in a thunderstorm. Generally the worst that happens is that the plane gets roughed up a little and comes out the other side no worse for wear. However, a passenger, particularly if it is his first airplane trip, may think this happens all the time and may decide that next time he will take the train.

Even light planes can usually survive a thunderstorm. Pilot Don Downie flew a small Cessna 182 into growing cumulonimbus clouds near Flagstaff, Arizona, during investigations of thunderstorms for the National Science Foundation and the Cambridge Research Center of the Air Force. At one point, with the throttle fully closed, the plane was sucked upward by the draft at a rate of 1300 feet per minute. But in two seasons of research flying, "not a single rivet was popped." When encountering turbulence, a pilot can avoid trouble by flying slowly, with enough airspeed to maintain control, and by keeping on a consistent heading. Eventually the plane will come out the other side. A good speed would be about halfway between the top speed of the plane and its stalling speed. If you are a pilot and unavoidably find yourself in a thunderstorm, try to keep about 6000 feet above the terrain, when making a low penetration, or else fly as high as possible within the safe operating capabilities of the plane. Be careful about possible freezing and icing conditions near the freezing level. For a small plane without oxygen for the crew it is better to use the low-level penetration. Don't try to correct for gain or loss of altitude from up- and downdrafts unless it is absolutely necessary to clear some ground obstruction. Concentrate on maintaining a level attitude and heading, and in a few minutes you'll be in the clear. The best practice of all, however, is to keep out of the thunderstorm in the first place.

The possibility of hail is another good reason to stay out of thunderstorms. Thunderstorm hail can damage an airplane. One of the most severe cases involved a Strategic Air Command B-52 jet bomber which ran into a violent frontal area in 1959 while cruising at 8000 feet. The plane was doing about 400 miles per hour when suddenly it was pelted with baseball-size hailstones. The windshield was shattered, the radome was torn off and the leading edges of the wings were almost hammered flat. The hail punctured holes in the wings and engine nacelles, pieces of metal were swallowed by the jet engines, and the electrical system temporarily failed. For a brief moment the plane went out of control, so the captain radioed a distress call and the crew readied to bail out. But the battle lasted only 47 seconds, and the big jet passed out through the storm almost as quickly as it entered. The plane's commander found that the engines were still putting out full power, so he climbed to 23,000 feet to take stock. After checking out his instruments, he brought the plane and its nine-man crew safely back to Carswell Air Force Base about two hours later. The $8-million airplane was battered, but repairs restored it to duty some months later. Encounters with hail are rarely fatal.

Uninvited Electricity

Airplanes often encounter uninvited electricity near storms, which may take several forms: *St. Elmo's fire* (brush discharge or corona), a glow discharge from the airplane, which interferes with radio communication and occurs after an airplane has built up an electrical charge from flying through precipitation particles or charged cloud regions; *disruptive discharges* or lightning strokes that may be initiated by the airplane distorting the electric fields in and between clouds; and *natural lightning*, which may strike the airplane if the craft happens to be in the path of the flash. Most of the discharges occur in regions where the temperatures are from −10° to +10° C. The Lightning and Transients Research Institute of Minneapolis studied lightning damage reports for 275 airplanes that had been struck by lightning. Approximately 30 per cent occurred right at the freezing altitude.

St. Elmo's fire is a visible corona glow on parts of the airplane. An airplane in flight can become electrically charged and then, because of mutual repulsion, the charges tend to concentrate at the sharp extremities of the plane, such as the wing tips, antennas, and nose or tail and propeller blades. Corona may even bathe the entire plane in light. One pilot, who experienced this over Africa a few years ago, remarked that the plane "was lit up like a Christmas tree."

The charge is built up in several ways. An airplane flying through particles such as sleet, hail, snowflakes, or dust picks up a charge by friction or contact, much as a piece of glass becomes charged when rubbed with a piece of silk. Collision with water moisture particles can cause them to rupture, which also separates charge. Another source of charge is collision with particles in the air that are already charged, such as the torrential rain below a thunderstorm. Induction can also charge a plane. If a plane flies in or near a heavily charged cloud region, the plane's metallic structure will have an opposite charge induced in it. Engineers have found that the amount of charge picked up by a plane depends not only upon the region in which it is flying, but also upon the plane's size and speed. The bigger the plane and the faster its speed, the greater is the likelihood of building up a charge.

St. Elmo's fire usually, but not always, precedes a disruptive discharge by a few minutes to a fraction of a second and announces its presence as precipitation static in the radio and by glowing brush discharge from the nose, wing tips, or propellers of the plane. The radio indicates this as a "frying" or "hissing" sound that runs up and down the musical scale and makes normal communications difficult or impossible. Wing tips may start to glow, and the propeller disc can be surrounded by a bluish or reddish glow. A Convair 440 twin-engine transport, flying over Nebraska on a June night in 1957, was carrying the Brooklyn Dodgers baseball team to Minneapolis when St. Elmo came to entertain them. All weather stations between Denver and Minneapolis were reporting thunderstorms and lightning flashed so frequently on all sides that the pilot said "it was so bright you could read a newspaper." As the ship climbed to 19,000 feet, well above the rain below, the small flickering bluish light of St. Elmo's fire played across the windshield.

Electrostatic phenomena do not create serious problems. The magnitude of the current in St. Elmo's fire or corona is so weak that aircraft are not damaged by this type of discharge. However, if a plane is forced to lighten its load by dumping fuel because of some emergency, St. Elmo's fire might ignite the vapors and cause a fire. Aircraft are equipped with "static dischargers" that are intended to leak off surplus charges picked up during flight. These dischargers usually take the form of wicks, attached to the trailing edges of the wings and tail surfaces. The wick is a cotton rope, impregnated with graphite to make it a conductor. The idea is that the strands at the end of the wick serve as points and provide a convenient place for surplus charge to leak off just as Franklin's needle point threw off its charge.

Dr. Robert L. Tanner of the Stanford Research Institute has developed a new static discharger that replaces the wicks with a conducting coated-glass fiber rod about a foot long from which extend tungsten needles. The needles facilitate charge leakage at a point isolated from the aircraft structure where the discharge will not interfere with the performance of the radio antennas. These are now being tested on modern airliners.

An airplane may hold a charge picked up in flight and, like the automobile that has just rolled to a stop after a fast drive on a dry day, can hold a charge. It is insulated from the ground by its rubber tires. The first person to connect the vehicle to earth gets a rude spark. A metal airplane should always be grounded before a person touches it. Some planes have a small wire on the landing gear that scrapes on the ground to act as a discharger.

Discharge

A pilot can't see St. Elmo's fire during the day, but he can hear it in his earphones. Often St. Elmo's stays for a while then goes away. More frequently, however, it precedes a disruptive discharge or natural lightning stroke. If the charge on the ship builds up enough, the corona begins to extend farther from the airplane as a streamer, from a few inches to ten or fifteen feet long. A long streamer may be six inches wide and project forward from a propeller or wing tip like a long, forked finger. A streamer halo may envelope the nose or engine nacelles. When the streamer appears, the pilot should prepare himself for a more brilliant discharge or lightning stroke that has been "triggered" by the airplane.

The mere presence of a metal airplane can trigger a lightning flash that might not have otherwise occurred. If a good long conductor, like the wing of an airplane, is inserted in a strong electric field, the potential gradient is distorted and may increase to the point needed for a cloud-to-cloud discharge.

The streamer reaches out, like a streamer rising from the ground, toward a charged cloud region. An ionized path is completed and a rush of electrons passes between the plane and the cloud. This rush of electrons creates a brilliant flash of light and high current flow. The flash may be composed of several discharges. The flash is not a "spark" resulting from the removal of the electrical charges that have accumulated on the plane. The flash is lightning, triggered by the airplane's charge, but produced by charges in the clouds.

The effects of intercepting a natural lightning stroke are similar to those of a disruptive or triggered discharge, but may produce greater damage because greater currents and longer discharge times are involved. The airplane's crew may not know whether their ship has been struck by natural lightning or has taken part in a disruptive discharge. A plane flying underneath a thundercloud may find itself in the path of a cloud-ground stroke, but more commonly a plane in or between thunderclouds may find itself offering a cloud-to-cloud stroke with an easy path between charge centers.

Fig. 67 Lightning usually goes the long way when passing on an airplane. Most common strikes are from nose to tail or from wing tip to wing tip.

Frequently lightning travels the long way on an airplane. Since the airplane is a better conductor than air, the lightning tends to travel as great a distance as possible on the plane before continuing through the air to its earth or cloud destination. Many incident reports show that lightning traveled from the nose to tail or from wing tip to wing tip. The exact route, of course, depends upon how the airplane is oriented in the electric field at the time of the stroke.

Lightning can hit an airplane more than once on the same flight. A European airliner was slightly damaged by two separate strokes over France in 1958. On another occasion a four-engine Air Force transport was hit twice within fifteen minutes.

Airplanes can and do get hit by lightning. What effect does this have upon the plane?

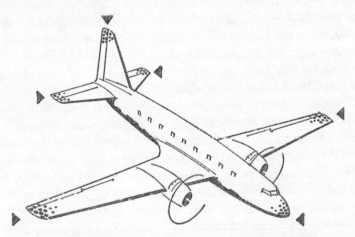

Fig. 68 Lightning is most likely to strike the extremities of an aircraft. Small burn holes or pitting are common types of lightning damage.

Protruding antennas are frequently damaged. Other popular lightning-damage areas are the wing tips, ailerons, elevators, rudder, and fuselage nose. The damage to metal parts usually takes the form of small burns, pitting, or holes.

On an afternoon in 1955 a four-engine Constellation was climbing through wet snow at about 16,000 feet over the west coast of Greece when lightning struck the nose. An antenna was destroyed and part of the plane's radio was put out of commission, so the plane put down at the nearest airport. The crew looked the plane over and found that lightning had left a trace, from the nose to the tail, of thirty-seven burned areas, up to six inches across, and twenty-two tiny holes.

A Lockheed Electra, flying at about 9000 feet in 1960, was struck by lightning while turning near Boston. More than two dozen burn marks were found on the fuselage and almost a dozen on the radome. The nose was apparently magnetized because the compass failed to operate properly after the strike. Radio equipment was unaffected. A month earlier a Boeing 707 was coming into New York from the southwest when lightning damaged the leading edge of the vertical fin. Infrequently the plane's magnetic compass is thrown out of whack. Steel and iron alloys are used in various parts of modern aircraft structures, and an electrical discharge can cause these to become magnetized. A Boeing 707, en route to Hong Kong, was struck by lightning in 1959. The steel of the windshield apparently became magnetized, causing the magnetic compass to give erroneous readings of about 45 degrees. The discharge did no other damage.

Lightning discharges to aircraft are usually the "hot"-lightning type, composed of long-duration strokes.

Electrical engineers have found that the total amount of heating (H) resulting when electricity flows through a material is equal to the square of the current (I) times the resistance (R) of the material times the length of time (t) or $H = I^2Rt$. The magnitude of the current (I) and the duration (t) of the stroke are determined by Nature, therefore the only way to minimize the heating is to keep the resistance (R) as low as possible. To avoid intensive heating and possible pitting or fusing of bearings between the movable parts of the airplane, such as ailerons and elevators, most manufacturers use flexible bonding *jumpers* to connect the movable parts. This also reduces any sparking at these places during St. Elmo's fire that might aggravate the static in the radio equipment.

Light-gauge skin can have holes burned in it and this has led to studies to determine the lightning hazards to aircraft fuel tanks. In 1958 J. D. Robb and his associates at the Lightning and Transients Research Institute in Minneapolis subjected aircraft tip tanks and pieces of aluminum skin to simulated natural lightning and found that fuel-tank skins should be at least .081 inch thick to obviate fuel-tank explosions due to lightning. Most modern turbine-powered airliners, whose fuel is carried in the wings, have skins up to .25 inch thick. Smaller planes with thin fuel-tank skins should use fuel-tank liners and/or lightning-diverter rods or conductors to avoid possible concentrated heating or burn holes near the tanks.

Nonmetal airplane parts, such as plastic radomes, have high resistance and are vulnerable to more intense heating from a lightning stroke.

Radome Protection

The dish-shaped antenna of the weather radar, which must be in a position to see forward, is logically placed on the nose of the aircraft. However, its streamline radome cover must be nonmetallic to permit the radar beam to pass through the dome. This nonconducting radome is most vulnerable to lightning damage and may be heated so intensely by a heavy lightning discharge that it may explode or have holes torn in it. A Military Air Transport Service C-124 Globemaster, fifty miles from Tokyo on a flight to Wake Island in 1957, experienced a disruptive discharge that tore a jagged hole about fourteen inches in diameter in its nose radome. At the point where the fabric-reinforced plastic radome joined to the metal fuselage a number of fused areas, about half an inch in diameter, were found. The rest of the aircraft was undamaged. Lightning knocked the radome off the nose of an Air Force C-133 Cargomaster near Point Richmond, California, in January 1960. The radome fell into San Francisco Bay but the plane returned safely to Travis Air Force Base with its ten-man crew uninjured.

Aircraft engineers have developed new ways to maintain the radome's ability to pass the radar beam and still provide a conducting path for lightning. Douglas Aircraft Company, builders of the DC-8 airliners, have developed a unique solution that uses several thin strips of aluminum taped to the outside of the radome, running from the nose of the radome aft to a point where they make electrical contact with the metal fuselage of the airplane. The strips, just three-eighths of an inch wide and only .003 inch thick, vaporize when lightning passes through them, but this creates an ionized path that carries the lightning charge safely past the radome. The lightning completes its trip before the ionized metallic vapor is blown away. Douglas tested a full-

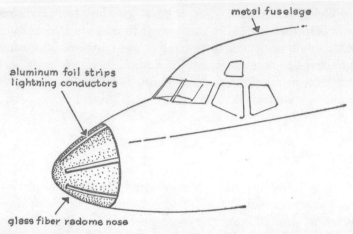

Fig. 69   Scheme developed for DC-8 jetliner used "consumable" light-ning-conductor strips to protect plastic nose without interfering with the beam of the weather radar inside.

scale DC-8 radome by bombarding it with artificial 1,500,000-volt light-ning at the Lightning and Transients Research Institute laboratory. M. P. Amason, Douglas Radiation Systems Engineer, reported in *Space Aeronautics* magazine in 1959 that "Even under heavy discharges . . . with current crests of over 100,000 amperes and charge transfer in the order of 100 coulombs, which completely vaporized the protective strip . . . the skin of the radome remained undamaged. All the main-tenance that was needed consisted of taping a new strip in place."

Douglas engineers believe that it is improbable that on the same flight two lightning strokes will come from the same direction, but they feel that the second would probably be diverted to one of the remain-ing conductor strips.

Airplane designers also test small models to determine exactly where lightning is most liable to strike a particular airplane design. Grumman Aircraft builds a twin-engine airplane for the Navy, the WF–2 Tracer, that carries the largest radome ever mounted on an air-craft. To reveal where lightning rods or conductors would be most effective for protecting this giant radome, Grumman engineers had tests conducted to determine what portions of the airplane would be struck, with the plane in various orientations. They built a 1/32-scale model and blasted it with high-voltage electrical discharges in the

Ryan High Voltage Laboratory at Stanford University. As a result
of these tests and analysis, Grumman designed a three-foot-tall combination communications antenna and lightning rod that sits on
top the huge 18 x 30-foot radome. Additional metal straps in the
structure of the radome act as conductors that "ground" the radome
to the rest of the plane.

Effect on Pilots and Passengers

A lightning stroke can have several effects upon a pilot. He may
become upset—particularly if he has been flying through a turbulent
area and is tense from the violent rock and roll of rough drafts.

He may become disturbed by the noise, too. The thunder of a
lightning stroke to a plane has been described by pilots as a snapping
sound or dull thump. Some liken it to the sound of a 75-millimeter
gun, others recall a sharp crack like a shotgun or rifle. Usually it also
produces a sharp loud click in the pilot's earphones. The sudden noise
of a discharge can sometimes disturb even a veteran pilot. One senior
captain of Pan American reported that he had been flying the Atlantic
for eight years without his aircraft ever having a discharge. Then, in
just two months, he had seven of them. One night, at about 8000 feet,
radio static warned him that a charge was building up. Nevertheless,
when the sudden discharge came "the bang scared hell out of me."
Another Pan American captain tells the story of the time he was
carrying a famous movie star aboard a DC-6B on a flight between the
Azores and New York. Shortly after dinner, about two and a half
hours out of Santa Maria, the captain invited the actor to come up
to the cockpit. The copilot offered the star his seat on the right side of
the cockpit. Just as the visitor sat down, there was the loud bang of
a discharge. The star cut his visit short, and returned to the passenger
cabin without saying a word.

The brilliant lightning flash can temporarily blind a pilot, particularly at night when his eyes are keyed to darkness. One crewman was
blinded for eight minutes, but perhaps ten seconds is par. Official
investigations blamed the fatal 1940 crash of a DC-3, on a training
flight over Lovettsville, Virginia, on a nearby lightning flash that
blinded the crew. This is the only crash of a U.S. airliner on record
that points the finger of blame on lightning. Today's pilots, when

flying near lightning areas at night, make a practice of turning up the cockpit lights and keeping their eyes down away from the windows. Some pilots even use special sunglasses under these conditions.

On rare occasions the pilots inside an all-metal airplane have felt electrical effects of a lightning strike. A few pilots have reported sparks in the cockpit, and one pilot felt a mild shock in his hands and feet when the airplane nose took part in a brilliant flash. The copilot of one plane got a slight shock in his hand as he was touching a metal portion of his seat.

The Miami *Herald* reported in February 1959 that a crewman, who was sitting up forward in the clear plastic nose of a Navy P2V patrol bomber, had his shoe set on fire when lightning hit the plane. This antisubmarine bomber was flying at about 7000 feet near San Francisco when lightning struck. The bolt evidently hit just below the plastic bubble, and part of the current passed up the man's right leg, along his back to his shoulder, where it passed into the metal seat. The man, an aviation machinist's mate, was reported by the *Herald* as saying, "I didn't know what hit me. I didn't see a flash or anything. All I know, my feet hurt all of a sudden and I looked down and saw my right shoe burning. I pulled the shoe off and grabbed the intercom and yelled for help." The lightning sheared off the heads of a few rivets and damaged the plane's tail, but the pilot brought the plane safely into Alameda Naval Air Station where Navy doctors treated the crewman for minor burns and shock. It is possible that if he had been in another part of the airplane, surrounded by metal structure as were his crewmates, he would have been unhurt. All-metal aircraft, like all-metal cars, guard their occupants by enclosing them in a conducting "Faraday cage."

Modern airplanes are considerably safer than planes of the past. Greater safety margins and thorough design analysis assures that the modern airliner can weather a thunderstorm without difficulty. The best lightning protection for an airplane, of course, is to avoid flying through areas in which thunderstorms or large cumulonimbus clouds are forecast. Frontal storms, which may take the form of a line of thunderstorms hundreds of miles long, may be hard to avoid. The airborne weather radar can help minimize the probability of turbulence and lightning strikes by providing the pilot with guidance through relatively safe areas. Modern jet transports can cruise at up to 40,000 feet, well above many of the thunderstorms. But since storms can grow as tall as 60,000 feet, it is not always possible to fly over them, so pilots must fly around these giants.

Weather radars have reduced a plane's exposure to lightning by pinpointing areas of heavy turbulence, hail, lightning, and precipitation. But occasionally a plane may be unable to thread its way through the storms and may have to buck the storm and thereby risk lightning and turbulence.

Serious accidents are extremely rare, however. Each year the scheduled airlines in the United States make millions of flights and yet, during the fourteen-year period between 1940 and 1953, for example, just nine passenger-carrying airplanes crashed because of thunderstorms. A total of 243 people perished in the crashes—less than the number killed in automobiles on a single Fourth-of-July weekend.

The National Advisory Committee for Aeronautics* concluded that "the damage from electrical discharges in the case of aircraft with electrically conducting skin, and all metallic parts well bonded, is ordinarily not of a serious nature."

There has been a marked reduction in thunderstorm incidents as more and more weather radars have been installed in planes.

---

* Now the National Aeronautics and Space Administration.

17 FALSE BLAME AND USEFUL PRANKS

Lightning is often blamed for destruction that was actually due to some other cause.

Lightning is frequently suspected in airplane crashes. An early instance was a headline of a New York newspaper in September 1929 proclaiming "8 KILLED WHEN AIR LINER, HIT BY LIGHTNING, FALLS IN NEW MEXICO WILDS." A few days later the same paper reported that the airplane, an all-metal Ford trimotor transport, had been found on Mount Taylor and that the plane had hit the mountain while trying to dodge a thunderstorm. The Viscount crash discussed in Chapter 16 was first attributed to lightning by some people, but subsequent investigation revealed that turbulence, rather than lightning, was the primary factor in the accident.

On other occasions, such as the Lake Denmark ammunition-dump explosion, lightning merely triggered some other destructive forces. On August 5, 1946, the 10,000-ton tanker *Homestead* burned while unloading gasoline at a dock in Jacksonville, Florida. The early reports said that lightning struck the 550-foot ship, setting it afire. Gasoline spilled and burned on the St. John's River, with flames leaping higher than 100 feet in the air. The smoke was visible for more than 20 miles. Actually, there would not have been a fire if an accident had not occurred before the lightning struck.

Tied up with its port side next to the dock, the ship was pumping gasoline into some shore tanks through an 8-inch hose. A sudden squall and windstorm came up that pushed the *Homestead* away from the dock. The breast line, that had been holding the ship, broke under the strain. The ship then swung away from the dock, throwing a strain on the hose and flanges. The hose flange broke and, before the pumps could be turned off, hundreds of gallons of gasoline spilled onto the dock and into the water. About ten or fifteen minutes later, lightning struck the water near the starboard side of the ship, igniting the gasoline. The fire quickly spread to the ship and totally destroyed it.

In August 1947 lightning struck the Broad Street Bridge, a 679-foot-long reinforced concrete structure that spans the Scioto River, in Columbus, Ohio. The news reports said that the lightning knocked a 40-foot concrete section off the bridge, hurling four people into the water below. One of the four, a middle-aged woman, died the next day. On the basis of the syndicated national news reports, a reader would conclude that it was the power of lightning that broke up the bridge. Actually the lightning did not knock the bridge apart: a gas explosion did. The bridge, built in 1917, carried utility lines and gas pipes under its sidewalk. Apparently the lightning stroke produced a spark that ignited gas, which then exploded, damaging the bridge. Normally a reinforced concrete structure is relatively immune from lightning damage because the steel reinforcing rods, imbedded in the concrete, are bonded together with wire wrapped around them wherever they lap or cross one another. However, if electrical continuity between reinforcing rods did not exist in this bridge for some reason, it is conceivable that any lightning currents carried by the rods would spark across the gap. If the gas pipes were nonmetal or if a leak existed, the spark could set off a gas explosion.

The most widely known lightning incident is probably a misconception. Every schoolchild is taught that Benjamin Franklin's kite was struck by lightning. This concept is imbedded throughout American literature, but it is extremely doubtful that the famous kite was actually struck by a lightning bolt. It is true that Franklin did collect "electrical fluid" from the end of his kite string, but there appears to be little justification for believing that the kite was hit by lightning. If the kite had intercepted a lightning stroke, Dr. Franklin might not have lived to tell about it or, at the very least, the string would have been burned beyond recognition. In all probability the sparks drawn from the end of the damp kite string were caused by a small current produced by a strong potential difference between the top and the bottom of the string. The existence of a thundercloud overhead facilitated the phenomenon because the strongly charged cloud intensified the potential gradient in the air. But the presence of a thundercloud was unnecessary, for, as Lemonnier and De Romas had shown, sparks can be drawn from a kite string or tall rod even on a clear day.

Lightning is powerful and lightning is capricious too, but some of the strange stories you may have heard are just too implausible. Modern newspapers strive for accurate, factual reporting but many newspapers years ago were unable to achieve such high standards, and some lightning legends may have had their basis in erroneous news reports. For example, here are four news items, quoted from the collection of newspaper stories assembled in 1895 by Henry F. Kretzer, lightning-rod manufacturer.

1. *Pittsburgh, Pa., July 30, 1892*

A curious phenomenon in connection with the death of the negroes Wm. Cassell and Solomon Richardson, in Highland Park yesterday, from a bolt of lightning, was that the foliage of the tree under which they sought shelter was photographed on the breast of one of the victims. The men were killed instantly. When the clothing was removed from Cassell's body an astounding sight met the eyes of the undertakers. Across Cassell's breasts was a picture true to nature. The browned oak leaf of autumn was there. Twined among the foliage were a number of ferns. These, too, with the exception that they were brown, were as natural as their model. So plain were the leaves and ferns that even the minutest vein was discernible. It was 4:20 o'clock when the men were killed. At 8 o'clock in the evening the impressions began to fade. Slowly the dark brown gave way to a purple color. After the fading process had been working a half hour many of the leaves became indistinct. An hour later the photograph had entirely faded and only the purple coloring remained. There was another curious thing about Cassell. When his trousers were removed his lower limbs were found to have turned to ashen white. They kept this color. This is a greater mystery than the photographic freak.

2. *Walnut Ridge, Ark., August 2, 1894*

This town is all excitement to-day over the terrible answer that was made to a prayer at a camp meeting near the town last night. Rev. Robinson, a local preacher of strong lungs was praying. He asked the Lord to bless them now with rain, saying: "Lord, come down now and pour out a blessing of some nature upon us; one of such a nature as we can remember; one that we can feel certain that it is from you, and come now."

Here the prayer stopped, not because the "Amen" was reached, but because a flash of lightning came down with the roar of ten or more cannons, shattering a huge tree near by, scattering its branches over the entire audience, knocking some senseless, wounding others and frightening all, most of the audience believing that the end of the world had come. They had scarcely recovered from the shock when such a volume of water came down as to almost drown them.

This would not seem so peculiar were it not for the fact that until the flash of lightning no cloud was visible and stars were shining brightly everywhere; but at that moment a small coffin-shaped cloud hovered over the audience, and from it came the deluge of water.

The lightning stroke was heard several miles away and the small cloud was noticed, but no water fell except in the small area of the camp meeting ground.

It was a remarkable occurrence, and, whether it came in wrath or a blessing, it broke up the meeting, and but a few of those present can be induced to go near the ground again. Those who have examined the ground think that not less than 15 inches of water fell, and that in less than five minutes.

3. *Sandersville, Ga., August 21, 1893*

During a thunder storm yesterday afternoon, a well on the farm of Col. J. N. Gilmore was struck by lightning. A dense volume of steam at once emanated from the well and the water boiled at a terrific rate. A pail was lowered into the well and the water set out to cool. In the course of an hour a man named Bill Ford put his finger in the water when he received an electrical shock. Everyone in the neighborhood is afraid of the water. A bottle of it has been sent to the State Chemist.

4. *Boston, Mass., July 10, 1891*

A freak of lightning probably more remarkable than any hitherto recorded has occurred near the small village of New Salem, Vt., at the foot of the Heldeberg Mountains. Arent S. Vandyck occupies an old mansion in the parlor of which hung a collection of revolutionary swords, one of which was heavily plated with silver. A terrific thunder-storm came night before last and one terrible crash aroused the household. All were stunned for a moment, but recovering they hastened to discover what damage was done.

Suddenly the younger Vandyck pointed to an old-fashioned sofa. Upon it lay what was apparently the silver image of a cat curled up in an exceedingly comfortable position. As far as the shape and posture of the animal were concerned it might have been a live cat. Each glittering hair was separate and distinct, and each silvery bristle of the whiskers described a graceful curve as in life. Father and son turned towards the swords which hung upon the wall just above the sofa and there saw that the sword had been stripped of all its silver. The hilt was gone and the scabbard was but a strip of blackened steel. The family cat had been electroplated by lightning.

In one of the panes of glass in the window was found a round hole about the size of a half-dollar, where the lightning had evidently entered. There was a charred streak across the sash, where the electrical fluid had made its way to the sword, down which it had passed to the cat, carrying with it the silver which it deposited upon the animal. Of course the cat was instantly killed, and therefore remained in the position in which it was quietly sleeping when the flash came. It is thought the plating of the cat's body will prevent decay and that probably it may be retained among the collection of curiosities, which is more remarkable than all.

Helpful Pranks of Lightning

Sometimes lightning's capricious behavior performs what some consider a service.

Back in 1891 law officers of Montana had the difficult chore of enforcing the Chinese Exclusion Act by preventing aliens from entering the state. The state was sparsely populated and roadblocks were nonexistent, so many aliens sneaked across the border. Even when working closely with the Canadian mounted police, the officers found it difficult to track down and capture violators of the exclusion act. One Sunday morning in August, officers received a tip that a large party of men had been seen on a trail near the town of Benton. The officers scoured the area without success. But a few days later, lightning intervened to aid the search. Sim Heron, a rancher, was headed toward Benton when he was caught in a thundershower five miles from town. A sudden flash of lightning struck the trail a few hundred yards ahead and Heron heard a scream. He rode ahead and found a wagon, with its driver dead from a lightning stroke. Heron examined the wagon, and was surprised to find nine frightened Chinese crouched beneath the canvas. He ushered them to town, where they were arrested.

Lightning is sometimes credited with medical cures. A thirteen-year-old New York girl is said to have recovered from a childhood handicap when lightning stunned her in 1894. Eight years before, the girl had lost her speech and hearing from a severe case of malaria. She and her mother were visiting friends on Long Island when lightning struck the house and flashed through the kitchen, knocking the girl to the floor. She got up, pointed to her ear, and said, "Mamma, I heard that; let's go home." Relatives said that these were the first words she had spoken in eight years.

Central Hudson Rail Road train No. 9 was roaring from Buffalo to Lockport, New York, with about 200 passengers when lightning prevented a train wreck in 1894. It was a dark rainy night and Engineer Schaffer squinted to see past the limited beam from his locomotive's headlight. He could only see about 50 yards ahead. Suddenly a flash of lightning, followed by a loud clap of thunder, lit up the track a half mile ahead. Schaffer saw a sight that made him grab the reverse lever and call to the fireman to put on the brakes. The wheels screeched and the train came to a halt with the cowcatcher just one foot from the caboose of a stalled freight train. Railroad men claimed that the flash of lightning was all that saved the lives of the passengers.

Sometimes lightning's destructive prowess aids historians. The age of what is now believed to be the oldest protestant church in the United States was established by a lightning stroke. The old St. Luke's church, near Smithfield, Virginia, had fallen into disrepair in 1852. Weeds had nearly enveloped the building and the Gothic buttresses were crumbling when lightning restored the church to historical importance with a direct hit during a thunderstorm in the summer of 1887. A few hand-hewn beams were dislodged and several bricks came tumbling down. One of the bricks had the date 1632 chiseled on it. The New York *Times* reported in 1954 that "the circumstance has since been called a 'fortuitous blessing' of the storm from heaven, for it fixed the date of the church's construction, at least for mundane historians." A nationwide drive began in 1954 to raise funds to restore St. Luke's.

On June 30, 1960, a thunderstorm struck the Columbia, Missouri, area and made time not only stand still, but go backward. The Columbia *Missourian* reported that Mr. C. W. Brenton looked at his electrical clock at 7:55 P.M. and was startled to see that the clock was running backward. During the storm a surge of lightning had entered his home along the power lines and fused some of the wiring in the clock. This apparently reversed the magnetic field of the motor, causing the hands to turn in the wrong direction.

Although lightning causes much damage and performs strange pranks, it is now helping man to study the upper atmosphere, the ionosphere, and the earth's magnetic field. How can lightning, which flashes close to the earth, possibly be useful in studying regions hundreds and thousands of miles up? This surprising application of lightning will be discussed in the next chapter, along with some other interesting aspects of lightning that are now the frontiers of lightning research.

Centuries of research have been devoted to unraveling the mysteries of lightning, but there is still much to be learned. For example, lightning arresters on new high-voltage power lines do not behave as they should when lightning strikes. Apparently we need better information about the make-up of the lightning bolt. Our lack of understanding of the mechanism of cloud electrification continues to hamper attempts to suppress lightning through cloud modification. The efforts of scientists and engineers to solve these and other lightning unknowns are reviewed on the next few pages.

Whistlers

During the recent International Geophysical Year, scientists of many countries stepped up investigations of a strange lightning phenomenon known as "whistlers." A whistler is a musical sound that follows a stroke of lightning and can be heard by a radio receiver tuned to very low frequencies. The phenomenon of the whistler may provide more information about the electrical character of the ionosphere and ultimately result in improved long-distance communications.

Special radio receivers, tuned to frequencies of below 20 kilocycles (20,000 cycles) and lower, often pick up strange sounds now called *tweeks* or *chinks*, brief metallic clinking noises; the *dawn chorus*, a strange twittering noise similar to that produced by flocks of birds in those noisy sunrise minutes in springtime; and *whistlers*, a whine that may start at a frequency of about 10,000 cycles (well above the highest note of a piccolo) and sweep down through several octaves in a matter of a second or so, stopping at about the limit of a high soprano singer.

While all of these strange noises may be produced somehow by light-ning, only the whistler is reasonably well understood.

The atmospheric disturbance created by a stroke of lightning is a conglomeration of electromagnetic emanations covering a broad spec-trum of frequencies. The ordinary household radio, tuned to the broadcast band of 550 to 1650 kilocycles, hears the lightning stroke as a sharp noise or crash of brief duration. This is *static* or *sferic* which, as described in Chapter 5, can be used to locate thunderstorm activity. This same sharp noise can be detected at other frequencies as well. The picture on your TV set, which may be tuned to about 150,000 kilocycles, will be disturbed or momentarily flicker when lightning flashes. On very-low-frequency receivers, the sharp noise is also heard; however, it is often followed a few seconds later by a whistler. (Such a receiver can be made from a hi-fi amplifier by merely attaching a long antenna—several hundred feet long or longer—directly to the am-plifier input terminals. No tuner is needed.)

How can lightning create a whistler that is heard seconds after the first crash of static? The electromagnetic disturbance produced by the lightning stroke spreads out in all directions. The highest-frequency portion passes straight through the ionosphere and out into space. Some of the low-frequency energy is reflected by the ionosphere back to earth and some is refracted. The refracted portions of the energy apparently follow the same course as a line of force of the earth's magnetic field, soaring up through the ionosphere and away from the earth to several thousands of miles into space, across the equator,

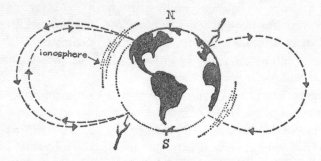

Fig. 70   A musical "whistler" may be heard on special low-frequency radio receivers in the hemisphere opposite to where a lightning stroke occurred. Electromagnetic disturbance of the flash apparently follows same path as line of force of earth's magnetic field.

and back down to earth in the opposite hemisphere. In passing through the ionosphere, the click becomes modified or "spread out" in time because the higher frequencies travel faster through the ionosphere than the lower frequencies. As a result, what had been a click has now been stretched out, with the highest frequency arriving first and the lowest frequency arriving last. Therefore a low-frequency radio receiver in the hemisphere opposite to where the lightning stroke occurred hears a noise that starts as a high pitch and sweeps downward in pitch: a whistler. The signal may be reflected from the earth at this point and go back along the line of force to where it started, being stretched out some more as it goes. A receiver located near the original lightning flash would pick up a sharp crash of static, followed a couple of seconds later by a whistler. The time interval between the click and the whistler represents the time required for the signal to make a round trip. Sometimes the signal may bounce back and forth along the line of force several times, with each subsequent whistler getting weaker and more and more stretched out.

For lightning to be heard in the opposite hemisphere as a whistler, the receiver must be located near the opposite end of the line of magnetic force that passes through the point of the original lightning stroke. For example, if lightning struck at 40 degrees north magnetic latitude it could be detected as a whistler at 40 degrees south magnetic latitude. The signal is strongest if both points are on the same longitude.

The theory of the whistler was demonstrated in 1955 by Millett G. Morgan and G. McK. Allcock, using synchronized recording receivers in New Zealand and in the Aleutian Islands, which are on opposite ends of a line of magnetic force. On August 28, lightning struck New Zealand. Almost immediately the New Zealand receiver heard a sharp click. About one and a half seconds later the Aleutian receiver heard a whistler. After about another one and a half seconds the New Zealand receiver heard the whistler. Records covered a period of more than nine seconds, during which time each receiver heard the whistler at least three times, and each subsequent whistler was more drawn out and weaker than the one before.

By correlating whistlers with lightning discharges, scientists are able to detect irregularities of the ionosphere and variations of the earth's magnetic field. Ultimately this information may improve world communication. Long-range communication depends upon the ability of the ionosphere to reflect certain radio waves. High-frequency radio signals, like those used for television broadcasting, can normally be detected only by receivers within direct line of sight of the transmitting antenna because radio waves travel in straight lines, on past the horizon and into space. Some lower-frequency radio signals, however, are reflected by the ionosphere and may therefore be skipped between the earth and the ionosphere so as to follow around the curvature of the earth. These are the frequencies used for long-distance communication. Unfortunately the ionosphere's ability to reflect these waves varies with time of day, time of year, and with activity or eruptions on the sun's surface. Sunspots and solar flares can severely disrupt long-range communications because this solar activity affects the ionosphere. Much more must be learned about the ionosphere to improve round-the-clock dependability of skip-broadcasting techniques.

The whistler may prove to be an inexpensive way to study the ionosphere. Satellites are useful for probing the upper atmosphere and ionosphere but they are expensive and may not be in the right position at the exact time a solar disturbance occurs. Any change in the ionosphere will cause changes in the behavior of the whistlers. Therefore, analysis of variations in the whistlers' travel time and "stretch-out" can reveal variations in the ionization density of the ionosphere. Since lightning is always flashing somewhere on the globe, whistler equipment can be on duty around the clock and needs relatively simple instruments that only listen and record, without involving expensive launching rockets, transmitters, and the like.

Particle streams from the sun may be trapped by the earth's magnetic field and cause whistlers to become amplified and may generate low-frequency noises of their own that are sometimes called "hooks" and "hisses." Intensive study of whistlers began during the International Geophysical Year and the results are now being analyzed. The U.S. Air Force is supporting research in the experimentation, measurement, and analysis of whistlers and is sponsoring the development of special receivers to study lightning effects down in the 2-cycle to 1000-cycle (1-kilocycle) range. As more scientific attention is directed to the study of whistlers, we will learn more about the ionosphere and its relationship to the sun and perhaps more about the sun itself.

Power Problems

The continued need to send electric power over greater distances has led power companies to experiment with higher transmission voltages in order to minimize heating losses. Sections of 345,000-volt transmission lines, and recent experiments with 750,000-volt lines, have required larger insulators and improved lightning-arrester designs. Engineers have discovered that the established design criteria fall short. In conflict with previous theory, unpredictable failures have resulted on these lines during thunderstorms. Present methods of predicting lightning arrester performance have not matched what has actually been experienced. The A.C. power from the lines often shorts out across the power-line insulators and is not adequately arrested by lightning arresters designed in accordance with accepted practice. It was this unexpected trend of higher-than-predicted power-line flashovers that prompted Westinghouse engineer Sam Griscom to postulate his "prestrike theory" described in an earlier chapter. Power engineers have also become increasingly concerned and are now vigorously attempting to gather more data on the transient characteristics of lightning strokes.

In order to avoid the expense of installing cathode-ray oscillographs on transmission towers, both General Electric and Westinghouse have developed inexpensive new high-speed instruments to measure lightning strokes that are easy to install, need no electric power, and may be left unattended. As fast or faster than the cathode-ray oscillograph, the *Kine-Klydonograph* developed by Griscom, and the *Teinograph* developed by J. G. Anderson and R. U. Giacomoni of General Electric, utilize the technique of the Lichtenberg figure, or klydonogram, formed when current passes through a piece of photographic film. Unlike the surge-voltage recorders developed in the 1920's, which made a single klydonogram, these new devices utilize many pairs of electrodes that produce a sequence of klydonograms, each made slightly after the previous image, displaced in time (and dispersed on the film) through the use of circuitry that "delays" the current racing through the instrument. These new devices are to the surge-voltage recorder what the Boys camera is to a time-exposure camera. Each klydonogram represents the magnitude of the current at a different time, and all images are made on a single sheet of film. For example, Griscom's device records as many as thirty-six different images which can be analyzed to determine the wave form and crest magnitude of the current that had passed through the instrument.

These new devices are installed on lightning rods of power-line towers where lightning strokes are anticipated, and can be left unattended until after a lightning stroke. Then the film is replaced. The Westinghouse instrument requires electrical connections to shunt some of the lightning current into the device. General Electric's unit needs no direct connection, using an induction coil to "sense" the current passing down the lightning rod. Engineers began installing these devices in 1959 and now scores of Kine-Klydonographs and Teinographs are on watch at power-line towers. The results that should be coming in shortly will give new data on the time history of a lightning stroke and lead to improved arrester design and protection systems.

Lightning and Tornadoes

Each year in the United States millions of dollars in property is destroyed and more than 200 people are killed by tornadoes. More than 500 of these violent "twisters" or "cyclones" smashed the United States during 1953, killing 514 people. Meteorologists find the tornado a particularly puzzling weather phenomenon. The main characteristic of the tornado is a narrow funnel-shaped cloud, generally several hundred yards across, that rotates at speeds of several hundred miles per hour and travels along the ground at up to fifty miles per hour. The funnel first grows down from the base of a severe thunderstorm-type cloud and has a brief life. Its base travels along, or just above, the ground from several to fifty miles before disappearing in the base of its parent cloud. During its tempestuous life it may pick up debris, explode buildings, toss automobiles about, and generally destroy everything in its path. Why does it behave the way it does? What causes the violent winds? Is there some way to prevent a tornado?

The tornado is associated with very large or intense thunderstorms. Some witnesses report that intense electrical displays accompany a tornado. Bernard Vonnegut, meteorologist with Arthur D. Little, Inc., a research company, believes that the tornado may be a manifestation of lightning and thunderstorm electricity. He admits that this idea is not new: Lucretius, back in 60 B.C., and Francis Bacon, in 1622, had suggested that the tornado may be caused by electricity. Dr. Herbert L. Jones, professor at Oklahoma A. & M. College, announced in 1957 that thunderstorms with frequent lightning discharges within the cloud are harbingers of tornadoes. Vonnegut recommends a new approach to understanding the mechanism of the tornado. If the mechanism of the twister can be determined, improved forecasting and warning methods could be developed.

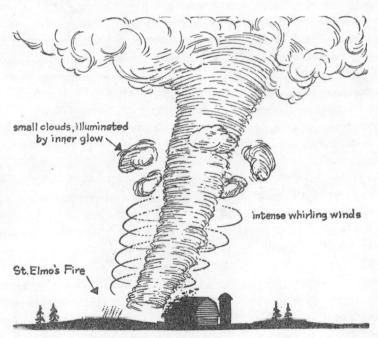

small clouds, illuminated by inner glow

intense whirling winds

St. Elmo's Fire

Fig. 71   Riddle of tornado's strong winds may be solved by more study of associated electrical phenomena. Tornado is accompanied by severe lightning activity and some reports describe electrical glow in and near the funnel.

The tornado may originate as a small ordinary whirlwind, later becoming intensified by the electrical energy released by a severe thunderstorm. The tornado is usually accompanied by incessant lightning and a loud buzzing or hissing sound. Often there is a bluish glow around the bottom edge of the funnel and St. Elmo's fire or corona may play from sharp objects on the ground. Odors like those from sparking electrical equipment are produced. Those rare witnesses who have survived a look up into the funnel report seeing inside a brilliant, glowing band of light. Other observers have seen a band of bright, blue light that swirls around the funnel perhaps 900 to 1000 feet above the ground. The tornado often dehydrates or scorches vegetation in its path.

It is possible that this unusual electrical activity may produce the winds. The violent winds cannot be explained on the basis of heating due to air temperature differences. Even concentrated falling hail could not provide enough of a temperature contrast to supply enough heat energy to drive the winds. Vonnegut computed the amount of energy needed to propel the tornado's winds and found that ample electrical energy is available, even in an ordinary thunderstorm. Sferics measurements show that the tornado is accompanied by ten times as many lightning discharges as a typical thunderstorm. Vonnegut suggests that continuous corona or glow discharges, or repetitive lightning discharges (each following the ionized path of the previous one), could produce intense winds. The strong electromagnetic field created by the discharge currents could propel charged air or ions in the same manner as the electromagnetic field in an electric motor moves the current-carrying conductors of the armature. The discharges, concentrated in a small area, might also produce heat that could cause intense local convection.

The reader may wonder if the electrical display of the tornado is the result, rather than the cause, of the tornado. This seems unlikely, since observers at the Air Weather Service sferics center have noticed that intense electrical activity not only accompanies the tornado funnel, but also precedes it.

Vonnegut does not pretend to have all the answers, but he believes that enough evidence exists to justify studying the tornado from this new point of view. He calls for more investigation into the relationship between the tornado and its extraordinary electrical activity. If modern instruments for measuring sferics and electric field could be brought into play and the findings combined with comprehensive photographic coverage and systematic accumulation of eyewitness reports, perhaps the riddle of the tornado could be solved. Once the tornado and its mechanism is understood, man will be better able to predict its impending birth, and perhaps, ultimately, even prevent its formation.

Lightning Suppression

During recent years, scientists have been investigating ways of suppressing lightning by modifying the clouds from which it comes. The effort is concentrated on trying to develop practical methods of inhibiting the growth of thunderheads by preventing cumulus clouds from maturing into cumulonimbus clouds. In 1946 Dr. Vincent Schaefer accidentally discovered in a home freezer that dry ice could trigger precipitation by causing the formation of ice crystals in miniature supercooled clouds. Bernard Vonnegut, then an associate of Schaefer at General Electric, found that tiny particles of smoke of silver-iodide crystals served as nuclei for ice crystals that formed at temperatures warmer than natural nuclei. Since these discoveries, meteorologists have been using dry ice and silver-iodide smoke to modify clouds. The dry ice can be dispensed from airplanes flying near the clouds. The dry-ice crystals accelerate the process of changing liquid water into ice and stimulate the growth of ice crystals that then become heavy enough to fall from the cloud as precipitation. Silver-iodide smoke can be generated by ground-based breeders and drawn into the clouds by convection. The French have tried sending the silver-iodide crystals up in an explosive mortar shell.

One of the more extensive investigations in cloud modification is known as *Project Skyfire*. Begun in 1953 as a joint program of the U.S. Forest Service, the Department of Agriculture, and the Munitalp Foundation, Project Skyfire has gained support from the U S Weather Bureau, the National Parks Service, the President's Advisory Committee on Weather Control, and the National Science Foundation. Its original purpose was to help protect national forests by gaining a better understanding of lightning fires and testing methods of suppressing lightning severity by modifying clouds. Field tests were conducted near Flagstaff, Arizona, and in Montana.

Project personnel used a small, four-place Cessna airplane to try several methods of cloud seeding. One method was to fly slowly in small circles around the updraft and just below a growing cumulus while dumping ice crystals or dispensing silver-iodide smoke. Observers found that the draft would carry the "seeds" up into the cloud, and then—perhaps ten or twenty minutes later—the updrafts ceased and sometimes downdrafts appeared or light rain fell from the cloud. Another technique found the airplane flying upwind of a line of clouds, again relying on the updraft to carry the seeds into the cloud.

These early tests showed that cloud seeding can modify local air-mass clouds by inhibiting cloud growth and causing precipitation. The effect upon lightning production was not evident. Sometimes the plane flew just above the tower of a growing cumulus before dumping ice pellets, but again the results were mixed. Sometimes rain fell a few minutes later and on other occasions the whole section of cloud that had been treated dissipated completely.

A different approach to cloud modification was tried by the Naval Research Laboratory and the U.S. Navy Weather Service. Instead of dispensing condensing nuclei such as silver-iodide particles, or cooling accelerators such as dry ice, the Navy tried dumping carbon black (soot) particles to absorb radiant energy. During the summer of 1958 a Navy Super Constellation flew along the Georgia-Florida coast, releasing from one and a half to six pounds of carbon black for each test over a cumulus cloud. Seven runs showed that the clouds dissipated five to twenty minutes after "carboning." The Navy also dropped the carbon into layers of humid, clear air and found that clouds could be made to form.

With the support of the U.S. Forest Service, the University of Arizona has also been investigating the effect of airborne cloud-seeding upon cloud behavior and lightning production. The Arizona approach was to fly a small Piper Super Cub upwind of a mountain range in the Catalina Mountains while dispensing a solution of silver iodide in acetone from a generator hung under a wing of the plane. Ten gallons of the solution, of which 20 per cent was silver iodide, was slowly released while the plane flew back and forth. Some flights lasted up to four hours before the solution was all gone. Project personnel used a meticulous random-sampling technique, running seeding tests on sixteen days picked at random and comparing the results with sixteen nonseeded days, also picked at random during the summer of 1957. Clouds were kept under observation around the clock during the thirty-two days. Observers were surprised to discover that the total number of lightning strokes on the sixteen seeded days was nine times greater than on the sixteen nonseeded days. Observers also found that there were actually slightly fewer forest fires on the seeded days. Louis J. Battan and A. R. Kassander, Jr., in analyzing the results, concluded that there was more rain on seeded days so the chances of ignition and fire spread was reduced, in spite of the increased lightning activity.

In 1957 a major attempt at large-scale cloud modification was begun in Montana, using thirty silver-iodide generators scattered through the Bitterroot mountain range to determine the effects upon mountain cumulus clouds. This study is still under way. A similar investigation conducted by the Division of Forestry of the State of California in 1957 halved the normal number of lightning fires in a test area of Northeastern California. But Arnold Court, meteorologist with the California Forest and Range Experiment Station, feels that these results are somewhat inconclusive and points out that the decrease has about one chance in six of being accidental. In a paper presented to the American Meteorological Society in June 1958, Court concluded, "In the present state of ignorance about the exact mechanism of charge formation, and also about the manner in which silver iodide affects natural clouds, whether cloud seeding should increase or decrease lightning is completely uncertain."

The results, then, of attempts at lightning suppression through cloud modification are ambiguous, and hardly permit, as yet, any quantitative predictions. Continued experimentation is needed and will surely continue. Extensive seeding operations, meticulous observation, measurement, and analysis will help clarify the effects of seeding and when these results are correlated with theories of cloud electrification, perhaps a new understanding of the thunderstorm mechanism will evolve, and with it will come practical techniques for suppressing lightning.

The key unknown, of course, is the process of thunderstorm electrification. Only by knowing what goes on in the thunderstorm will we be able to modify the mechanism and thereby reduce lightning. Will this mean someday that we will shoot small rockets into thunderstorms to dispense particles that will stunt the cloud's growth and inhibit its output of lightning? Will we have networks of wires on the ground that "seed" the air with electrical charge that would be drawn into the updraft of a growing cumulus to prevent its maturing into a thunderhead? Only time will tell, but it seems clear that to achieve true knowledge of the thunderstorms we need more data about thunderstorm activity over the oceans.

Answers from the Oceans?

The role of the seas, which cover more than two-thirds of the surface of the earth, may be a significant factor in the world's atmospheric electricity process. Duncan Blanchard, scientist at the Woods Hole Oceanographic Institution, suggested in 1958 that the breaking up of bubbles at the surface of waves may result in a net flow of electrons into the oceans from the air. Using an experimental laboratory apparatus, Blanchard found that burst droplets ejected from a container of sea water were generally positively charged, indicating that they left electrons behind. It is possible that intense wave action may release droplets of moisture that, through turbulent mixing, are carried aloft, leaving the oceans with a surplus of electrons. This leads to the consideration that the waves of the sea, like point discharge under thunderstorms on land, help combat the loss of electrons to the ionosphere. The implications of this interesting possibility may require amendment of some established theories of the atmosphere's electricity budget and should be explored in greater detail.

While most data indicates that lightning is generated by clouds whose tops are at temperatures below freezing, recent observations made at sea in subtropical zones have shown that a few lightning flashes are occasionally produced by low, warm clouds which have not yet grown to altitudes where the air temperature is at freezing. Since some of the theories of thunderstorm electrification depend upon the presence of ice in the clouds, these theories may have to be re-examined. The observations of lightning from low, warm clouds were made at sea, where cloud studies are not usually conducted. It is clear that more effort and observation should be directed to the study of thunderstorms and atmospheric electricity at sea.

Lightning in the Arsenal

Hypersonic-speed space vehicles, like small meteors, may get red-hot from friction when re-entering the earth's atmosphere. The film of hot air surrounding the vehicle exhibits abnormal electrical properties because it is ionized and dissociated into what is popularly known as a *plasma*.

Research scientists of many large American corporations are now engaged in the study of plasmas. A plasma is a high temperature (perhaps 15,000° C.) gaseous mixture, composed of a nearly equal number of electrons and positive ions, that can be produced in the laboratory by subjecting a gas to high temperature or by passing a gas through an electric arc. The hot, ionized gas stream produced by laboratory generators is a good conductor of electricity and may emulate the core of a lightning channel. While scientists concentrate on learning more about plasmas and their relationship to space-vehicle re-entry problems and possible use in nonmechanical electrical power stations, further understanding of lightning may be a by-product of this research. While unwilling to publicly admit their interest, more than one plasma-research physicist hopes that knowledge of plasmas may lead to the development of a ball-lightning "gun" that could be used as a weapon.

Can lightning itself be harnessed and used as a weapon? Back in 1958 Congressmen heard a rumor that the Soviets had learned how to control lightning. Their concern was allayed when, in closed session, an intelligence expert from the Pentagon assured them that the rumor was untrue. The harnessing of lightning may be a technical achievement that will permanently elude man, but it is less improbable than antigravity devices or perpetual-motion machines.

While the scientists and engineers wrestle with lightning on the frontiers of research, there is already a wealth of knowledge at hand that you can apply to protect yourself and your property. Install lightning rods. Invented by Franklin more than 200 years ago, they have stood the test of time. They work. And over the years, basic rules of behavior have evolved that can reduce your chances of being a lightning statistic. In the next chapter these basic rules of personal behavior are reviewed.

By the time you have reached this point in the book, you should have a reasonable acquaintance with lightning and a fair understanding of its behavior.

Lightning behaves in terms of a complete electrical circuit. The charge in the thundercloud wants to reach and distribute itself through the ground. Lightning tends to utilize tall objects to ease its route to the earth. Good conductors, such as metal masts and towers, are most tempting and can usually carry the lightning current without being damaged. Nonmetallic objects, such as trees, wooden buildings, or masonry chimneys are poor conductors but do offer lightning an easier path than air. These objects may explode from the heat and throw debris that can harm nearby objects or people. Upon reaching the ground, lightning currents spread out in search of good conducting soil that will allow the charges to distribute themselves in the earth. Electrical current travels more easily in wet soil than dry, so dry soil around a tall object that has been struck will have more hazardous voltages produced in it. A lightning stroke can induce strong currents in long metal objects nearby, such as fences, railroad tracks, and pipes.

Lightning can, and frequently does, strike the same place twice. If your home has been struck by lightning, don't assume that you are now immune. Quite the contrary. Chances are that your home will be struck again before your neighbor's.

If you are in a building that is struck by lightning, check it over immediately to determine if a fire has been started. If so, follow the fire-safety rules: get the family out of the house right away and call the fire department.

If someone near you is stunned by lightning, administer artificial respiration immediately and call a doctor.

While every mischievous inclination of lightning cannot be anticipated, certain guides for personal conduct are endorsed by scientists, engineers, and insurance men. Generally, don't wait for the first nearby lightning stroke before you take cover. When the thunderstorm approaches, make your move for safety.

In transit: If you are in a train, bus, subway, or car with an all-metal body, stay in it. If you are driving, slow down. Don't park under a tree. If you are flying your own plane, stay away from areas where thunderstorms are predicted. If it looks as though you may become hemmed in by cumulonimbus clouds, set down at the nearest airport. If you are in a modern airliner, relax and enjoy the view. If you are walking in town or in the city, get off the street and into a cab or into a large building, the larger the better.

Buildings: If you have a choice of shelter, pick in this order: large metal or metal-frame buildings, buildings with lightning-protection systems, large buildings without lightning-protection systems, and lastly, small unprotected buildings. If you are at work in a large store, office building, or factory, go about your business but avoid handling electrical equipment and telephones unless necessary.

Camping or hiking: Get off hilltops, avoid lone trees and buildings, stay out of small sheds. Keep your distance from metal fences, pipes, and railroad tracks. Get into a ravine, canyon, or cave or next to the foot of a cliff. It is believed wise to crouch in the open away from trees, but if you can't stand getting wet and feel you must be under trees, choose a thick grove of uniform-height trees rather than tall, isolated trees. If you are caught in a large flat area where it is impossible to reach adequate cover, crouch down and don't worry if your clothes become wet: this may be an advantage. (It is not necessary to follow recommendations made by John Simmons in 1775 that "it would be right for them to put the Money out of their Pockets and the Buckles out of their shoes.")

Working out of doors: Finish working on a rooftop after the storm: get down and into the building. If you are near a water tank or metal tower, you will be protected from direct strokes, but you are not safe because currents coming down the tank or tower will radiate along the ground. Get into your truck or all-metal car. Don't stay near or on railroad tracks, fences, or pipes.

On the golf course: Get off the course and into the clubhouse. Small sheds will keep you dry but will not protect you from lightning. It won't make much difference whether you are carrying a metal club or not.

At play or at the beach: Positively don't fly a kite. Get out of the water and into your car or into a large building.

At sea: Large modern ships provide good protection, but stay off the deck and in the cabin. If aboard a wooden ship or small pleasure craft, get below deck. A lightning-conductor system will protect the boat, but don't touch the conductors. If you are in a small skiff or open runabout, head for shore when you first see the storm approaching and get into your car or a large building. If you can't make shore, crouch down in the middle of the boat: don't feel you have to jump overboard!

Houses: Stay away from windows or open doors that face large trees. Shut the door and draw the curtains to help stop flying splinters if the trees are struck. A pane of glass will hardly deter a lightning bolt that can jump several thousand feet through the air. A closed window may stop ball lightning, however, and will definitely keep the rain out. If you want to watch lightning through a window, don't lean against a radiator.

Stay away from sinks and don't take a bath: remember that the plumbing system is connected with a metal vent pipe that protrudes up through the roof.

Large metal objects, such as refrigerators, stoves, pianos, washing machines, etc., can have currents induced in them if lightning strikes very close, so avoid touching them.

Avoid handling the telephone, electrical appliances, or wires. It makes little difference whether your radio or TV set is turned off or on, but the static can be annoying.

Stay away from the fireplace or chimney, these are favorite lightning targets.

A modern home has a network of wires and pipes running in the walls. If lightning should strike your house, it will seek these conductors out and probably ignore you. The best place to sit is in the middle of a downstairs room, away from the walls.

Turn up the hi-fi, sit back in a comfortable chair and read your newspaper or a good book. If you have already gone to bed, shut your eyes and try to go to sleep. An old-fashioned bed with a metal frame at the head and foot provides good protection, as long as you don't hang half in and half out of bed.

The odds are remote: Don't worry yourself too much about being killed by lightning: the odds are about a million to one per year. Following the simple precautions listed above can improve your chances manyfold, since more than two-thirds of all lightning victims were out-of-doors—at the beach, on a golf course or farm, fixing a roof, or under a tree. The late Karl McEachron made this consoling observation: "If you heard the thunder, the lightning did not strike you. If you saw the lightning, it missed you; and if it did strike you, you would not have known it."

CODES & HANDBOOKS WORTH SENDING FOR:

CODE FOR PROTECTION AGAINST LIGHTNING—88 pages of recommended practice for installation of lightning-protection equipment. Sponsored by the American Institute of Electrical Engineers, the National Fire Protection Association, and the National Bureau of Standards. Issued by the National Bureau of Standards of the U.S. Department of Commerce, this code is known as Handbook 46. Price 45 cents. Available from the Superintendent of Documents, Government Printing Office, Washington 25, D.C.

MASTER LABELED LIGHTNING PROTECTION SYSTEMS INSTALLATION REQUIRE-MENTS—47-page document describing installation requirements to qualify for Master Label of the Underwriters' Laboratories, Inc., which is an organization sponsored by the National Board of Fire Underwriters. Available on request from Underwriters' Laboratories, Inc., 207 East Ohio Street, Chicago 11, Illinois.

CODE FOR PROTECTION AGAINST LIGHTNING—48-page guide for protection to persons, buildings, and structures. Price 50 cents. Available as Code NFPA No. 78 from the National Fire Protection Association, 60 Batterymarch Street, Boston 10, Massachusetts.

LIGHTNING PROTECTION FOR THE FARM—12 page folder describing special lightning protection methods for farms. Published by the U.S. Department of Agriculture as Farmers' Bulletin No. 2136. Price 10 cents. Available from the Superintendent of Documents, Government Printing Office, Washington 25, D.C.

TELEVISION AND FM ANTENNAS—15-page discussion of installation techniques for electrical and lightning safety. Price 15 cents. Available as NFPA No. Q 45-1 from the National Fire Protection Association, 60 Batterymarch Street, Boston 10, Massachusetts.

FIRE PROTECTION STANDARDS FOR MOTOR CRAFT—48-page discussion of recommended standards for fire, electrical, and lightning safety of commercial and pleasure boats. Particular emphasis on power boats. Price 50 cents. Available as NFPA No. 302 from the National Fire Protection Association, 60 Batterymarch Street, Boston 10, Massachusetts.

NATIONAL ELECTRICAL CODE—More than 500 pages of recommended practice for electrical wiring, installations, ground connections, etc. Approved by the National Fire Protection Association, American Standards Association, and National Board of Fire Underwriters. Price $1.00. Available as Code NFPA No. 70 from the National Fire Protection Association, 60 Batterymarch Street, Boston 10, Massachusetts.

MEAN NUMBER OF THUNDERSTORM DAYS IN THE UNITED STATES—24-page summary of average number of thunderstorm days recorded each month for 266 weather-bureau stations in major cities of United States and its territories. Includes monthly frequency maps. Prepared by the Weather Bureau as Technical Paper No. 19. Price 15 cents. Available from the Superintendent of Documents, Government Printing Office, Washington 25, D.C.

MANUFACTURERS:

LIGHTNING RODS AND PROTECTION EQUIPMENT
    Aetna Protection Co., 100 Race Street, Meadeville, Pennsylvania
    American Chimney Corp., 145 4th Avenue, New York 3, New York
    American Lightning Rod Co., Inc., 274 Franklin Street, Boston 10, Massachusetts
    Blackburn Jasper Corp., 1527 Woodson Road, St. Louis, Missouri
    Carl Bajohr Co., 5052 South 38th Street, St. Louis, Missouri
    Electra Protection Co., Inc., 121 North Lake Avenue, Albany 6, New York
    Independent Protection Co., Inc., 1605 South Main Street, Goshen, Indiana
    National Lightning Protection Co., 2340 Eugenie Street, St. Louis, Missouri
    Security Mfg. & Contracting Co., Jefferson & Pine Streets, Burlington, Wisconsin
    Sewell Mfg. Co., 2288 University Avenue, St. Paul, Minnesota
    Thompson Lightning Protection, 616 41st Avenue North, Minneapolis 12, Minnesota
    West Dodd Lightning Conductor Corp., West Lafayette & Thomas Streets, Goshen, Indiana

CONDUCTOR CABLE
    General Cable Corp., 420 Lexington Avenue, New York, New York
    Rome Cable Corp., 332–400 Ridge Street, Rome, New York

BRACES, POINTS & MISCELLANEOUS FITTINGS
American Brass Co., Fabricated Metals Division, Waterbury, Connecticut
Champion Hardware Co., 3300 Miller Street, Geneva, Ohio
Cambridge Instrument Co., 3778 Grand Central Terminal Bldg., New York, New York
John A. Roebling's Sons Co., 640 South Broad Street, Trenton, New Jersey

ARRESTERS & PROTECTORS
Electronic Specialties Co., Inc., Island at Thomas Streets, Batavia, Illinois
General Electric Company, Schenectady, New York
Robbins Lightning Protection Co., 124A East 2nd Street, Maryville, Missouri
Westinghouse Electric Corp., P.O. Box 868, Pittsburgh, Pennsylvania

MANUFACTURER'S TRADE ASSOCIATION:

Lightning Protection Institute, 53 West Jackson Street, Chicago 4, Illinois

INSTALLERS TRADE ASSOCIATION:

United Lightning Protection Assoc., Box 9, Onondaga, New York

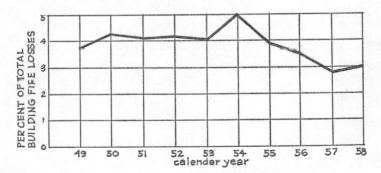

Fig. 72   Share of building fire losses due to lightning in the United States. For example, lightning accounted for 5 per cent of all building fire losses in 1954.   DATA COURTESY OF NATIONAL FIRE PROTECTION ASSOCIATION

FIRES RESULTING FROM KNOWN CAUSES—NUMBER OF INSURANCE CLAIMS AND PROPERTY LOSS: 1948-57

(In thousands of dollars. Figures are for reported fires where the cause is ascertainable, excluding incendiarism, and do not represent either total number of fires or total property loss in the United States. Excludes all unreported losses as well as all fires resulting from unknown causes.)

| | Claims | | Property Loss | |
	Number	Per cent	Amount ($1000)	Per cent
Total	2,518,308	100.0	3,539,214	100.0
Matches and smoking	642,108	25.5	546,109	15.4
Misuse of electricity	404,979	16.1	854,131	24.1
Lightning	273,374	10.9	213,996	6.1
Stoves, furnaces, boilers, and their pipes	162,304	6.5	251,391	7.1
Petroleum and its products	148,838	5.9	311,312	8.8
Exposure (fire originating off premises)	155,062	6.2	283,054	8.0
Ignition of hot grease, etc.	125,329	5.0	61,631	1.7
Hot ashes and coals—open fires	100,720	4.0	120,519	3.4
Overheated or defective chimneys, flues, etc.	99,319	3.9	137,939	3.9
Open lights	66,042	2.6	64,033	1.8
Rubbish and litter	65,348	2.6	82,703	2.3
Sparks on roofs	47,837	1.9	63,404	1.8
Gas, natural and artificial	42,989	1.7	102,296	2.9
Spontaneous combustion	40,812	1.6	143,366	4.1
Friction, sparks from running machinery	20,729	0.8	74,270	2.1
Explosions	18,645	0.7	45,369	1.3
Sparks arising from combustion	17,966	0.7	47,932	1.4
Fireworks, balloons, etc.	3,589	0.1	3,968	0.1
Miscellaneous	82,318	3.3	131,783	3.7

Based upon National Board of Fire Underwriters, New York, New York. *Report of the Committee on Statistics and Origin of Losses* as published in *Statistical Abstract of the United States, 1959,* U.S. Department of Commerce.

BIBLIOGRAPHY FOR FURTHER READING
(Also See Appendix)

CHAPTER 1 THROUGH THE AGES

How Old Is the Earth?, Patrick M. Hurley, Anchor (Doubleday), 1959.
The Ocean of Air, D. Blumenstock, Rutgers University Press, 1959.
The Bible (King James Version), Oxford University Press, 1934.
The Age of Fable, Thomas Bulfinch, 1855, Heritage Press, 1942.
Mythology, Edith Hamilton, 1940, Mentor (New American Library), 1959.
The Masks of God; Primitive Mythology, J. Campbell, Viking Press, 1959.
Flight of the Thunderbolts, B. F. J. Schonland, Oxford University Press, 1950.
The Golden Bough, Sir James George Frazer, 1922, Macmillan, 1951.
World's Great Religions, Editors of Life. Time, Inc., 1957.
Naval Customs, Traditions and Usage, L. P. Lovette, U.S. Naval Institute, 1939.
The Bantu Speaking Tribes of South Africa, Isaac Schapera, G. Routledge & Sons, Ltd., 1937.
A Pictorial History of the American Indian, O. LaFarge, Crown Publishers, 1957.
Sun, Sea and Sky, I. P. Krick and R. Fleming, J. B. Lippincott Co., 1954.
Book about a Thousand Things, George Stimson, Harper & Brothers, 1946.
The Notebooks of Leonardo da Vinci, Ed. E. A. McCurdy, G. Braziller, 1958.
Electricity, P. Viemeister, Nelson Doubleday, Inc., 1959.
Medieval and Early Modern Science, Vol. I, A. C. Crombie, Anchor (Doubleday), 1959.
Physics, the Pioneer Science, Vol. II, L. M. Taylor, 1941, Dover, 1959.
"Origin of Life," C. Wald, *The Physics and Chemistry of Life*. (A Scientific American Book), Simon and Schuster, 1955.
Directions for Insuring Personal Safety During Storms of Thunder and Lightning and for the Right Application of Conductors to Houses and Other Buildings, John Leigh, Jun., Esq., Pamphlet, 1835.
"Folklore of Lightning," K. B. McEachron, *Encyclopaedia Britannica*, Vol. 14, 1957.
"The First Fire," *Life*, November 2, 1959.

CHAPTER 2 BENJAMIN FRANKLIN

Franklin, the Apostle of Modern Times, B. Fay, Little Brown, 1929.
Benjamin Franklin, Carl Van Doren, Viking Press, 1938.
Benjamin Franklin's Experiments. A New Edition of Franklin's Experiments and Observations on Electricity, Ed. I. B. Cohen, Harvard University Press, 1941.
Benjamin Franklin's Autobiographical Writings, Carl Van Doren, Viking, 1945.
Franklin and Newton, I. B. Cohen, American Philosophical Society, 1956.

"Benjamin Franklin," I. B. Cohen, *Lives in Science*, (A Scientific American Book),
Simon and Schuster, 1957.
"The Work of Benjamin Franklin on Thunderstorms and the Development of
the Lightning Rod," B. F. J. Schonland, *Journal of the Franklin Institute*, Vol.
253, No. 5 (May 1952), p. 375.
"Prejudice against the Introduction of Lightning Rods," I. B. Cohen, *Journal of
the Franklin Institute*, Vol. 253, No. 5 (May 1952), p. 393.
"America's Pioneer Man of Science," *Life*, February 29, 1960, p. 51.

CHAPTER 3   LIGHTNING RESEARCH

Lightning Reference Book 1918–1935, American Institute of Electrical Engineers,
1937.
A Treasury of the World's Great Letters, M. L. Schuster, Simon and Schuster,
1940.
The Thunderstorm, H. R. Byers and R. R. Braham, Jr., Weather Bureau, Depart-
ment of Commerce, 1949.
Workshop for Engineers, J. A. Miller, Maqua Company, 1952.
A History of Technology, Vol. IV, C. Singer, E. J. Howard, A. R. Hall and T. I.
Williams, Oxford University Press, 1958.
Modern Jupiter—The Story of Charles Proteus Steinmetz, J. A. Miller, American
Society of Mechanical Engineers, 1958.
The Ocean of Air, D. I. Blumenstock, Rutgers University Press, 1959.
Electricity, P. Viemeister, Nelson Doubleday, Inc., 1959.
World Almanac and Book of Facts, Ed. by H. Hansen, New York World-Tele-
gram and The Sun, 1960.
"Experimental Lightning Research," H. Norinder, *Journal of the Franklin Insti-
tute*, Vol. 253, No. 5 (May 1952), p. 471.
"Meteorology—Newest Region of Exploration," E. Robinson, *Stanford Research
Institute Journal*, Vol. 3, 2nd Quarter 1959, p. 37.
"Probing the Thunderstorm," H. R. Byers, *Weatherwise*, Vol. 1 (June 1948),
p. 47.
"Ben Franklin Was Lucky," I. W. Brunk, *Weatherwise*, Vol. 11 (June 1958),
p. 92.
"Lightning Death During Kite Flight," I. W. Brunk, *Weatherwise*, Vol. 11 (De-
cember 1958), p. 204.
"The Automatic Oscillograph and Its Utility," A. D. MacAffer, *General Electric
Review*, March 1935, p. 146.
"Photos Show EHV-Line Noise Sources," L. N. Robertson and J. E. O'Neil,
Electrical World, July 20, 1959.

CHAPTER 4   BIRTH OF A STORM

The Thunderstorm, H. R. Byers and R. R. Braham, Jr., Weather Bureau, Depart-
ment of Commerce, 1949.
How You Can Forecast the Weather, E. Sloane, Premier (Fawcett), 1957.
Weather, P. E. Lehr, R. W. Burnett, H. S. Zim, Simon and Schuster, 1957.
Introduction to Meteorology, S. Petterssen, McGraw-Hill, 1958.
Meteorology for Naval Aviators, Office of the Chief of Naval Operations, U.S.
Navy, 1958.
"Eighteen Hundred Thunderstorms," *Weatherwise*, Vol. 2, 1949, p. 139.
"Rainclouds," B. J. Mason, *Shell Aviation News*, No. 242 (August 1958), p. 2.
"It Rained Everywhere But Here!, The Thunderstorm-Encirclement Illusion,"
J. E. McDonald, *Weatherwise*, Vol. 12, No. 4 (August 1959), p. 158.

"Vertical Motions in Thunderstorm Cells Indicated by Balloon Flight Incidents," A. Gaalswyk, Paper given to meeting of American Meteorological Society, Washington, May 1959.

"Thunderstorms," *Pilots Weather Handbook*, Department of Commerce, C.A.A. Technical Manual No. 104, 1955, p. 55.

CHAPTER 5   GLOBAL VAGABONDS

Lightning and the Protection of Electrical Systems, General Electric Co., Maqua Company, 1939.

Introduction to Meteorology, S. Petterssen, McGraw-Hill, 1958.

Weather, P. E. Lehr, R. W. Burnett, H. S. Zim, Simon and Schuster, 1957.

The Wind and the Weather, J. Bolton, Thomas Y. Crowell Co., 1957.

Weather Elements, T. A. Blair, Revised by R. C. Fite, Prentice-Hall, 4th Ed., 1957.

Descriptive Meteorology, H. C. Willett and F. Sanders, Academic Press, 2nd Ed., 1959.

Meteorology for Naval Aviators, Office of the Chief of Naval Operations, U.S. Navy, 1958.

Radar Meteorology, L. J. Battan, University of Chicago Press, 1959.

Atmospheric Techniques, World Meteorological Organization, Geneva, 1955.

World Distribution of Thunderstorm Days, World Meteorological Organization, Geneva, 1953.

Mean Number of Thunderstorm Days in the United States, Weather Bureau Technical Paper No. 19, Department of Commerce, 1952.

"Circulation of the Atmosphere," H. Wexler, *The Planet Earth* (A Scientific American Book), Simon and Schuster, 1957, p. 101.

"Circulation of the Oceans," W. H. Munk, *The Planet Earth* (A Scientific American Book), Simon and Schuster, 1957, p. 113.

"The Circulation of Radioactive Isotopes," J. R. Arnold and E. A. Martell, *Scientific American*, September 1959, p. 85.

"Thunderstorms," H. R. Byers, *Compendium of Meteorology*, American Meteorological Society, 1951, p. 681.

"Physics of Clouds," H. J. Aufm Kampe and H. J. Weickmann, *Meteorological Monographs*, Vol. 3, American Meteorological Society, July 1957, p. 182.

"New Concepts of Cumulonimbus," F. H. Ludlam, *The Aeroplane*, May 10, 1957.

A Basis for the Prediction of Severe Local Thunderstorms, D. C. House, Institute of Aeronautical Sciences, Paper No. 60-2, 1960.

"Radar—New Weather Eye," M. G. H. Ligda, *Stanford Research Institute Journal*, Vol. 3, 2nd Quarter 1959, p. 49.

"Sferics System May Track Tornadoes," J. A. Fusca, *Aviation Week*, June 15, 1959, p. 87.

"U.S. Planning Nationwide Weather Radar Network," J. A. Fusca, *Aviation Week*, May 2, 1959, p. 56.

"New Weather Warning System Under Test," *Weatherwise*, Vol. 13, No. 2 (April 1960), p. 63.

"Lightning Geography Key to Protection," W. C. Smith and A. F. Ayers, *Electrical West*, Vol. 85, December 1940, p. 45.

CHAPTER 6   ELECTRICITY IN THE AIR

Thunderstorm Electricity, Ed. H. R. Byers, University of Chicago Press, 1953.

Atmospheric Electricity, J. A. Chalmers, Pergamon Press, 1957.

Proceedings on the Conference on Atmospheric Electricity, Eds. R. E. Holzer and W. E. Smith, Geophysics Research Directorate, Air Force Cambridge Research Center, 1955.

Recent Advances in Atmospheric Electricity, Ed. L. G. Smith, Pergamon Press, 1958.

The Face of the Sun, H. W. Newton, Penguin Books, 1958.

Physics of the Earth, Vol. VIII, *Terrestrial Magnetism and Electricity*, Ed. J. A. Fleming, McGraw-Hill, 1939.

"Atmospheric Electricity," H. J. Aufm Kampe, *Meteorological Monographs*, Vol. 3, American Meteorological Society, 1957, p. 256.

"Atmospheric Electricity," B. B. Phillips, *American Institute of Physics Handbook*, McGraw-Hill, 1957.

"The Formation of Electric Charges in Thunderstorms," J. P. Kuettner, *Atmospheric Explorations*, Ed. H. G. Houghton, John Wiley & Sons, 1958, p. 25.

"Airborne Electricity," J. W. Ford, *Research Trends* of Cornell Aeronautical Laboratory, Vol. II, No. 4, 1959, p. 5.

"Relationship between Thunderstorm and Fair Weather Electricity," B. Vonnegut, *Research Reviews*, U.S. Navy, Office of Naval Research, July 1958, p. 12.

"An Assessment of Mechanisms Proposed to Explain Thunderstorm Electrification," C. B. Moore and B. Vonnegut, Unpublished paper, Arthur D. Little, Inc., 1959.

"The Earth's Electricity," J. E. McDonald, *Scientific American*, April 1953, p. 33.

"Investigation on Lightning Discharges and on the Electric Field of Thunderstorms," C. T. R. Wilson, *Philosophical Transactions of the Royal Society*, Series A, Vol. 220, June 1920, p. 73.

"A Theory of Thundercloud Electricity," C. T. R. Wilson, *Royal Society Proceedings*, Series A, Vol. 236, No. 1206 (August 2, 1956), p. 297.

"The Electrification of Precipitation and Thunderstorms," R. Gunn, *Proceedings of the I.R.E.*, Vol. 45, No. 10 (October 1957), p. 1331.

"The Electrification of Clouds and Raindrops," R. Gunn, in *Atmospheric Explorations*, Ed. H. G. Houghton, John Wiley & Sons, 1958, p. 3.

"Estimates of Raindrop Collection Efficiencies in Electrified Clouds," C. B. Moore and B. Vonnegut in *Monograph No. 5, Physics of Precipitation*, American Geophysical Union, 1960.

Observations of Thunderstorms in New Mexico, C. B. Moore, B. Vonnegut and A. G. Emslie, Arthur D. Little, Inc., 1959.

"Proposes New Theory of Lightning Formation," *Science Newsletter*, Vol. 67, No. 7 (February 12, 1955), p. 110.

"A Possible Effect of Lightning Discharge on Precipitation Formation Process," B. Vonnegut and C. B. Moore, *Monograph No. 5, Physics of Precipitation*, American Geophysical Union, 1960, p. 287.

"Thunder and Lightning," E. T. Pierce, *Shell Aviation News*, December 1958, p. 9.

"Cosmic Thunderstorms," C. E. R. Bruce, *Journal of the Franklin Institute*, Vol. 286, No. 6 (December 1959), p. 425.

"Yearly Variation of the Potential Gradient of Atmospheric Electricity," N. A. Paramonov, *Doklady Akademii Nauk SSR*, Vol. 71, No. 1, 1950, p. 39.

"Electric Currents in the Ionosphere—The Conductivity," W. G. Baker and D. F. Martyn, *Philosophical Transactions of the Royal Society*, Series A, Vol. 246, No. 913 (December 16, 1953).

CHAPTER 7   THE LIGHTNING BOLT

Flight of the Thunderbolts, B. F. J. Schonland, Oxford University Press, 1950.

Gaseous Conductors Theory and Engineering Applications, J. D. Cobine, Dover, 1958.

"Lightning Phenomena," E. L. Harder and J. M. Clayton, *Westinghouse Engineer*, Vol. II, No. 4 (July 1951), p. 106.

"Properties of Lightning Strokes," E. L. Harder and J. M. Clayton, *Electrical World*, June 2, 1952, p. 106.

"The Lightning Prestrike," S. B. Griscom, *A.I.E.E. Transactions, Part III*, Vol. 77, (A.I.E.E. Paper 58–829), 1958.

"Lightning and the Protection of Lines and Structures from Lightning," J. H. Hagenguth, *Standard Handbook for Electrical Engineers*, McGraw-Hill, 9th Ed., 1957, p. 2154.

"The Lightning Stroke," C. F. Wagner and A. R. Hileman, *A.I.E.E. Transactions, Part III*, Vol. 77, No. 36, (A.I.E.E. Paper 58–24), 1958.

"Atmospheric Electricity," H. J. Aufm Kampe, *Meteorological Monographs*, Vol. 3, American Meteorological Society, 1957, p. 272.

Lightning Discharges to Aircraft and Associated Meteorological Conditions, L. P. Harrison, National Advisory Committee for Aeronautics, Technical Note No. 1001, May 1946.

"Lightning Flash," E. Sloane, *Weatherwise*, Vol. 1 (June 1948), p. 56.

"Progressive Lightning, VII," D. J. Malan and B. F. J. Schonland, *Proceedings of the Royal Society*, Series A, Vol. 191, No. 1027 (December 3, 1947), p. 485.

"The Pilot Streamer and the Long Spark," B. F. J. Schonland, *Proceedings of the Royal Society*, Series A, Vol. 220, No. 1140 (October 22, 1953), p. 25.

"Photographic Study of Lightning," J. H. Hagenguth, *A.I.E.E. Transactions*, Vol. 66, (A.I.E.E. Paper 47–98), 1947.

"Positive Streamer Sparks in Air Relating to the Lightning Stroke," L. B. Loeb, *Atmospheric Explorations*, Ed. H. G. Houghton, John Wiley & Sons, 1958, p. 46.

"Experimental Lightning Discharges," H. Norinder and O. Karsten, *Journal of the Franklin Institute*, Vol. 253, No. 3 (March 1952), p. 225.

"Upward Stepped Leaders from the Empire State Building," B. F. J. Schonland and D. J. Malan, *Journal of the Franklin Institute*, Vol. 258, No. 4 (October 1954), p. 271.

"Note on 'Upward Stepped Leaders from the Empire State Building'," C. E. R. Bruce, *Journal of the Franklin Institute*, Vol. 260, No. 2 (August 1955), p. 127.

Propagation Mechanism of Impulse Corona and Breakdown in Oil, T. W. Liao and J. G. Anderson, A.I.E.E. Paper 54–280, 1953.

The Propagation Mechanism of Impulse Creepage Discharges Over Oil-Immersed Surfaces, J. G. Anderson and T. W. Liao, A.I.E.E. Paper 55–36, 1954.

"The Distribution and Discharge of Thunderstorm Charge Centers," S. E. Reynolds and H. W. Neill, *Journal of Meteorology*, Vol. 12, No. 1 (February 1955), p. 1.

"Some Thunderstorm Statistics for the Northern Rocky Mountain Region," D. M. Fuquay, Paper given to Research Programs in Weather Modification conference, Shenandoah National Park, Virginia, May 1959.

CHAPTER 8   THUNDER AND LIGHTNING

Physics of the Air, W. J. Humphreys, McGraw-Hill, 3rd Ed., 1940.

1001 Questions Answered About the Weather, F. Forrester, Dodd Mead, 1957.

Weather Elements, T. A. Blair, Revised by R. C. Fite, Prentice-Hall, 4th Ed., 1957, p. 229.

Henry F. Kretzer's Lightning Record, H. F. Kretzer, Henry F. Kretzer, 1895.

Flight of the Thunderbolts, B. F. J. Schonland, Oxford University Press, 1950.

"The Rumbling of Thunder," A. T. Jones, *Science*, Vol. 102, No. 2651 (October 19, 1945), p. 407.

"The Rumbling of Thunder," S. R. Cook, *Science*, Vol. 103, No. 2662 (January 4, 1946), p. 26.

"Thunder in the Clear Sky," A. D. Zamorskiy, *Meteorologiya i gidgrologiya*, No. 6, November–December 1955, p. 37.

"Remarkable Lightning Bolt," H. A. Allard, *Science*, Vol. 84, No. 2171 (August 7, 1936), p. 136.

"The Thunder-storm as a Chemical Phenomena," R. V. Konow, *Journal of the Franklin Institute*, Vol. 269, No. 6 (June 1960), p. 439.

"How Dangerous Is Lightning?", H. M. Lacey, *Country Life*, September 3, 1959, p. 166.

"Thunderbolts: the Electrical Phenomena of Thunderstorms," E. Golde, *Nature*, Vol. 169, No. 4031 (April 5, 1952), p. 563.

"Ball Lightning Observations," M. Rodewald, *Zeitschrift fur Meteorologie*, Vol. 8, No. 1, (January 1954), p. 27.

"Nature of the Lightning Ball," P. L. Kapitza, *Compt. Rend Acad. Sci. USSR*, Vol. 101, No. 2, 1955, p. 245.

"Chemical and Electric Explosions," D. M. Hillebrand, *Tekn. T.*, (Sweden), Vol. 85, No. 23, (June 7, 1955), p. 541.

CHAPTER 9   EARTH, MOUNTAIN, AND SEA

"Characteristics of Rocky Mountain Lightning Storms," R. G. Baughman and D. M. Fuquay, Paper given to Western Forest Fire Research Council meeting, Spokane, Washington, December 1959.

Lightning Investigations at High Altitudes in Colorado, L. M. Robertson, W. W. Lewis and C. M. Foust, A.I.E.E. Paper No. 42–16, 1941.

Lightning Stroke Protection at High Altitude in Peru, C. M. Foust, B. C. Maine and C. Lee, A.I.E.E. Paper No. 53–93, 1952.

"The Dodge, Nebraska Fireball," J. C. Jensen, *Science*, Vol. 83, No. 2163 (June 12, 1936), p. 574.

"Unusual Phenomena in Illinois," *Weatherwise*, Vol. 12, (June 1959), p. 133.

"Klydonogram Reproduced on Golf Green by Lightning Stroke," *Electrical Engineering*, Vol. 63, February 1944, p. 56.

———, A. A. Julien, *Journal of Geology*, Vol. 9, 1901, p. 679.

———, W. W. Meyers and A. B. Peck, *American Minerologist*, Vol. 10, 1925, p. 152.

"A Unique Occurrence of Lechatelierite or Silica Glass," A. F. Rogers, *American Journal of Science*, Vol. 19, March 1930, p. 195.

"Sand Fulgurites with Enclosed Lechatelierite from Riverside County, California," A. F. Rogers, *Journal of Geology*, Vol. 54, No. 2 (March 1946), p. 117.

CHAPTER 11   FORESTS AND TREES

Trees—The Yearbook of Agriculture, Department of Agriculture, 1949.

Trees, H. S. Zim and A. C. Martin, Golden Press, 1956.

Trees of the Eastern and Central United States and Canada, W. M. Harlow, Dover, 1957.

Tree Maintenance, P. P. Pirone, Oxford University Press, 1959, p. 172.

Big Trees, W. Fry and J. R. White, Stanford University Press, 1959.

Wood Structural Design Data, Vol. 1, National Lumber Manufacturers Association, 2nd Ed., 1953.

Wood Handbook, Forest Products Laboratory, Department of Agriculture, Handbook No. 72, 1955.

The Fiber-Saturation Point of Wood, A. J. Stamm, Forest Products Laboratory, Report No. R859, Department of Agriculture, April 1929.

Forest Fires in the Northern Rocky Mountains, J. S. Barrows, Forest Station (Missoula) Paper No. 28, Department of Agriculture, April 1951.

Project Skyfire—A Progress Report on Lightning Fire and Atmospheric Research, J. S. Barrows, V. J. Schaefer and P. B. MacReady, Forest Service Research Paper No. 35, Department of Agriculture, 1954.

"Characteristics of Rocky Mountain Lightning Storms," R. G. Baughman and D. M. Fuquay, Paper given to Western Forest Fire Research Council meeting, Spokane, Washington, December 1959.

"Lightning and Trees," J. F. Shipley, *Weather*, Vol. 1, No. 7 (November 1946), p. 206.

"Atmospheric Electricity," C. Chree, *Encyclopaedia Britannica, Vol. II*, 11th Ed., 1910, p. 860.

"Final Report of the Lightning Struck Tree Survey," A. R. Thompson, 22nd *National Shade Tree Conference Proceedings*, 1946.

The Giant Sequoias of California, L. R. Cook, National Park Service Pamphlet, 1955.

"Giant Sequoias Draw Millions to California Parks," J. M. Kauffmann, *National Geographic Magazine*, Vol. 116, No. 2 (August 1959), p. 147.

"Death Comes to a Giant Sequoia," J. W. McFarland, *Yosemite Nature Notes*, Vol. 28, No. 1 (January 1949), p. 2.

CHAPTER 12   RODS AND ROOFS

Protection of Transmission Systems Against Lightning, W. W. Lewis, John Wiley & Sons, 1950.

Lightning Protection for Electric Systems, E. Beck, McGraw-Hill, 1954.

Henry F. Kretzer's Lightning Record, H. F. Kretzer, Henry F. Kretzer, 1895.

Flight of the Thunderbolts, B. F. J. Schonland, Oxford University Press, 1950.

Lightning Reference Book 1918–1935, American Institute of Electrical Engineers, 1937.

Lightning: Its Behavior and What To Do About It, H. M. Towne, United Lightning Protection Association, 1956.

High Voltage Laboratory Technique, J. D. Craggs and J. M. Meek, Butterworth's Scientific Publications, 1954.

Statistical Abstract of the United States, Department of Commerce, 1959, p. 527.

"Lightning Protection Since Franklin's Day," K. F. McEachron, *Journal of the Franklin Institute*, Vol. 253, No. 5 (May 1952), p. 444.

Master Labeled Lightning Protection Systems, Installation Requirements (see Appendix).

Code For Protection against Lightning (see Appendix).

"Theory of the Lightning Rod," V. I. Arabadzhi, *Uchanyya Zapiski*, Vol. 6, Jubilee, 1958, p. 327.

"The Lightning Prestrike," S. B. Griscom, *A.I.E.E. Transactions, Part III*, Vol. 77, (A.I.E.E. Paper 58–829), 1958.

"Lightning Strokes Prefer Tall Structures," E. Beck, *Westinghouse Engineer*, July 1949, p. 124.

"Observations upon Lightning, and the Method of Securing Buildings from its Effects in a Letter to Sir Charles Frederick, etc., etc.," B. Wilson and others, *Philosophical Transactions*, Vol. 64, Part I, 1773.

"Lightning Arrester—Electrical Protector," E. Beck, *Westinghouse Engineer*, May 1950, p. 148.

"Data Confirms Worth of Lightning Protections," J. S. Maloy, *Electrical World*, Vol. 123, March 3, 1945, p. 104.

"17 Year Lightning Study Gets Results," G. W. Maihl, *Electrical World*, Vol. 129, April 10, 1948, p. 105.

"Why Lightning Rods?" H. M. Lashier, *American Journal of Physics*, Vol. 27, No. 6 (September 1959), p. 446.

"Certified Protection Against Lightning," *Journal of the Franklin Institute*, Vol. 253, No. 2 (February 1953), p. 193.

"Telephony," H. A. Affel, *Radio Engineering Handbook*, McGraw-Hill, 5th Ed., 1959, p. 28.8.

Underground Corrosion of Anchor Rods, Rural Electrification Administration Bulletin 169–30, Department of Agriculture, 1958.

Television and FM Antennas, C. L. Smith, National Fire Protection Association, Bulletin No. Q 45-1, 1953.

Occupancy Fire Record, 1 & 2 Family Dwellings, National Fire Protection Association, Bulletin No. FR 56–2, 1956.

Fires and Fire Losses Classified, 1956, National Fire Protection Association, Bulletin No. Q 51-4, 1957.

Thunderbolts in Harness, General Electric Co., Pamphlet APD–62A, 1953.

High Voltage Laboratory, General Electric Co., Pamphlet GET–2433, 1954.

Testing for Safety, Underwriters' Laboratories, Inc., Pamphlet, October 1958.

Lightning Facts and Figures, Lightning Protection Institute, (no date).

"Lightning in Action," F. B. Colton, *National Geographic Magazine*, Vol. 97, No. 6 (June 1950), p. 809.

New Low Cost Lightning Arrester, General Electric Co., Pamphlet GED–3865A, 1960.

How to Build or Remodel for the Safety of Your Family, Home Insurance Co., Pamphlet, 1956.

CHAPTER 13   FARMS, FENCES, AND FERTILIZER

Code for Protection against Lightning (see Appendix).

Book about a Thousand Things, G. Stimson, Harper & Brothers, 1946.

Henry F. Kretzer's Lightning Record, H. F. Kretzer, Henry F. Kretzer, 1895.

Lightning Protection for the Farm (see Appendix).

Your Farm and Fire Safety, National Board of Fire Underwriters, Pamphlet (no date).

Occupancy Fire Record, Farm Property, National Fire Protection Association, Bulletin No. FR 54–6, 1954.

"Safe Lightning Protection," R. D. Bienemann, *Agricultural Engineering*, Vol. 28, No. 11 (November 1947), p. 505.

"Lightning Protection for Farm Structures," R. D. Bienemann, *Agricultural Engineering*, Vol. 30, No. 4 (April 1949), pp. 172, 176.

"Lightning—Friend or Foe," R. D. Bienemann, *Electricity on the Farm*, June–July 1958, p. 8.

"Lightning and the Origin of Nitrates in Precipitation," P. E. Viemeister, *Journal of Meteorology*, Vol. 17, No. 6 (December 1960).

"Biochemistry of the Terrestrial Atmosphere," G. E. Hutchinson, *Earth as a Planet*, Ed. by G. P. Kuiper, University of Chicago Press, 1954, p. 397.

"Results of Scientific Investigations Made by Soviet Sputniks and Cosmic Rockets," V. I. Krassovskii, *American Rocket Society Journal*, Vol. 30, No. 1, (January) 1960, p. 27.

"The Awesome Miracle of Lightning," I. Wolfert, *Reader's Digest*, August 1959, p. 187.

CHAPTER 14   MAN IN THE OPEN AND ON THE MOVE

Henry F. Kretzer's Lightning Record, H. F. Kretzer, Henry F. Kretzer, 1895.
The Autobiography of Mark Twain, C. Neider, Harper & Brothers, 1959.
Electric Shock—Its Causes and Its Prevention, R. L. Kline, and J. B. Friauf, Bureau of Ships, Document Navships 250–660–42, U.S. Navy, 1954.
"Electrical Shock, Fact and Fiction," D. P. Peters, *Aircraft Accident and Maintenance Review* (U.S. Air Force), December 1959, p. 12.
The Effects of Electric Shock on Man, C. F. Dalziel, U.S. Atomic Energy Commission, Safety and Fire Protection Technical Bulletin No. 7, 1960.
Field Treatment in Electric Shock Cases—II, W. B. Kouwenhoven, G. G. Knickerbocker, W. R. Milnor, J. R. Jude, A.I.E.E. Paper 60–171, 1960.
"Effects of Electricity on the Human Body," W. B. Kouwenhoven, *Electrical Engineering*, Vol. 68, (March 1949), p. 199.
"Lightning Strikes on the Job in Apalachia Tunnel," G. K. Leonard, *Civil Engineering*, Vol. 15, December 1945, p. 545.
"Lightning in Action," F. B. Colton, *National Geographic Mazazine*, Vol. 97, No. 6 (June 1950), p. 809.

CHAPTER 15   SHIPS AND BOATS

The Age of Fable, T. Bulfinch, 1855, Heritage Press, 1942.
Fire Protection Standards for Motor Craft (see Appendix).
Remarkable Instances of the Protection of Certain Ships of Her Majesty's Navy from the Destructive Effects of Lightning, W. S. Harris, Pamphlet, 1847.
Occupancy Fire Record, Motor Boats, National Fire Protection Association, Bulletin FR 55–3, 1955.
"Lightning Protection for U.S.N. Ships and Boats," Bureau of Ships, Navy Department Informal Memo, 1958.
"Recommended Practices and Standards for Lightning Protection (Tentative)," American Boat & Yacht Council, *The Boating Industry*, January 15, 1957.
"When Lightning Strikes," H. E. Isaacks, *Yachting*, April 1955.
"Prepare for Lightning," E. Robberson, *Yachting*, May 1957.

CHAPTER 16   AIRCRAFT

Ships in the Sky, J. Toland, Frederick Muller, 1957.
Danger in the Air, O. Stewart, Philosophical Library, 1958.
Zeppelins over England, Von Buttlar Bandenfels, Harcourt Brace, 1932.
Song of the Sky, G. Murchie, Houghton Mifflin Co., 1954.
Radar Meteorology, L. J. Battan, University of Chicago Press, 1959.
Proceedings: Symposium on Lightning Protection for Aircraft, Lightning and Transients Research Institute, 1948.
Lightning Discharges to Aircraft and Associated Meteorological Conditions, L. P. Harrison, National Advisory Commission for Aeronautics, Technical Note No. 1001, 1946.
Thunderstorm Conditions Affecting Flight Operations, Weather Bureau, Department of Commerce, Technical Paper No. 7, 1949.
Hazards of Lightning Discharges to Aircraft, G. A. Faucher and H. O. Curtis, Air Force Surveys in Geophysics No. 103, ASTIA Document AD–152595, 1958.
Lightning Hazards to Aircraft Fuel Tanks, J. D. Robb, E. L. Hill, M. M. Newman, and J. R. Stahmann, National Advisory Commission for Aeronautics, Technical Note No. 4326, 1958.

Aircraft Accident Report SA–341, Civil Aeronautics Board, File No. 1–0050, October 15, 1959.

"Lightning Stroke Damage to Aircraft," J. H. Hagenguth, *Transactions of the A.I.E.E.*, Vol. 68, 1949.

"The Radar Observation of Lightning," M. G. H. Ligda, *Journal of Atmospheric and Terrestrial Physics*, Vol. 9, No. 5/6, 1956, p. 329.

Observation of Hail Storms by Means of Airborne Radar, L. J. Battan, I.A.S. Paper 60–1, 1960.

The Occurrence of Damaging Hail at High Altitudes, H. S. Appleman and P. E. Lehr, I.A.S. Paper 60–3, 1960.

"Hailstones Damage Boeing B52 Bomber," *Aviation Week*, December 29, 1958.

"J57 Titanium Engines Save 9-man Crew," *Aviation Week*, February 23, 1959, p. 62.

"Hailstones Severely Damage C133 Transport," *Aviation Week*, April 13, 1959, p. 109.

"Inside the Cloud Barrier," D. Downie, *New Frontiers* (Garret Corp.), Fall 1959, p. 16.

"Inside Story of the Cumulus," D. Downie, AOPA *Pilot*, April 1960, p. 24.

"Hail and Thunderstorm Damage," H. W. Fleming, *Skyways*, March 1960, p. 42.

"Squall Blamed for South African Accident," *Aviation Daily*, August 17, 1959.

"Discussing Wind Shear," T. H. Farnsworth, *Skyways*, March 1960, p. 42.

"Thunderstorms," H. B. Kaster, *Weatherwise*, Vol. 1 (June 1948), p. 61.

"Summer Weather," *Safety Suggestions* (Beech Aircraft Corp.), No. 20, 1959.

"Compliance Time Stretched in Weather Radar Rule," *Aviation Daily*, January 11, 1960.

"And Then There Were None," *Approach, The Naval Aviation Safety Review*, Vol. 1, No. 5 (November 1955), p. 4.

"Uninvited Electricity," L. G. Hill, *Flight* (London), April 10, 1959, p. 487.

"Explosive Electrostatic Discharges," *The MATS Flyer*, July 1958, p. 24.

"Lightning Strikes Twice," W. A. Redman, *The MATS Flyer*, July 1958, p. 24.

"How to Protect Radomes from Lightning," M. P. Amason, *Space/Aeronautics*, December 1959, p. 177.

"Corona Static Discharger Replaces Wicks," P. J. Klass, *Aviation Week*, March 14, 1960, p. 52.

"Early Warning WF–2 Joins Squadrons," B. Tully, *Aviation Week*, January 11, 1960, p. 87.

CHAPTER 17   FALSE BLAME AND USEFUL PRANKS

Henry F. Kretzer's Lightning Record, H. F. Kretzer, Henry F. Kretzer, 1895.

Flight of the Thunderbolts, B. F. J. Schonland, Oxford University Press, 1950.

Atmospheric Electricity, J. A. Chalmers, Pergamon Press, 1957.

"United States of America v. Standard Oil Co. of Kentucky," No. 12095, in the U.S. Court of Appeals for the Sixth Circuit, Brief for the Appellee.

"Tanker Homestead Struck; Destroyed by Fire," New York *Times*, August 6, 1946.

"Lightning Strikes Bridge, 6 Hurt," New York *Times*, August 23, 1947.

"Lightning Sets Age of 'Oldest Church'," New York *Times*, April 18, 1954.

CHAPTER 18   FRONTIERS

WHISTLERS

International Geophysical Year, National Academy of Sciences, for U.S. Senate, 84th Congress, 2nd Session, Doc. No. 124, 1956.

Manual on Rockets and Satellites, L. V. Berkner, Annals of the International Geophysical Year, Vol. IV, Pergamon Press, 1958, p. 7.

IGY: Year of Discovery, S. Chapman, University of Michigan Press, 1959.

Basic Research Resumes, AFOSR TR 59–204, Office of Technical Services, Department of Commerce, 1959, pp. 154, 156, 161.

"The Voyage of the *Atka,*" P. A. Humphrey, *Scientific American,* September 1955, p. 55.

"Whistlers," L. R. O. Storey, *Scientific American,* January 1956, p. 34.

"Observations of Whistling Atmospherics at Geomagnetically Conjugate Points," M. G. Morgan, H. E. Dinger, and G. McK. Allcock, *Nature,* Vol. 177, January 7, 1956, p. 29.

"Electromagnetic Radiation from Lightning Strokes," E. L. Hill, *Journal of the Franklin Institute,* Vol. 263, No. 2 (February 1957), p. 107.

"Worldwide Propagation of Super Low Frequency Lightning Radiation," P. A. Goldberg, *American Journal of Physics,* Vol. 25, No. 4 (April 1957), p. 268.

"Radio Noise From Planets," F. Horner, *Nature,* Vol. 180, December 7, 1957, p. 1253.

"Radio Noise from Lightning Discharges," F. Horner and C. Clarke, *Nature,* Vol. 181, March 8, 1958, p. 688.

"Atmospheric Whistlers," R. A. Helliwell, M. G. Morgan, *Proceedings of The I.R.E.,* Vol. 47, No. 2 (February 1959), p. 200.

"A Preliminary Meteorological Study of the Origin of Whistlers," C. P. Mook, *Journal of Geophysical Research,* Vol. 64, No. 7 (July 1959), p. 745.

"Note on Conjugate Points of Geomagnetic Field Lines for Some Selected Auroral and Whistler Stations of the IGY," E. H. Vestine, *Journal of Geophysical Research,* Vol. 64, No. 10 (October 1959), p. 1411.

"A Comparison of Spherics as Observed in the Very Low Frequency and Extremely Low Frequency Bands," L. R. Tepley, *Journal of Geophysical Research,* Vol. 64, No. 12 (December 1959), p. 2315.

"Radio Wave Propagation," *Reference Data for Radio Engineers,* International Telephone and Telegraph Corp., 4th Ed., 1959, p. 170.

POWER PROBLEMS

"The Teinograph—A New High-Voltage Surge Recorder," J. G. Anderson and R. U. Giacomoni, Paper given to meeting of A.I.E.E. at Baltimore, May 1959.

"The Kine-Klydonograph—A Transient Wave-Form Recorder," S. B. Griscom, Paper given to meeting of A.I.E.E. at Providence, Rhode Island, May 1960.

"A Hypothesis Concerning Lightning Phenomena and Transmission-Line Flashover," I. B. Johnson and A. J. Schultz, *Power and Apparatus Systems,* February 1958.

TORNADOES

Tornado Deaths in the United States, U. J. Linehan, Weather Bureau, Department of Commerce, Technical Paper No. 30, March 1957.

It Looks Like a Tornado, Weather Bureau, Department of Commerce, January 1959.

"Duration of Tornadoes," L. J. Battan, *Bulletin of the American Meteorological Society,* Vol. 40, No. 7 (July 1959), p. 340.

"Giant Electrical Storms," B. Vonnegut and C. B. Moore, *Recent Advances in Atmospheric Electricity,* Pergamon Press, 1959, p. 339.

"Electrical Theory of Tornadoes," B. Vonnegut, *Journal of Geophysical Research,* Vol. 65, No. 1 (January 1960), p. 203.

LIGHTNING SUPPRESSION

Project Skyfire—A Progress Report on Lightning Fire and Atmospheric Research, J. S. Barrows, V. J. Schaefer, P. B. MacReady, Department of Agriculture, Forest Service Research Paper No. 35, 1954.

Project Skyfire, Picture Story No. 104, Office of Information, Department of Agriculture, 1957.

"Final Report of the Advisory Committee on Weather Control," H. T. Orville, *Bulletin of the American Meteorological Society,* Vol. 39, No. 11 (November 1958), p. 583.

"Decrease in Lightning-Caused Forest Fires through Cloud Seeding," A. Court, Paper given to 166th National Meeting of the American Meteorological Society at Logan, Utah, June 1958.

"Lightning Suppression Studies in the Northern Rocky Mountains," C. A. O'Dell, Paper given to 166th National Meeting of the American Meteorological Society at Logan, Utah, June 1958.

Cloud Modification and Lightning, L. J. Battan and A. R. Kassander, Jr., Final Report under Supplemental Memorandum No. 1, Contract No. 12-11-332-58 of Rocky Mountain Forest and Range Experiment Station, U.S. Forest Service, University of Arizona, Tucson, 1959.

"Generator Technology for Cloud Seeding," D. M. Fuquay, Paper given to joint meeting of American Society of Civil Engineers and American Meteorological Society at Denver, Colorado, August 1959.

"Cloud Modification by 'Carboning'," F. W. van Straten, R. E. Ruskin, J. E. Dinger, and H. J. Mastenbrook, *Research Reviews,* U.S. Navy, Office of Naval Research, December 1958, p. 15.

"Preliminary Attempts to Influence Convective Electrification in Cumulus Clouds by the Introduction of Space Charge into the Lower Atmosphere," B. Vonnegut and C. B. Moore, *Recent Advances in Atmospheric Electricity,* Pergamon Press, 1959, p. 317.

"Active Influence on the Weather—USSR," V. A. Shtal' and V. G. Morachevskiy, *Priroda,* Vol. 47, No. 9 (September 1958), p. 85.

"New Grant for Project Skyfire," *Bulletin of the American Meteorological Society,* Vol. 41, No. 4 (April 1960), p. 224.

OCEANS AND LIGHTNING

"Electrically Charged Drops from Bubbles in Sea Water and Their Meteorological Significance," D. C. Blanchard, *Journal of Meteorology,* Vol. 15, No. 4 (August 1958).

"Observations of Electrification and Lightning in Warm Clouds," B. Vonnegut, C. B. Moore, B. Stein and H. J. Survilas, *Journal of Geophysical Research,* Vol. 65, No. 7 (July 1960).

PLASMA STUDIES, etc.

Project Sherwood, A. S. Bishop, Anchor (Doubleday), 1960.

"Weather Control and National Strategy," W. J. Kotsch, *U.S. Naval Institute Proceedings,* Vol. 86, No. 7 (July 1960), p. 74.

"Magnetohydrodynamics: Hope for Space," J. S. Butz, Jr., *Aviation Week,* May 12, 1958, p. 48.

"Magnetohydrodynamics Opens Up New Electronic Vistas," I. Stambler, *Space/Aeronautics,* January 1959, p. 28.

"Pentagon Experts Deny USSR Has Harnessed Lightning," New York *Times,* April 28, 1958.

"Sudden Zeus," *Time,* March 28, 1960, p. 44.

"Exotic Power Packages," G. A. W. Boehm, *Fortune,* July 1960, p. 124.

CHAPTER 19 GUIDES TO LIVE BY

Playing with Lightning, K. B. McEachron and K. G. Patrick, Random House, 1940.

Lightning—Its Behavior and What To Do About It, H. M. Towne, United Lightning Protection Association, 1956.

Lightning, C. L. G. Fortescue, Unpublished paper, Westinghouse Electric Mfg. Co., ca. 1935.

Lightning, Weather Bureau, Department of Commerce, 1960.

Protection from Lightning, A. McAdie, Weather Bureau, Department of Agriculture, 3rd Ed., 1894.

An Essay on the Cause of Lightning and the manners by which the Thunderclouds become possessed of their electricity, deduced from Known facts and properties of that Matter. To which are added, Plain Directions for constructing and erecting Safe conductors. J. Simmons, Pamphlet, 1775.